TEACHER'S GUIDE

CONNECTED MATHEMATICS

Say It With Symbols x x $x+5$

Making Sense of Symbols

Glenda Lappan, Elizabeth Difanis Phillips,
James T. Fey, Susan N. Friel

PEARSON

Boston, Massachusetts • Chandler, Arizona • Glenview, Illinois • Upper Saddle River, New Jersey

Connected Mathematics™ was developed at Michigan State University with financial support from the Michigan State University Office of the Provost, Computing and Technology, and the College of Natural Science.

This material is based upon work supported by the National Science Foundation under Grant No. MDR 9150217 and Grant No. ESI 9986372. Opinions expressed are those of the authors and not necessarily those of the Foundation.

As with prior editions of this work, the authors and administration of Michigan State University preserve a tradition of devoting royalties from this publication to support activities sponsored by the MSU Mathematics Education Enrichment Fund.

Acknowledgments appear on page 297, which constitutes an extension of this copyright page.

PEARSON

13-digit ISBN 978-0-13-327667-1
10-digit ISBN 0-13-327667-8
1 2 3 4 5 6 7 8 9 10 V001 17 16 15 14 13

Authors

A Team of Experts

Glenda Lappan is a University Distinguished Professor in the Program in Mathematics Education (PRIME) and the Department of Mathematics at Michigan State University. Her research and development interests are in the connected areas of students' learning of mathematics and mathematics teachers' professional growth and change related to the development and enactment of K–12 curriculum materials.

Elizabeth Difanis Phillips is a Senior Academic Specialist in the Program in Mathematics Education (PRIME) and the Department of Mathematics at Michigan State University. She is interested in teaching and learning mathematics for both teachers and students. These interests have led to curriculum and professional development projects at the middle school and high school levels, as well as projects related to the teaching and learning of algebra across the grades.

James T. Fey is a Professor Emeritus at the University of Maryland. His consistent professional interest has been development and research focused on curriculum materials that engage middle and high school students in problem-based collaborative investigations of mathematical ideas and their applications.

Susan N. Friel is a Professor of Mathematics Education in the School of Education at the University of North Carolina at Chapel Hill. Her research interests focus on statistics education for middle-grade students and, more broadly, on teachers' professional development and growth in teaching mathematics K–8.

With... Yvonne Grant and Jacqueline Stewart

Yvonne Grant teaches mathematics at Portland Middle School in Portland, Michigan. Jacqueline Stewart is a recently retired high school teacher of mathematics at Okemos High School in Okemos, Michigan. Both Yvonne and Jacqueline have worked on all aspects of the development, implementation, and professional development of the CMP curriculum from its beginnings in 1991.

Development Team

CMP3 Authors

Glenda Lappan, University Distinguished Professor, Michigan State University

Elizabeth Difanis Phillips, Senior Academic Specialist, Michigan State University

James T. Fey, Professor Emeritus, University of Maryland

Susan N. Friel, Professor, University of North Carolina – Chapel Hill

With...

Yvonne Grant, Portland Middle School, Michigan

Jacqueline Stewart, Mathematics Consultant, Mason, Michigan

In Memory of... William M. Fitzgerald, Professor (Deceased), Michigan State University, who made substantial contributions to conceptualizing and creating CMP1.

Administrative Assistant

Michigan State University
Judith Martus Miller

Support Staff

Michigan State University
Undergraduate Assistants:
Bradley Robert Corlett, Carly Fleming,
Erin Lucian, Scooter Nowak

Development Assistants

Michigan State University
Graduate Research Assistants:
Richard "Abe" Edwards, Nic Gilbertson,
Funda Gonulates, Aladar Horvath,
Eun Mi Kim, Kevin Lawrence, Jennifer Nimtz,
Joanne Philhower, Sasha Wang

Assessment Team

Maine
Falmouth Public Schools
Falmouth Middle School: Shawn Towle

Michigan
Ann Arbor Public Schools
Tappan Middle School:
Anne Marie Nicoll-Turner

Portland Public Schools
Portland Middle School:
Holly DeRosia, Yvonne Grant

Traverse City Area Public Schools
Traverse City East Middle School:
Jane Porath, Mary Beth Schmitt

Traverse City West Middle School:
Jennifer Rundio, Karrie Tufts

Ohio
Clark-Shawnee Local Schools
Rockway Middle School: Jim Mamer

Content Consultants

Michigan State University
Peter Lappan, Professor Emeritus,
Department of Mathematics

Normandale Community College
Christopher Danielson, Instructor,
Department of Mathematics & Statistics

University of North Carolina – Wilmington
Dargan Frierson, Jr., Professor,
Department of Mathematics & Statistics

Student Activities
Michigan State University
Brin Keller, Associate Professor,
Department of Mathematics

Consultants

Indiana
Purdue University
Mary Bouck, Mathematics Consultant

Michigan
Oakland Schools
Valerie Mills, Mathematics Education Supervisor

Mathematics Education Consultants:
Geraldine Devine, Dana Gosen

Ellen Bacon, Independent Mathematics Consultant

New York
University of Rochester
Jeffrey Choppin, Associate Professor

Ohio
University of Toledo
Debra Johanning, Associate Professor

Pennsylvania
University of Pittsburgh
Margaret Smith, Professor

Texas
University of Texas at Austin
Emma Trevino, Supervisor of
Mathematics Programs, The Dana Center

Mathematics for All Consulting
Carmen Whitman, Mathematics Consultant

Reviewers

Michigan
Ionia Public Schools
Kathy Dole, Director of Curriculum
and Instruction

Grand Valley State University
Lisa Kasmer, Assistant Professor

Portland Public Schools
Teri Keusch, Classroom Teacher

Minnesota
Hopkins School District 270
Michele Luke, Mathematics Coordinator

Field Test Sites for CMP3

Michigan
Ann Arbor Public Schools
Tappan Middle School: Anne Marie Nicoll-Turner*

Portland Public Schools
Portland Middle School: Mark Braun,
Angela Buckland, Holly DeRosia, Holly Feldpausch,
Angela Foote, Yvonne Grant*, Kristin Roberts,
Angie Stump, Tammi Wardwell

Traverse City Area Public Schools
Traverse City East Middle School:
Ivanka Baic Berkshire, Brenda Dunscombe,
Tracie Herzberg, Deb Larimer, Jan Palkowski,
Rebecca Perreault, Jane Porath*, Robert Sagan,
Mary Beth Schmitt*

Traverse City West Middle School:
Pamela Alfieri, Jennifer Rundio,
Maria Taplin, Karrie Tufts*

Maine
Falmouth Public Schools
Falmouth Middle School: Sally Bennett,
Chris Driscoll, Sara Jones, Shawn Towle*

Minnesota
Minneapolis Public Schools
Jefferson Community School:
Leif Carlson*,
Katrina Hayek Munsisoumang*

Ohio
Clark-Shawnee Local Schools
Reid School: Joanne Gilley
Rockway Middle School: Jim Mamer*
Possum School: Tami Thomas

*Indicates a Field Test Site Coordinator

Contents

Say It With Symbols
Making Sense of Symbols

▼ Unit Overview

Unit Description

Traditionally, the goal of Algebra instruction has been to develop of students' proficiency in working with expressions and equations. This work includes simplifying, factoring, expanding, evaluating, or solving expressions and equations. In addition to these traditional tasks, *Say It With Symbols* develops the understanding of using symbolic expressions to represent and reason about relationships. The students will write and interpret equivalent expressions, combine expressions to form new expressions, predict patterns of change represented by an equation or expression, and solve equations. This manipulation of symbolic expressions is explored using the properties of equality and the Distributive and Commutative Properties. They will see that the properties reveal new information about a given context by critically examining each part of an expression and explaining how each part relates to the original expression.

This Unit also puts emphasis on multiple representations, such as graphic, tabular, and symbolic representations. Students examine the graph and table of an expression as well as the context the expression models. Having access to graphing calculators and computers will provide students with a natural focus on functions and modeling patterns of quantitative change. If you are teaching this Unit for Grade 8 content only, you may skip Problems 3.3, 3.4, 4.2, 4.3, 4.4 and 5.3. However, parts of Problem 4.4 should be assigned as students need experience in recognizing which function is needed to solve the problem.

Summary of Investigations

Investigation 1: Making Sense of Symbols: Equivalent Expressions

Students have an opportunity to generate and justify, in their own ways, the equivalence of two or more symbolic expressions for the same situation. They are encouraged to think about problems in a variety of ways, leading to different, yet equivalent, expressions. Equivalency is discussed in terms of graphs, tables, and the validity of the reasoning each expression or equation represents. In addition, the structures of the problems reintroduce the important properties of numbers, especially the Distributive Property. By the end of this Investigation, students will have developed a strong sense of the Distributive Property independent of a specific context.

Investigation 2: **Combining Expressions**

In this Investigation, students combine expressions to write new expressions either by adding or subtracting expressions or by substituting an equivalent expression for a given quantity in an expression or equation. They also explore the relationship among the volumes of cylinders, cones, and spheres that have the same height and radius. They describe these relationships with algebraic equations that lead to formulas for the volumes. They use the properties of real numbers to write equivalent expressions as they continue to connect symbolic expressions with real-world contexts.

Investigation 3: **Solving Equations**

In the two previous Investigations, students used the Distributive and Commutative Properties to write equivalent expressions. In this Investigation, they continue to use these properties, as well as the properties of equality, to solve linear equations with parentheses and to solve quadratic equations by factoring.

Investigation 4: **Solving Equations**

In this Investigation, students describe the underlying pattern of change represented by a symbolic equation. They also write symbolic equations to represent specific patterns of change found in a problem and to find answers to specific questions. The last Problem provides several problem situations. Students have to decide which function can be used to represent and solve the problem. This Investigation pulls many of the algebraic ideas from the algebra strand together.

Investigation 5: **Reasoning With Symbols**

Another important aspect of understanding symbols and writing equivalent expressions is their role in confirming or proving a conjecture. Sometimes, as we have seen in writing equivalent expressions, the symbolic statements can reveal additional patterns in the context. In this Investigation, students use their algebraic knowledge to explore why number puzzles work. They also make conjectures about the relationships between the operations on even and odd numbers and use algebraic expressions to confirm their conjectures. They also explore patterns that emerge from squaring an odd number and then subtracting one and again use algebra to confirm their conjecture.

Unit Vocabulary

- Commutative Property of Addition
- Commutative Property of Multiplication
- Distributive Property
- equivalent expressions
- expanded form
- factored form
- properties of equality
- roots

Planning Charts

Investigations & Assessments	Pacing	Materials	Resources
Unit Readiness	Optional		• Unit Readiness*
1 Making Sense of Symbols	4 days	**Labsheet 1.1** Pool Problem **Labsheet 1ACE:** Exercise 3 (accessibility) **Labsheet 1.3** The Community Pool Problem unit squares or tiles (optional)	**Teaching Aid 1.1** Tiling Pools **Teaching Aid 1.3** The Community Pool Problem **Teaching Aid 1.4** Different Dimensions
Mathematical Reflections	½ day		
Assessment: Check Up 1	½ day		• Check Up 1 • Spanish Check Up 1
2 Combining Expressions	4 days	**Labsheet 2ACE:** Exercise 1 (accessibility) graphing calculators (optional); equal dimension plastic geometric cones, cylinders, and spheres (optional); poster paper; markers	• Pouring and Filling
Mathematical Reflections	½ day		
Assessment: Partner Quiz	1 day		• Partner Quiz • Partner Quiz (optional) • Spanish Partner Quiz

continued on next page

▶ UNIT
OVERVIEW   GOALS AND
STANDARDS   MATHEMATICS
BACKGROUND   UNIT
INTRODUCTION   UNIT
PROJECT

Planning Charts *continued*

Investigations & Assessments	Pacing	Materials	Resources
3 Solving Equations	4 days	**Labsheet 3ACE:** Exercise 9 (accessibility) graphing calculators (optional); poster paper; markers	**Teaching Aid 3.1** Solving Linear Equations **Teaching Aid 3.3A** Factoring Quadratic Equations **Teaching Aid 3.3B** Quadratic Expression Model **Teaching Aid 3.4** Solving Quadratic Equations
Mathematical Reflections	½ day		
Assessment: Check Up 2	½ day		• Check Up 2 • Spanish Check Up 2
4 Looking Back at Functions	4 days	**Labsheet 4ACE:** Exercises 1 and 2 (accessibility) **Labsheet 4ACE:** Exercise 25 (accessibility) **Labsheet 4.4** Function Matching graphing calculators (optional); poster paper	**Teaching Aid 4.3** Check for Understanding
Mathematical Reflections	½ day		

continued on next page

Planning Charts *continued*

Investigations & Assessments	Pacing	Materials	Resources
5 Reasoning With Symbols	3 days	**Labsheet 5ACE:** Exercises 1–3 (accessibility) graphing calculators (optional); poster paper (optional); grid paper (optional)	**Teaching Aid 5.2** Bianca's Method **Teaching Aid 5.3** Student Examples
Mathematical Reflections	½ day		
Looking Back	½ day		
Assessment: Unit Project	Optional	Cuisenaire® rods	
Assessment: Self-Assessment	Take Home		• Self-Assessment • Notebook Checklist • Spanish Self-Assessment • Spanish Notebook Checklist
Assessment: Unit Test	1 day		• Unit Test • Spanish Unit Test
Total	25 days	**Materials for All Investigations:** rulers, angle rulers or protractors, miras or mirrors, tracing paper, grid paper, meter sticks	

* Also available as an assignment in MathXL.

Block Pacing (Scheduling for 90-minute class periods)

Investigation	Block Pacing
1 Expressing Equivalence	4½ days
Problem 1.1	1 day
Problem 1.2	1 day
Problem 1.3	1 day
Problem 1.4	1 day
Mathematical Reflections	½ day
2 Combining Expressions	4½ days
Problem 2.1	1 day
Problem 2.2	1 day
Problem 2.3	1 day
Problem 2.4	1 day
Mathematical Reflections	½ day
3 Solving Equations	4½ days
Problem 3.1	1 day
Problem 3.2	1 day
Problem 3.3	1 day
Problem 3.4	1 day
Mathematical Reflections	½ day

Investigation	Block Pacing
4 Looking Back at Functions	4½ days
Problem 4.1	1 day
Problem 4.2	1 day
Problem 4.3	1 day
Problem 4.3	1 day
Mathematical Reflections	½ day
5 Reasoning With Symbols	3½ days
Problem 5.1	1 day
Problem 5.2	1 day
Problem 5.3	1 day
Mathematical Reflections	½ day

Parent Letter

- Parent Letter (English)
- Parent Letter (Spanish)

▼ Goals and Standards

Goals

1. **Equivalence** Develop understanding of equivalent expressions and equations.

   - Model situations with symbolic statements

   - Recognize when two or more symbolic statements represent the same context

   - Use the properties of real numbers, such as the Distributive Property, to write equivalent expressions

   - Determine if different symbolic expressions are mathematically equivalent

   - Interpret the information that equivalent expressions represent in a given context

   - Determine the equivalent expression or equation that is most helpful in answering a particular question about a relationship

   - Use algebraic equations to describe the relationship among the volumes of cylinders, cones and spheres that have the same height and radius

   - Solve linear equations involving parentheses

   - Determine if a linear equation has a finite number of solutions, an infinite number of solutions, or no solution

   - Develop understanding and some fluency with factoring quadratic expressions

   - Solve quadratic equations by factoring

   - Recognize how and when to use symbols, rather than tables or graphs, to display relationships, generalizations, and proofs

2. **Functions** Develop an understanding of specific functions such as linear, exponential, and quadratic functions.

   - Develop proficiency in identifying and representing relationships expressed in problem contexts with appropriate functions and use these relationships to solve the problem

   - Analyze equations to determine the patterns of change in the tables and graphs that the equations represent

   - Relate parts of a symbolic statement or expression to the underlying properties of the relationship they represent and to the context of the problem

   - Determine characteristics of a graph (intercepts, maxima and minima, shape, etc.) of an equation by looking at its symbolic representation

Standards

Common Core Content Standards

8.EE.A.2 Use square root and cube root symbols to represent solutions to equations of the form $x^2 = p$ and $x^3 = p$, where p is a positive rational number. Evaluate square roots of small perfect squares and cube roots of small perfect cubes. Know that $\sqrt{2}$ is irrational. *Investigation 3*

8.EE.C.7 Solve linear equations in one variable. *Investigations 1, 2, 3, and 4*

8.EE.C.7a Give examples of linear equations in one variable with one solution, infinitely many solutions, or no solutions. Show which of these possibilities is the case by successively transforming the given equation into simpler forms, until an equivalent equation of the form $x = a$, $a = a$, or $a = b$ results (where a and b are different numbers). *Investigation 3*

8.EE.C.7b Solve linear equations with rational number coefficients, including equations whose solutions require expanding expressions using the distributive property and collecting like terms. *Investigations 1, 2, 3, 4, and 5*

8.EE.C.8 Analyze and solve pairs of simultaneous linear equations. *Investigation 3*

8.EE.C.8a Understand that solutions to a system of two linear equations in two variables correspond to points of intersection of their graphs, because points of intersection satisfy both equations simultaneously. *Investigation 3*

8.EE.C.8b Solve systems of two linear equations in two variables algebraically, and estimate solutions by graphing the equations. Solve simple cases by inspection. *Investigation 3*

8.EE.C.8c Solve real-world and mathematical problems leading to two linear equations in two variables. *Investigation 3*

8.F.A.1 Understand that a function is a rule that assigns to each input exactly one output. The graph of a function is the set of ordered pairs consisting of an input and the corresponding output. *Investigations 2, 3, 4, and 5*

8.F.A.2 Compare properties of two functions each represented in a different way (algebraically, graphically, numerically in tables, or by verbal descriptions). *Investigations 2, 4, and 5*

8.F.A.3 Interpret the equation $y = mx + b$ as defining a linear function, whose graph is a straight line; give examples of functions that are not linear. *Investigations 1, 2, and 4*

8.F.B.4 Construct a function to model a linear relationship between two quantities. Determine the rate of change and initial value of the function from a description of a relationship or from two (x, y) values, including reading these from a table or from a graph. Interpret the rate of change and initial value of a linear function in terms of the situation it models, and in terms of its graph or a table of values. *Investigations 4 and 5*

8.F.B.5 Describe qualitatively the functional relationship between two quantities by analyzing a graph (e.g., where the function is increasing or decreasing, linear or nonlinear). Sketch a graph that exhibits the qualitative features of a function that has been described verbally. *Investigation 4*

8.G.C.9 Know the formulas for the volumes of cones, cylinders, and spheres and use them to solve real-world and mathematical problems. *Investigation 2*

N-RN.B.3 Explain why the sum or product of two rational numbers is rational; that the sum of a rational number and an irrational number is irrational; and that the product of a nonzero rational number and an irrational number is irrational. *Investigation 5*

N-Q.A.1 Use units as a way to understand problems and do guide the solution of multi-step problems; choose and interpret units consistently in formulas; choose and interpret the scale and the origin in graphs and data displays. *Investigations 2, 3, and 4*

N-Q.A.2 Define appropriate quantities for the purpose of descriptive modeling. *Investigations 2, 3, and 4*

A-SSE.A.1 Interpret expressions that represent a quantity in terms of its context. *Investigations 1, 2, 3, 4, and 5*

A-SSE.A.1a Interpret parts of an expression, such as terms, factors, and coefficients. *Investigations 1, 2, 3, 4, and 5*

A-SSE.A.1b Interpret complicated expressions by viewing one or more of their parts as a single entity. *Investigations 1, 2, 3, 4, and 5*

A-SSE.A.2 Use the structure of an expression to identify ways to rewrite it. *Investigations 1, 2, 3, 4, and 5*

A-SSE.B.3 Choose and produce an equivalent form of an expression to reveal and explain properties of the quantity represented by the expression. *Investigations 1, 2, 3, 4, and 5*

A-SSE.B.3a Factor a quadratic expression to reveal the zeros of the function it defines. *Investigations 3 and 4*

A-CED.A.1 Create equations and inequalities in one variable and use them to solve problems. *Investigations 1, 2, 3, 4, and 5*

A-CED.A.2 Create equations in two or more variables to represent relationships between quantities; graph equations on coordinate axes with labels and scales. *Investigations 3, 4, and 5*

A-REI.A.1 Explain each step in solving a simple equation as following from the equality of numbers asserted at the previous step, starting from the assumption that the original equation has a solution. Construct a viable argument to justify a solution method. *Investigation 3*

UNIT
OVERVIEW

▶ GOALS AND
STANDARDS

MATHEMATICS
BACKGROUND

UNIT
INTRODUCTION

UNIT
PROJECT

A-REI.B.3 Solve linear equations and inequalities in one variable, including equations with coefficients represented by letters. *Investigations 1, 2, 3, and 4*

A-REI.B.4 Solve quadratic equations in one variable. *Investigations 3 and 4*

A-REI.B.4b Solve quadratic equations by inspection (e.g., for $x^2 = 49$), taking square roots, completing the square, the quadratic formula and factoring, as appropriate to the initial form of the equation. Recognize when the quadratic formula gives complex solutions and write them as $a \pm bi$ for real numbers a and b. *Investigations 3 and 4*

A-REI.C.6 Solve systems of linear equations exactly and approximately (e.g., with graphs), focusing on pairs of linear equations in two variables. *Investigation 3*

A-REI.D.10 Understand that the graph of an equation in two variables is the set of all its solutions plotted in the coordinate plane, often forming a curve (which could be a line). *Investigation 3*

A-REI.D.11 Explain why the *x*-coordinates of the points where the graphs of the equations $y = f(x)$ and $y = g(x)$ intersect are the solutions of the equation $f(x) = g(x)$; find the solutions approximately, e.g., using technology to graph the functions, make tables of values, or find successive approximations. Include cases where $f(x)$ and/or $g(x)$ are linear, polynomial, rational, absolute value, exponential, and logarithmic functions. *Investigation 3*

F-IF.C.9 Compare properties of two functions each represented in a different way (algebraically, graphically, numerically in tables, or by verbal descriptions). *Investigations 1, 2, and 4*

F-BF.A.1 Write a function that describes a relationship between two quantities. *Investigations 2, 4, and 5*

F-BF.A.1a Determine an explicit expression, a recursive process, or steps for calculation from a context. *Investigations 1, 2, 3, 4, and 5*

F-LE.A.1 Distinguish between situations that can be modeled with linear functions and with exponential functions. *Investigation 4*

F-LE.A.2 Construct linear and exponential functions, including arithmetic and geometric sequences, given a graph, a description of a relationship, or two input-output pairs (including reading these from a table). *Investigation 4*

F-LE.B.5 Interpret the parameters in a linear or exponential function in terms of a context. *Investigation 4*

Facilitating the Mathematical Practices

Students in *Connected Mathematics* classrooms display evidence of multiple Standards for Mathematical Practice every day. Here are just a few examples of when you might observe students demonstrating the Standards for Mathematical Practice during this Unit.

Practice 1: **Make sense of problems and persevere in solving them.**

Students are engaged every day in solving problems and, over time, learn to persevere in solving them. To be effective, the problems embody critical concepts and skills and have the potential to engage students in making sense of mathematics. Students build understanding by reflecting, connecting, and communicating. These student-centered problem situations engage students in articulating the "knowns" in a problem situation and determining a logical solution pathway. The student-student and student-teacher dialogues help students not only to make sense of the problems, but also to persevere in finding appropriate strategies to solve them. The suggested questions in the Teacher Guides provide the metacognitive scaffolding to help students monitor and refine their problem-solving strategies.

Practice 2: **Reason abstractly and quantitatively.**

In Problem 3.1, students interpret a linear equation in the context of the Problem. By examining the structure of the equation, they see that it shows the difference of two quantities, income and expenses. Similarly, without solving the equation for some value, they recognize that the only constant term is the fixed cost. For this reason, they can conclude that the school choir must sell more than $100 worth of greeting cards before making a profit.

Practice 3: **Construct viable arguments and critique the reasoning of others.**

In Problem 5.1, students use algebra to solve a puzzle that reveals a person's age. From the analysis of the puzzle, students determine how they can change the puzzle to make it work in other years besides the current year. Problems 5.2 and 5.3, present students with informal proofs, or arguments, of number patterns. First they analyze two proofs for the sum of two even numbers. Then they write their own arguments for the sum of an odd and even number and for sums and products involving rational and irrational numbers. They also look for patterns from squaring an odd number and subtracting one. This Problem is rich with opportunities to construct viable algebraic and geometric arguments for the number patterns. In the Summarize for Problem 5.3, they present and discuss their approaches with their classmates.

Practice 4: **Model with mathematics.**

In Problem 2.1, students explore situations that can be modeled using mathematical expressions. The first situation is a walkathon that involves three students who walk together the same distance. Students model, from the individual pledges for each student to a combined expression, the total pledges for the three. Problem 2.2 also involves expressions to model profit and the number of visitors. These two separate expressions are used to make a model for profit based on the probability of rain. In the last two Problems, students revisit volume formulas for cylinders, cones, and spheres to predict the amount of material required to make candles and cups of ice cream. Again, they develop expressions to model each situation and then they use the models to predict the amounts of material required for each situation.

UNIT
OVERVIEW
▶ GOALS AND
STANDARDS
MATHEMATICS
BACKGROUND
UNIT
INTRODUCTION
UNIT
PROJECT

Practice 5: **Use appropriate tools strategically.**

In Problem 2.3, students use clear plastic cylinders, cones, and spheres with the same radius and height to determine the relationship among their volumes. They use water to fill the various containers. In each group, they discover that a cone fills $\frac{1}{3}$ of a cylinder and a sphere fills $\frac{2}{3}$ of a cylinder. The students use this information and the formula for the volume of a cylinder to derive formulas for the volume of a cone and sphere.

Practice 6: **Attend to precision.**

Investigation 4 focuses students on the usage of functions to solve applied problems. In Problem 4.1, students analyze the measurement units associated with the terms of an equation to model pumping water from a pool over time. In Problem 4.2, students find the maximum area and profit. They can use tables and graphs to help identify the maximum. To find a maximum with a table, they must refine the precision of input values. This is done to get the best possible estimate for the maximum. In Problem 4.4 where students select appropriate functions as models for verbal descriptions, they can compare the outputs from a function to see if there is a match with the description. In Question B of Problem 4.4, they provide detailed descriptions of the graphs for the models. Here they give precise values for intercepts, maximums and minimums, as well as patterns of change.

Practice 7: **Look for and make use of structure.**

In Problem 3.2, students notice that there are different ways for solving a linear equation. In the case of determining when the cost of the two companies equal, the first step to the solution varies. Some students apply the Distributive Property while others subtract the fixed cost from both sides of the equations. They also find that graphs and tables are helpful for solving linear equations.

Practice 8: **Look for and express regularity in repeated reasoning.**

In Problem 3.4, students learn that the linear factors of a quadratic equation reveal a characteristic about its graph. When they rewrite an expanded quadratic equation into its factored form and set it equal to 0, the solutions of x are the x-intercepts of the graph associated with the equation. With this new discovery, they can use linear factors to help sketch the graphs of quadratic equations in expanded form.

Students identify and record their personal experiences with the Standards for Mathematical Practice during the Mathematical Reflections at the end of each Investigation.

▼ Mathematics Background

Making Sense of Symbols

Students come to this Unit with considerable experience working with symbolic expressions, tables, and graphs arising from their study of mathematics in Problems from prior Units. Beginning in Grade 6, students learn to examine multiple representations (equations, graphs, tables, diagrams, and verbal descriptions) to help them understand mathematical relationships and to represent mathematical relationships in a variety of ways. In Grade 6, students develop formulas for the area and perimeter of two-dimensional shapes by looking at the relationship between the dimensions of a shape and its perimeter or area. They are introduced to the basic language, concepts, and representations of algebra in *Variables and Patterns*.

In Grade 7, students study geometric relationships, such as the relationship between the number of sides and measures of angles of regular polygons. They also study numerical relationships, such as finding a missing factor or addend in a number sentence. In *Moving Straight Ahead*, they examine linear models in detail, including patterns of change that characterize linear relationships, and they solve equations using tables, graphs, and symbolic methods.

In Grade 8, *Thinking With Mathematical Models* continues the study of linear relationships, but shifts the focus to examining and comparing linear and nonlinear functions, in particular, inverse variation relationships. *Looking For Pythagoras* provides a geometric interpretation of the Pythagorean Theorem. It also provides a geometric interpretation of parallel and perpendicular lines. Questions about variables, relationships, patterns of change, and representations are raised in *Moving Straight Ahead* and applied to exponential functions in *Growing, Growing, Growing*. Quadratic relationships are studied and applied in *Frogs, Fleas, and Painted Cubes*. Up to this point in the development of algebra, representing patterns and reasoning about patterns of change using multiple representations has been the main focus. In addition, students have studied the properties of real numbers, such as the Commutative and Distributive properties, first in *Prime Time*. They have used these properties throughout the remaining Units.

In this Unit, *Say It With Symbols*, the emphasis shifts to using the properties of numbers to look at equivalent expressions and the information each expression represents in a given context and to interpreting the underlying patterns that a symbolic equation or statement represents. Students look critically at each part of an expression and how each part relates to the original expression. They examine the graph and table of an expression as well as the context the expression is modeling. The properties of equality and numbers are used extensively in this Unit as students write and interpret equivalent expressions, combine expressions to form new ones, predict patterns of change represented by an equation or expression, and solve equations. Students continue to develop their algebraic skills in the remaining Grade 8 and Algebra 1 Units. Collectively, the Algebra Units and, in particular, this Unit help to develop what we call "symbol sense."

This Unit develops students' facility in reasoning with purely symbolic expressions. They observe how symbolic expressions are used in real situations in the Problems. This Unit provides meaningful settings to motivate conventional algebraic notation and techniques. Thinking with symbolic expressions, in situations where mathematics is applied, plays a significant role in developing a student's "symbolic sense" or fluency with symbolic statements.

The Unit is organized around five aspects of symbolic expressions: creating and interpreting equivalent expressions, combining expressions, solving equations, observing patterns of change, and reasoning with symbols. Throughout all of the Investigations, the Problems require students to write symbolic statements to model a situation, interpret symbolic statements, write equivalent symbolic expressions, and make predictions using symbolic statements.

Equivalent Expressions

In *Variables and Patterns* and *Moving Straight Ahead*, students explored ways in which relationships can be expressed in tables, graphs, and equations. The contextual clues or the patterns in tables or graphs strongly influenced the construction of a single equation or expression, so students did not gain experience with equivalent equations. In this Unit, students are deliberately presented with situations in which contextual clues can be interpreted in several ways to produce different equations or expressions that are equivalent.

Example
Find the number of 1-foot-square tiles *N* needed to make a border around a square pool with sides of length *s* feet.

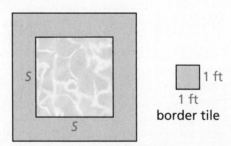

Different conceptualizations of the situation can lead to different equivalent expressions for the number of tiles; e.g., $N = 4(s + 1)$, $N = 4(s + 2) - 4$, or $N = (s + 2)^2 - s^2$.

continued on next page

Verifying Equivalence

At this stage of development, students may consider the reasonableness of the geometric reasoning represented by each equation. For example, the equation $N = 4(s + 1)$ represents the following geometric pattern: The border is divided into four rectangles with dimensions $(s + 1)$ and 1, resulting in the equation $N = 4(s + 1)$.

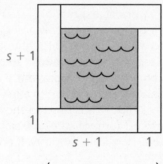

Or students might use the following geometric pattern for the equivalent equation $N = 4(s + 2) - 4$.

Example

Add the four long strips along the sides and then subtract the four corner tiles that are counted twice, resulting in the equation $N = 4(s + 2) - 4$.

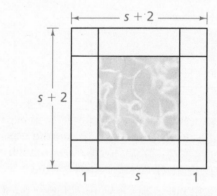

Students may also generate a table or graph to show that the expressions are equivalent for the number of border tiles. Some students may realize from the table and graph that the relationship is linear. They find that the constant rate of change is 4, the y-intercept is 4, and the equation is $N = 4s + 4$.

UNIT
OVERVIEW

GOALS AND
STANDARDS

▶ MATHEMATICS
BACKGROUND

UNIT
INTRODUCTION

UNIT
PROJECT

In Problem 1.2, students also verify that the expressions for the number of border tiles are equivalent using the Distributive and Commutative properties. They may have questions about the expression $(s + 2)^2 - s^2$ for the number of border tiles because it seems quadratic. Using the Distributive and Commutative properties, they verify that it is equivalent to $4s + 4$.

The Distributive Property

The Distributive Property was first introduced in *Prime Time* and then used in several sixth, seventh, and eighth grade Units in the linear form, $a(b + c) = ab + ac$. In *Frogs, Fleas, and Painted Cubes*, the Distributive Property was extended to binomials, $(a + b)(c + d)$. In each case, an area model was used to show the relationship between the expanded and factored form of an expression. The diagram below illustrates two aspects of the Distributive Property. If an expression is written as a factor multiplied by a sum of two or more terms, the Distributive Property can be applied to multiply the factor by each term in the sum. If an expression is written as a sum of terms, and the terms have a common factor, the Distributive Property can be applied to rewrite or factor the expression as the common factor multiplied by a sum of two or more terms.

The Distributive Property

$r(s + t) = rs + rt,$
for any real numbers r, s, and t.

multiply

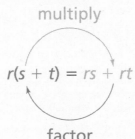

$r(s + t) = rs + rt$

factor

The Distributive Property allows students to group symbols or to expand an expression. It is one of the most important properties for writing equivalent expressions. In Investigation 3, a realistic context motivates a rule for distributing a negative sign. The following example provides some informal understanding for the general idea that $a - (b + c) = a - b - c$.

> ### Example
> Suppose a checking account contains $100 at the start of the week. Two checks are written during the week, one for $22 and one for $50. Find the balance in the account at the end of the week.
>
> **Method 1**
>
> $100 - (22 + 50) = 28$
>
> **Method 2**
>
> $100 - 22 - 50 = 28$

continued on next page

Mathematically, the relationship can be represented as an equation and rewritten.

$$a - (b + c) = a + (-1)(b + c)$$
$$= a + (-1)b + (-1)c$$
$$= a - b - c$$

Practice multiplying binomials and factoring simple quadratic expressions is provided throughout the Unit as students write equivalent quadratic expressions or solve quadratic equations.

Interpreting Expressions

Identifying and interpreting information that is represented by expressions occurs in all of the Problems. In the first two Problems, 1.1 and 1.2, students interpret the geometric patterns that are represented by each student's equation for the number of border tiles based on the dimensions of the square pool. In Problem 1.3, students interpret a symbolic expression that has the added complexity of being a quadratic expression.

Example

A community center is building a pool with part of it indoors and part of it outdoors. A diagram of the indoor part of the pool is shown. The indoor shape is made from a half-circle and a rectangle. The diagram does not show the shape of the outdoor part of the pool. The exact dimensions of the pool are unavailable, but the area A of the whole pool is given by $A = \frac{\pi x^2}{2} + x^2 + 8x^2 + \frac{\pi x^2}{4}$.

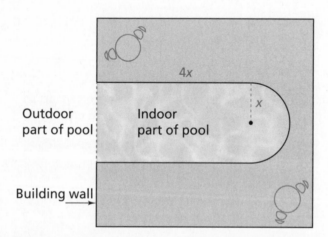

Students identify the part of the expression that represents the area of the indoor part $\left(\frac{\pi x^2}{2} + 8x^2\right)$ and also the part of the expression that represents the outdoor part $\left(x^2 + \frac{\pi x^2}{4}\right)$. Then they sketch a shape for the outdoor part of the pool, which has many possibilities.

UNIT
OVERVIEW

GOALS AND
STANDARDS

▶ MATHEMATICS
BACKGROUND

UNIT
INTRODUCTION

UNIT
PROJECT

Using Expressions and Equations

In the first example, students write expressions to represent the number of border tiles needed to surround a square pool. Some of these expressions are $4s + 4$, $4(s + 1)$, $4(s + 2) - 4$, and $2s + 2(s + 2)$. An expression represents a quantity, so there is a relationship implied by an expression. Here, each expression represents the quantity or the number of tiles N. In this situation, we can say $N =$ the expression. The expression could be any one of the expressions listed above or any other equivalent expression. The implied relationship that is represented by the equation in this example is linear. That is, the relationship between the number of tiles N and the length of the square pool s is a linear relationship.

Combining Expressions

In Investigation 2, students combine expressions to write new expressions either by adding or subtracting expressions, or by substituting an equivalent expression for a given quantity in another expression that contains the quantity.

Adding Expressions

Problem 2.1 revisits a walkathon from *Moving Straight Ahead*. It provides students an opportunity to apply the Distributive and Commutative properties to write equivalent expressions for the total amount of money raised by the students in a walkathon.

> ### Example
> Leanne, Gilberto, and Alana enter a walkathon as a team. This means that each person will walk the same distance in kilometers. The walkathon organizers offer a prize to the three-person team that raises the most money.
>
> The individual pledges for each student are as follows:
>
> - Leanne has pledges from 16 sponsors. All of her sponsors pledge $10 regardless of how far she walks.
>
> - Gilberto has pledges from 7 sponsors. Each sponsor pledges $2 for each kilometer he walks.
>
> - Alana has pledges from 11 sponsors. Each sponsor pledges $5 plus $50 for each kilometer she walks.

continued on next page

Students first write three expressions to represent the total amount of money raised by each student.

$$M_{Leane} = 16(10)$$
$$M_{Gilberto} = 7(2x)$$
$$M_{Alana} = 11(5 + 0.50x)$$

Then they use these equations to find the total by using them to calculate the money raised by each student, or by combining (adding) the three expressions to form one expression that represents the total amount of money M_{Total} raised by all three students if each walks x kilometers.

$$M_{Total} = 16(10) + 7(2x) + 11(5 + 0.50x)$$

Students then find an equivalent expression for the total amount of money. They interpret the information the variables and numbers represent in the new expression and discuss the advantages or disadvantages of each expression.

Making New Expressions by Substitution

In Problem 2.2, students write one linear equation to predict the profit P for an amusement park based on the probability of rain R by substituting an expression for the number of visitors into the profit equation.

> ### Example
> The manager of the Water Town amusement park uses data collected over the past several years to write equations that will help her make predictions about the daily operations of the park. The daily concession-stand profit in dollars P depends on the number of visitors V. To model this relationship, the manager writes $P = 2.5V - 500$. To predict the number of visitors V based on the probability of rain R, she uses $V = 600 - 500R$. Write an equation that can be used to predict the profit based on the probability of rain.

This requires students to replace V in the first equation with $600 - 500R$, the equivalent expression for the number of visitors from the second equation. The equation after the substitution is $P = 2.50(600 - 500R)$. Students then write an equivalent expression for profit and compare the information each expression represents for the amusement park.

UNIT
OVERVIEW

GOALS AND
STANDARDS

▶ MATHEMATICS
BACKGROUND

UNIT
INTRODUCTION

UNIT
PROJECT

Expressions Representing Relationships Among the Volumes of a Cylinder, Cone, and Sphere

Volume of cones, cylinders, and spheres is used as a context to generate interesting algebraic expressions. Students use plastic shapes of cylinders, cones, and spheres that have the same height and radius to explore how the volumes of these shapes are related when $h = 2r$. The Pouring and Filling activity allows them to do the same thing on a computer. Before this experiment, students determine a formula for the volume of a cylinder. Some of the relationships that they discover are shown in the table:

Relationships Among the Volumes of Cylinders, Cones, and Spheres

	$V_{cone} = \frac{1}{3}\pi r^2 h$ or $\frac{2}{3}\pi r^3$
	$V_{sphere} = \frac{2}{3}\pi r^2 h$ or $\frac{4}{3}\pi r^3$
	$V_{cone} + V_{sphere} = \pi r^2 h$ or $V_{cylinder}$
	$V_{cone} = \frac{1}{2}V_{sphere}$
	$V_{sphere} = 2V_{cone}$
	$V_{cylinder} = 3V_{cone}$
	$V_{cylinder} = 1\frac{1}{2}V_{sphere}$
	$V_{sphere} = V_{cylinder} - V_{cone}$

Students then use these relationships to determine formulas for finding the volumes of the three shapes.

Solving Equations

One aspect of developing students' facility with symbols is to use equations to make predictions or answer specific questions. This sometimes requires solving equations for a specific variable.

Solving Linear Equations

Students are quite comfortable using tables or graphs to solve equations, and they can solve simple linear equations of the form $y = mx + b$, $mx + b = nx + c$, or simple equations with parentheses, such as $y = a(x + b)$. In Investigation 3, students solve more complicated equations.

Example

A school choir is selling boxes of greeting cards to raise money for a trip. The equation for the profit in dollars P in terms of the number of boxes sold s is $P = 5s - (100 + 2s)$.

- What information do the expressions $5s$ and $100 + 2s$ represent?

  $5s$ represents the income for selling s boxes at $5 a box. $(100 + 2s)$ represents the cost of selling s boxes; that is, $2 per box and $100 for miscellaneous expenses, such as advertising.

- How many boxes must the choir sell to make a $200 profit? Explain.

  Students might use a calculator or they could substitute values for s. Some may be ready to try to solve this using the properties of equality and the Distributive Property.

- What is the break-even point?

  Students may recognize that income must be equal to cost to break even. They then set $5s = 100 + 2s$ and solve for s. Some students may use tables or graphs.

- Write an equivalent expression for profit. What new information does this expression represent?

- One of the choir members wrote the following expression for profit: $5s - 2(50 + s)$. Explain whether this expression is equivalent to the original expression for profit.

- Describe how to solve an equation that has parentheses without using a table or graph.

The first few questions are similar to those that have been asked early in this Unit or in previous Units, but this equation involves more work with the use of parentheses. Students use the Distributive Property to show that the two expressions for profit, $5s - (100 + 2s)$ and $5s - 2(50 + s)$, are equivalent. In this

UNIT
OVERVIEW

GOALS AND
STANDARDS

▶ MATHEMATICS
BACKGROUND

UNIT
INTRODUCTION

UNIT
PROJECT

Problem, the focus is on developing techniques for solving equations symbolically without using tables and graphs. The last question pushes students to think about solving linear equations, the properties of equality, and the numbers that solve this equation. Next, they apply these strategies to equations like $y = 5 + 2(3 + 4x)$ or $y = 5 - 2(3 - 4x)$.

Conditional Equations, Identities, and Contradictions

The basic property of equality states that performing the same operation to each side of an equation does not change its solution. That is, if the original equality is true, then applying the properties of equality will not affect the solution.

For each example, find a value of x that makes $y_1 = y_2$. **Note:** All graphs use the window setting shown below.

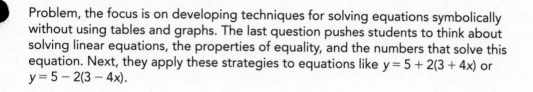

```
WINDOW
  Xmin=-20
  Xmax=20
  Xscl=2
  Ymin=-120
  Ymax=120
  Yscl=10
```

A *conditional equation* has at least one solution. For example, a linear equation has one solution.

Example

$y_1 = 3(2x - 5)$

$y_2 = 2(3x - 1) + x$

$3(2x - 5) = 2(3x - 1) + x$

$6x - 15 = 6x - 2 + x$

$6x - 15 = 7x - 2$

$-13 = x$

The graph of the equations is of a pair of intersecting lines, which have exactly one point in common.

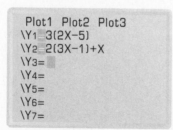

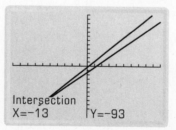

continued on next page

An *identity* has an infinite number of solutions. Its solutions are true for all values of the variable.

Example

$y_1 = 3(2x - 5)$

$y_2 = 2(3x - 1) - 13$

$3(2x - 5) = 2(3x - 1) - 13$

$6x - 15 = 6x - 2 - 13$

$6x - 15 = 6x - 15$

$0 = 0$ Always true.

This is an identity. All real numbers are a solution to this equation.

The graph of the equations is of a pair of equivalent lines, which have an infinite number of points in common. That is, their points all lie on the same line.

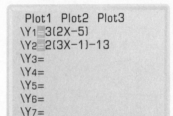   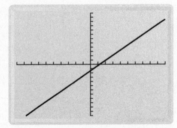

A *contradiction* has no solutions. This implies a contradiction of some known fact.

Example

$y_1 = 3(2x - 5)$

$y_2 = 2(3x - 1) + 7$

$3(2x - 5) = 2(3x - 1) + 7$

$6x - 15 = 6x - 2 + 7$

$6x - 15 = 6x + 5$

$-15 = 5$ False.

This is a contradiction. There is no solution.

The graph of the equations is of a pair of parallel lines, which have no points in common.

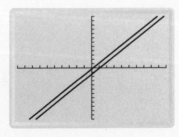

UNIT
OVERVIEW

GOALS AND
STANDARDS

▶ MATHEMATICS
BACKGROUND

UNIT
INTRODUCTION

UNIT
PROJECT

In summary, an equation is called

- a conditional equation if it has at least one solution. (A linear equation has one solution.)
- an identity if it has all the numbers in a specified set as solutions.
- a contradiction if it has no solutions. It implies a contradiction of some known fact.

Note: In the student book, we do not use the terms, conditional, identity, and contradiction because the definitions include information about conditional equations that students have not yet encountered. For example, the equation $\sin(x) = 0.5$ is conditional, but it has an infinite number of solutions. Instead we use the language from CCSS, which is to state whether the linear equation has one solution, no solution, or an infinite number of solutions.

Solving Quadratic Equations

To solve quadratic equations like $0 = 2x^2 + 8$ or $0 = x^2 + 5x + 6$, students recognize that these equations are specific cases of the equations, $y = 2x^2 + 8$ or $y = x^2 + 5x + 6$. Finding x when $y = 0$ is the same as finding the x-intercepts of the graphs of these equations. Students have already had experience solving quadratic equations in *Frogs, Fleas, and Painted Cubes* using tables and graphs. In Investigation 3, the connection is made between solving quadratic equations for x when $y = 0$ and finding x-intercepts. Students are introduced to solving quadratic equations by factoring and solve for x when $y = 0$. They solve equations of the form $y = ax(x + b)$, $y = x^2 + bx$, or $y = ax^2 + bx + c$ that are easily factored into the product of two binomials.

Example
If $y = 2x^2 + 8x$ find the values of x when $y = 0$.

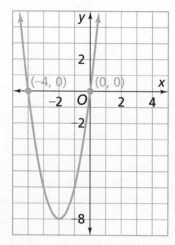

continued on next page

Students need to recognize that the expression $2x^2 + 8x$ can be rewritten in the equivalent form of $2x(x + 4)$. Next, they must recognize that this product can only be zero if one of the factors, $2x$ or $x + 4$, is equal to zero. This is known as the Zero Product Rule, if $ab = 0$, then $a = 0$ or $b = 0$. Thus, $2x = 0$ or $x + 4 = 0$. Solving each of these linear equations gives $x = 0$ or $x = -4$.

It is important that students understand that finding x when $y = 0$ is the same as finding the x-intercepts of the graph of $y = 2x^2 + 8x$. Important steps are factoring the quadratic expression and applying the fact that for any two real numbers, a and b, if $ab = 0$, then either $a = 0$ or $b = 0$.

Example

If $y = x^2 + 5x + 6$, find the values of x when $y = 0$.

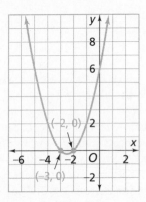

Students write $y = x^2 + 5x + 6$ in factored form $(x + 2)(x + 3)$ and then solve $0 = (x + 2)(x + 3)$. Thus, $x + 2 = 0$, which means $x = -2$, or $x + 3 = 0$, which means $x = -3$.

Students are asked to check their solutions when solving equations. Frequently, they are also asked to connect the solutions to a quadratic equation to its graph.

Factoring

Before quadratic equations are solved, students spend time factoring quadratic expressions in Problem 3.3. It is important to note that factoring is mostly trial and error using clues from the coefficients of x, x^2, and the constant term. Given any three real numbers for a, b, and c in $ax^2 + bx + c$, it is unlikely that the expression is easily factorable, even if a, b, and c are whole numbers between 1 and 10. Over a number of years, mathematicians developed the quadratic formula that can be applied to any quadratic equation. It states that if $0 = ax^2 + bx + c$, then $x = \frac{-b \pm \sqrt{b^2 - 4ac}}{2a}$. What is important is that students understand that quadratic expressions can be written in two equivalent forms, expanded form and a factored form, and that these two expressions represent different pieces of information about the underlying quadratic function or the context that it models. Students should be able to factor simple quadratic expressions and understand how factoring quadratic expressions uses the Distributive Property. The quadratic formula is developed in the Grade 8 *Unit Function Junction*.

Predicting the Underlying Patterns of Change

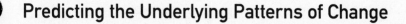

Prior to this Unit, the focus of the algebra strand has been the study of patterns of change between two variables. Students represented these relationships using tables, graphs, and symbolic statements. They used these representations to study the special patterns of change associated with linear, exponential, and quadratic functions and the used them to solve equations. For linear situations, the statements were in the form of $y = mx + b$; for exponential situations, the statements were in the form $y = a(b^x)$; and for quadratic situations, the statements were in the form $y = ax^2 + bx + c$ or $y = (x + p)(x + q)$. Students used contexts or representations to determine whether a situation is linear, exponential, quadratic, or none of these and to write an equation to model the situation. The following discussion reviews patterns of change associated with linear, exponential, and quadratic functions.

Patterns of Change

Example

$y = 70 - 5x$

x	0	1	2	3	4	5
y	70	65	60	55	50	45

first differences   −5   −5   −5   −5   −5

The coefficient of x, -5, is the constant rate of change and the slope for this linear relationship. The constant term, 70, is the y-intercept. When the equation represents a "real" situation, then parts of the equation are directly related to specific values in the situation. For example, a club has \$70 to spend on a trip. If the trip costs \$5 per person, then y or $y = 70 - 5x$ represents the amount of money left if x people go on the trip.

Example

$y = 3(2)^x$

x	0	1	2	3	4	5
y	3	6	12	24	48	96

constant factors   × 2   × 2   × 2   × 2   × 2

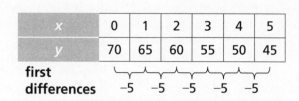

continued on next page

The base 2 is the constant growth factor and 3 is the y-intercept. As x increases by 1, y changes by a factor of 2. When the equation represents a "real" situation, then parts of the equation are directly related to specific values in the situation. For example, suppose the Queen of Montarek offers a peasant three rubas at the start and then doubles the amount of money each day. Then the equation $y = 3(2)^x$ represents the amount of money y on day x.

Example

$y = x(x + 1)$ or $y = x^2 + x$

x	0	1	2	3	4	5
y	0	2	6	12	20	30

first differences   2   4   6   8   10

second differences   2   2   2   2

Students can recognize quadratic equations by looking at second differences of successive values of y. Writing the associated quadratic equation is a bit more challenging. In quadratic situations, the y-value grows in some relation to the square of the x-value. In this example, the y-value grows as the square of the x-value, x^2 plus x. For large values of x, x^2 is much larger than x. The equation is characterized by a constant second difference, 2. In calculus, they will learn that this difference is the second derivative of the function.

Students also recognize that the graph of $y = x(x + 1)$ has a minimum point at $\left(-\frac{1}{2}, -\frac{1}{4}\right)$, and x-intercepts are $(0, 0)$ and $(-1, 0)$.

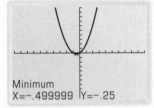

Minimum
X=−.499999 Y=−.25

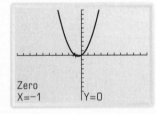

Zero
X=−1   Y=0

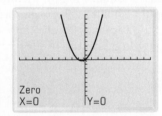

Zero
X=0   Y=0

This equation could represent the number of handshakes that take place between two teams, one with x members and one with $x + 1$ members. For quadratic equations, the expression for y can be written in expanded or factored form. The form to use depends on the information that is needed. To predict the y-intercept and patterns of change, the expression $x^2 + x$ is best to use. To predict the x-intercepts, line of symmetry, and the maximum or minimum points, the expression $x(x + 1)$ is best to use.

UNIT
OVERVIEW

GOALS AND
STANDARDS

▶ MATHEMATICS
BACKGROUND

UNIT
INTRODUCTION

UNIT
PROJECT

Even though the first three Investigations of this Unit focus on equivalent expressions and solving equations, students are frequently asked to describe the patterns of change that a situation or equation represent. Predicting patterns of change and interpreting the special features of a function is the focus of Investigation 4. This Investigation provides some contexts that involve more complex equations, including some that involve all three functions. Finally, Investigation 4 serves as a cumulative review for the algebra strand up to this point.

Predicting Linear Patterns of Change

In *Moving Straight Ahead*, students learned about linear relationships. In Investigation 4, students focus on a situation in which the pattern of change is linear, that is, the constant difference is the slope.

Example

Magnolia Middle School needs to empty their pool for resealing. Ms. Theodora's math class decides to collect data on the amount of water in the pool and the time it takes to empty it. They write an equation to represent the amount of water w (in gallons) in the pool after t hours.

$w = -250(t - 5)$

- How many gallons of water are pumped out each hour?

- How long will it take to empty the pool?

- How many gallons of water are in the pool at the start?

- Write an expression for the amount of water in the tank after t hours that is equivalent to the original expression.

- What information does this new expression tell you about the amount of water in the tank?

- Which expression is more useful in this situation? Explain

- Without graphing the equation, describe the shape of the graph.

This linear situation contains parentheses that students have briefly encountered in *Moving Straight Ahead* and *Thinking With Mathematical Models*. To find the rate at which water is being pumped out per hour, students may use a variety of strategies.

- They may make a table and note that as t increases by 1, the water decreases by 250 gallons.

- They may substitute values into the equations and note the difference between two consecutive hours.

- They may apply the Distributive Property and write $w = -250t + 1,250$ and then recognize that the coefficient of t is the constant rate of change for a linear relationship.

continued on next page

The amount of water at the start of the pumping is the w-intercept, which students may read from an equivalent expression for the amount of water in the tank, or they can use a table or graph. Similarly, to find how long it will take to empty the pool, they may solve the equation for $w = 0$, or use a table or graph. Some students may note that the expression is in factored form and if the amount of water w is 0, then one of the factors must be 0. So, $t - 5 = 0$ or $t = 5$. Students also describe the graph of the relationship without making a table or graph.

These questions are similar to questions asked in previous Units except that the expression for the amount of water contains parentheses. This is an example of interpreting symbolic statements to find specific information about the situation and describing the underlying relationship that the equation represents. This Problem is followed by a Problem in which students make a table of values for linear, exponential, and quadratic equations, given the same two points for each relationship.

Writing Equations for Linear, Exponential, and Quadratic Functions Given Two Points

In prior Units, students learned about linear, exponential, and quadratic relationships. In Problem 4.3, students focus on constructing patterns with a specific type of relationship from two coordinates.

Example

The first two rows in a table of numbers are given below. Write four more numbers in each column to make a linear relationship, an exponential relationship, and a quadratic relationship.

Data Points

x	Linear y	Exponential y	Quadratic y
1	1	1	1
2	4	4	4
3	▪	▪	▪
4	▪	▪	▪
5	▪	▪	▪
6	▪	▪	▪

- Explain why the relationship in each column works.

- Write an equation for each relationship. Explain what information the variables and numbers represent.

- Compare your equations with your classmates' equations. Do you all have the same equations? Explain.

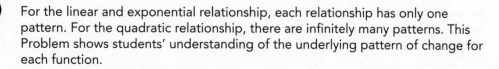

For the linear and exponential relationship, each relationship has only one pattern. For the quadratic relationship, there are infinitely many patterns. This Problem shows students' understanding of the underlying pattern of change for each function.

Finally, this Investigation ends with a Problem in which students match descriptions of situations with the appropriate function type. Then they write an equation to represent each situation and describe the shape of each graph with as much detail as possible, including the pattern of change, the *x*- and *y*-intercepts, the maximum or minimum points, and the line of symmetry.

Reasoning With Symbols

In Investigation 5, the central idea is to use symbolic statements and appropriate mathematical properties to confirm conjectures. In *Prime Time*, students conjectured that the sum of two odd numbers and the sum of two even numbers are even. They tried many examples that confirmed their conjecture, and they used geometric arrangements of square tiles to validate their conjecture. They arranged rectangular arrays whose dimensions were 2 and *n*, where *n* is a whole number, to represent even numbers. The arrays for odd numbers were the same as those for even except that they had one extra piece added to the rectangle.

Some students argued that even numbers have a factor of 2, so the sum of two even numbers will have a factor of 2. For odd numbers, they argued that you are combining the two extra 1's to end up with an even number. Using symbolic statements is a way to confirm these intuitive arguments.

Using Symbolic Statements to Confirm a Conjecture

If *n* is any integer, then $2n$ represents an even number and $2n + 1$ represents an odd number. The sum of two even numbers is even:

Let $2m$ and $2n$ represent any two even numbers.

$$2m + 2n = 2(m + n)$$

The number $2(m + n)$ is even, so the sum of two even numbers is even.

continued on next page

The sum of two odd numbers is even:

Let $2m + 1$ and $2n + 1$ represent any two odd numbers.

$$(2m + 1) + (2n + 1) = 2m + 2n + 2$$
$$= 2(n + m + 1)$$

The number $2(n + m + 1)$ is even, so the sum of two odd numbers is even.

Similar arguments can be used for the following:

- Sum of an odd and an even number
- Product of an odd and an even number

The symbolic arguments offer a very precise and convincing argument for all integers. In the next example, students look for patterns in a quadratic relationship, and then find a way to confirm their conjectures about the patterns.

Example

Perform the following operations on the first eight odd numbers. Record your information in a table.

- Pick an odd number.
- Square it.
- Subtract 1.

- What patterns do you see in the resulting numbers?
- Make conjectures about these numbers. Explain why your conjectures are true for any odd number.

If students try this procedure for the first few odd numbers, they quickly see that the numbers are multiples of 8. If they rewrite each number as a product of 8, they also see that each of these numbers is 8 times a triangular number.

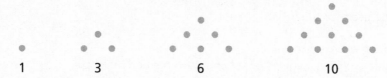

s	1	3	5	7
$s^2 - 1$	0	8	24	48
Pattern	8×0	8×1	8×3	8×6

The nth triangular number is represented by $\frac{n(n + 1)}{2}$.

1   3   6   10

So, $s^2 - 1 = \frac{8n(n + 1)}{2}$, where s is an odd number and $n = 1, 2, 3, \ldots$

$s^2 - 1$

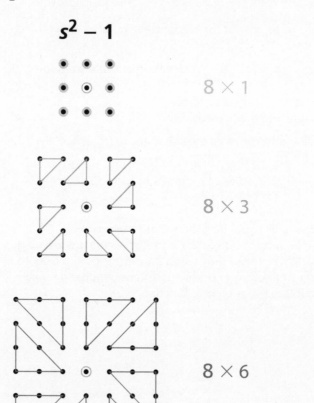

8×1

8×3

8×6

continued on next page

The inductive proof can be proven deductively in the following algebra proof.

Let $2n + 1$ represent an odd number.

$$(2n + 1)^2 - 1 = 4n^2 + 4n + 1 - 1$$
$$= 4n^2 + 4n$$
$$= 4n(n + 1)$$
$$= \frac{8n(n + 1)}{2}$$

Since $\frac{n(n + 1)}{2}$ is the nth triangular number, squaring an odd number and subtracting 1 is 8 times a triangular number.

The first part of this Problem, which involves observing patterns and making conjectures, is accessible to all students. Whether you want to help students develop a symbolic argument at this time is a decision you can make based on your students' needs. In this Unit, students

- Write symbolic expressions to represent the dependent variable in a situation

- Write equivalent expressions to reveal new information about a situation

- Interpret expressions

- Use expressions and equations to make decisions

- Solve equations and predict patterns of change that are represented by symbolic statements

- Use symbolic statements and properties of numbers to provide arguments for conjectures

Much of the work involved in this Unit could be thought of as developing traditional algebra skills, but an important difference is that students are learning these skills in a purposeful way. Not only are they using properties of numbers to write equivalent expressions, they are using expressions and equations to make important decisions about a problem situation or a function.

Unit Introduction

Introducing Your Students to Say It With Symbols

To begin the Unit, ask the class to give some examples of symbolic expressions or equations that represent exponential, linear and quadratic relationships in previous Units. You can post these examples in the classroom. Ask:

- What information do the numbers and symbols represent in the problem?

- If you know the value of one variable, explain how you could find the value of the other variable?

- Describe the shape of the graph.

- Describe a possible context or problem that this expression or equation could symbolize.

Using the Unit Opener

Refer students to the three questions posed on the Looking Ahead page in the Student Edition. You may want to have a class discussion about these questions so students can share their ideas about what is needed to give an answer. As you listen to the students, ask yourself:

- Can they evaluate expressions for a given value of one of the independent variables?

- Do they recognize the patterns of change associated with each relationship?

- Can they relate parts of the symbolic expression or equation for the relationship to the table and graph of the equation?

This introduction will raise issues related to reading, interpreting, and evaluating symbolic expressions. Therefore it is not important to look for "correct" answers at this time. You may want to revisit these questions as students learn the mathematical ideas and techniques necessary to find the answers.

Using the Mathematical Highlights

The Mathematical Highlights page in the Student Edition provides information to students, parents, and other family members. It gives students a preview of the mathematics and some of the overarching questions that they should ask themselves while studying *Say It With Symbols*.

As they work through the Unit, students can refer back to the Mathematical Highlights page to review what they have learned and to preview what is still to come. This page also tells students' families what mathematical ideas and activities will be covered as the class works through *Say It With Symbols*.

▼ Unit Project

Introduction

The Unit Project can be used as the final assessment to *Say It With Symbols*. It allows students to apply what they have learned about writing algebraic expressions to describe patterns and verifying the equivalence to those expressions.

In *Finding the Surface Area of Rod Stacks*, students find the surface areas of stacks of rods of certain lengths by varying the number of rods n. They describe a pattern and find the relationship between the number of rods n and the surface area of the stack A. The equation for the surface area is a linear relationship in terms of the number of rods used. Students will find that different but equivalent expressions can be used to model the data. You could include questions about volume by asking how many unit rods will be needed to build a stack of n rods of length x. Then ask the students to determine the function that can model this situation.

Materials

Cuisenaire® rods for each student:

4 to 6 rods in each of three colors

3 to 4 unit rods

Assigning

Provide a set of rods so students have a physical example of the rod stack in Unit Project pages of the Student Edition. Hold up one of the colored rods and ask students:

- How long is this rod?

Providing Additional Support

You may want to have students begin the Project in class so that they are able to share their results for rods of length 2–10 (Part 1, Questions 5 and 6). If you do not begin in class, make sure that students get a chance to share their equations with each other. There will be more than one way to find an expression for, say, the green rods. Encourage students to compare their symbolic expressions with other groups. Remind students to include and discuss examples of equivalent expressions for a given rod length in their final write up of this Project.

UNIT
OVERVIEW

GOALS AND
STANDARDS

MATHEMATICS
BACKGROUND

UNIT
INTRODUCTION

▶ **UNIT
PROJECT**

Grading

Suggested Scoring Rubric

This rubric for scoring the Project employs a scale that runs from 0 to 4, with a 4+ for work that goes beyond what has been asked for in some unique way. You may use the rubric as presented here or modify it to fit your district's requirements for evaluating and reporting students' work and understanding.

4+ Exemplary Response

- Complete, with clear, coherent explanations
- Shows understanding of the mathematical concepts and procedures
- Satisfies all essential conditions of the problem and goes beyond what is asked for in some unique way

4 Complete Response

- Complete, with clear, coherent explanations
- Shows understanding of the mathematical concepts and procedures
- Satisfies all essential conditions of the problem

3 Reasonably Complete Response

- Reasonably complete; may lack detail in explanations
- Shows understanding of most of the mathematical concepts and procedures
- Satisfies most of the essential conditions of the problem

2 Partial Response

- Gives response; explanation may be unclear or lack detail
- Shows some understanding of some of the mathematical concepts and procedures
- Satisfies some essential conditions of the problem

1 Inadequate Response

- Incomplete; explanation is insufficient or not understandable
- Shows little understanding of the mathematical concepts and procedures
- Fails to address essential conditions of problem

0 No Attempt

- Irrelevant response
- Does not attempt a solution
- Does not address conditions of the problem

Unit Project Answers

1. & 4. Students will choose different rods, so answers will vary from 2 by 1 by 1 to 10 by 1 by 1.

2. & 4.

Length 2

Number of Rods	Surface Area
1	10
2	18
3	26
4	34
5	42

Length 3

Number of Rods	Surface Area
1	14
2	24
3	34
4	44
5	54

Length 4

Number of Rods	Surface Area
1	18
2	30
3	42
4	54
5	66

Length 5

Number of Rods	Surface Area
1	22
2	36
3	50
4	64
5	78

Length 6

Number of Rods	Surface Area
1	26
2	42
3	58
4	74
5	90

Length 7

Number of Rods	Surface Area
1	30
2	48
3	66
4	84
5	102

Length 8

Number of Rods	Surface Area
1	34
2	54
3	74
4	94
5	114

Length 9

Number of Rods	Surface Area
1	38
2	60
3	82
4	104
5	126

Length 10

Number of Rods	Surface Area
1	42
2	66
3	90
4	114
5	138

For every set of rods, each additional rod adds the same amount to the surface area.

Length of Rod Added	Surface Area Increase
2	8
3	10
4	12
5	14
6	16
7	18
8	20
9	22
10	24

3. & 4.

Length (cm)	Equation in the Form $y = mx + b$
2	$A = 8n + 2$
3	$A = 10n + 4$
4	$A = 12n + 6$
5	$A = 14n + 8$
6	$A = 16n + 10$
7	$A = 18n + 12$
8	$A = 20n + 14$
9	$A = 22n + 16$
10	$A = 24n + 18$

Some strategies students may use are given. **Note:** All of the examples use a rod of length 4.

Strategy 1 Students may make a table and recognize the pattern as linear. Since an increase of 1 in the number of rods is related to an increase of 12 in the surface area, an equation is $A = 12n + 6$.

Length 4

Number of Rods	Surface Area
1	18
2	30
3	42
4	54
5	66
n	$12n + 6$

Strategy 2 Students may reason as follows: For one rod, the surface area is 18. For two rods, it is $12 + 18$. For three rods, it is $18 + 12 + 12$. For four rods, it is $18 + 12 + 12 + 12$. Thus, the surface area is always 18 plus $(n - 1)$ multiplied by 12, or $A = 18 + 12(n - 1)$.

Strategy 3 Students may analyze the number of surfaces with an area of 4 and the number of surfaces with an area of 1. The top and the front surfaces together have a surface area of $4(n + 1)$, and the right sides of the rods have a surface area of n. To account for the back, the bottom and the left sides, double the areas: $2[4(n + 1) + n]$. The number of additional surfaces with an area of 1, created by the staggering of the rods, is $2(n - 1)$. The total area is $2[4(n + 1) + n] + 2(n - 1)$.

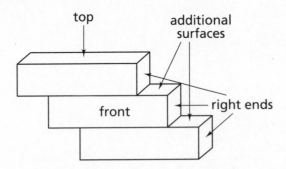

Strategy 4 Students may analyze the number of surfaces with an area of 4 and the number of surfaces with an area of 1 in a different way. The number of surfaces with an area of 4 is $2n + 2$: n in the front, n in the back, and 1 on the top and the bottom. This is a total surface area of $4(2n + 2)$. The number of surfaces with an area of 1 is $2n + 2(n - 1)$: each rod has 2 ends, for $2n$ surfaces, plus the $n - 1$ surfaces uncovered by the staggering on each end of the stack, for $2(n - 1)$. This expression is multiplied by 1 to get the surface area. The total surface area is thus $4(2n + 2) + 2n + 2(n - 1)$.

Strategy 5 Students might see a pattern in the number of surfaces with certain areas by making a table. Reasoning about the pattern leads to the equation $A = [2 + 4(n - 1)](1) + [4 + 2(n - 1)](4)$ or to the equation $A = (4n - 2)(1) + (2n + 2)(4)$.

Number of Rods	Faces With an Area of 1	Faces With an Area of 4	Total Surface Area
1	2	4	$2(1) + 4(4) = 18$
2	6	6	$6(1) + 6(4) = 30$
3	10	8	$10(1) + 8(4) = 42$
4	14	10	$14(1) + 10(4) = 54$
n	$2 + 4(n - 1)$ or $4n - 2$	$4 + 2(n - 1)$ or $2n + 2$	$[2 + 4(n - 1)](1) + [4 + 2(n - 1)](4)$ or $(4n - 2)(1) + (2n + 2)(4)$

Strategy 6 Some students may form the rods into a rectangular prism. For rods of length 4, this prism has dimensions n, 4, and 1. The surface area of the prism, $2(4n + n + 4)$, is then adjusted for the number of faces with a surface area of 1 that are hidden in the arrangement, a total of $2(n - 1)$.

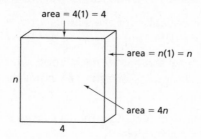

area = 4(1) = 4

area = n(1) = n

area = 4n

n

4

The area of each face of the prism plus the lost area is
$2[4(n) + 1(n) + 4(1)] + 2(n - 1)$, or $2[4(n + 1) + n] + 2(n - 1)$.

Strategy 7 Some students may analyze the surface area of the figure as seen from the front, the right side, and the top; add the three numbers; and then multiply the sum by 2 to account for the back, the left side, and the bottom.

For rods of length 4, they might then produce the table below, which leads to the equation $A = 2[4n + n + 4 + (n - 1)]$ or to $A = 2(4n + n + n + 3)$, or $A = 2(6n + 3)$ (Figure 2)

Number of Rods	Surface Area From Front	Surface Area From Right Side	Surface Area From Top	Total Surface Area
1	4	1	4	$2(4 + 1 + 4) = 18$
2	8	2	5	$2(8 + 2 + 5) = 30$
3	12	3	6	$2(12 + 3 + 6) = 42$
4	16	4	7	$2(16 + 4 + 7) = 54$
n	$4n$	n	$4 + (n - 1)$ or $n + 3$	$2[4n + n + 4 + (n - 1)]$ or $2(4n + n + n + 3) = 2(6n + 3)$

5. Students' expressions should be equivalent. Explanations will vary.

6. **a.** Students are asked to compare their equations with classmates. The simplified equations are given in the table below.

Length (cm)	Equation in the Form $y = mx + b$
2	$A = 8n + 2$
3	$A = 10n + 4$
4	$A = 12n + 6$
5	$A = 14n + 8$
6	$A = 16n + 10$
7	$A = 18n + 12$
8	$A = 20n + 14$
9	$A = 22n + 16$
10	$A = 24n + 18$

b. The expressions are all linear equations; the variable n is raised to the 1st power. Each equation has a graph which is a straight line and that has a constant rate of change. However, the slope and y-intercepts are different for all the equations. The slopes (and y-intercepts) are all multiples of 2. The slopes (and y-intercepts) increase by 2 as the rod length increase by 2.

c. Students are asked to write an equation for the surface area, A, of any stack of n rods of length ℓ. $A = 2[\ell(n + 1) + 1(n)] + 2(n - 1)$, or $(2\ell + 4)n + 2\ell - 2$.

Students do not have to start from scratch for each length of rod. They can use the strategy for the "4" rods and replace the "4" in the formula with the length of a new rod. For example:

Using Strategy 6 to make a compact rectangle that is 4 long, n high, and 1 wide, would lead eventually to the formula

$A = 2[1(n + 1) + 1(n)] + 2(n - 1)$. Replacing the "4" that represents the length of the rod we get

$A = 2[1(n + 1) + 1(n)] + 2(n - 1)$ for "1" rods,

$A = 2[3(n + 1) + 1(n)] + 2(n - 1)$ for "3" rods,

$A = 2[5(n + 1) + 1(n)] + 2(n - 1)$ for "5" rods, and so on. In general,

$A = 2[\ell(n + 1) + 1(n)] + 2(n - 1)$ or $(2\ell + 4)n + 2\ell - 2$ for any length of rod ℓ.

d. Students are asked to find the surface area of a stack of 50 rods each of length 10. Using the equation $A = 2[\ell(n + 1) + 1(n)] + 2(\ell - 1)$ for $\ell = 10$ and $n = 50$ we get that

$A = 2[10(50 + 1) + 1(50)] + 2(50 - 1) = 1{,}218$ square units.

Note: Answers are given below regarding the rectangular prism.

7. The dimensions are n, n, and 4.

8. An expression for the surface area is $2n^2 + 2(4n)$, or $2n^2 + 8n + 8n$, or $2n^2 + 16n$.

9. The surface area of a prism that is 10 rods high and 10 rods wide is $2(10)^2 + 16(10) = 360$ square units.

10. To change the expression if the rod length were something other than 4, one would replace the 4 in the expression. If the length were x, the expression would be $2n^2 + 2(xn) + 2(xn)$.

11. The relationship is quadratic. In the equation, the highest power of the variable is 2. The graph has the shape of a parabola.

Notes

Looking Ahead

In-ground swimming pools are often surrounded by borders of tiles. **How** many border tiles do you need to surround the pool?

A school is selling ice cream served in souvenir cups for charity. The cup is cone-shaped with a height of 16 centimeters and a radius of 3 centimeters. The cup is filled and then topped with half a scoop of ice cream. **How** much ice cream do you need to make 75 cups?

You can approximate the height h of a pole-vaulter from the ground after t seconds with the equation $h = 32t - 16t^2$. **Will** the pole-vaulter clear a height of 17.5 feet?

You have used many powerful tools, including graphs, tables, and equations, to represent relationships among variables. Graphs allow you to see the shape of a relationship. They also help you identify intercepts and maximum and minimum points. Tables help you to observe patterns of change in the values of the variables. Equations give you an efficient way to generalize relationships.

In this Unit, you will focus on symbolic expressions and equations. You will see that different ways of reasoning about a situation can lead to different but equivalent expressions. You will use mathematical properties to rewrite expressions. You may discover that an equivalent expression allows you to think about a problem in a new way. And, you will learn new ways to solve equations. As you work through the Investigations, you will solve problems, such as the concession-stand profit at a water park, as well as those on the previous page.

Looking Ahead   3

Notes _____

_____

_____

Mathematical Highlights

Say It With Symbols

Algebra provides ideas and symbols for expressing information about quantitative variables and relationships. In *Say It With Symbols*, you will solve problems designed to develop your understanding and skill in using symbolic expressions and equations in algebra.

You will learn how to

- Represent patterns and relationships in symbolic forms

- Determine when different symbolic expressions are mathematically equivalent

- Write algebraic expressions in useful equivalent forms

- Combine symbolic expressions using algebraic operations to form new expressions

- Analyze expressions or equations to determine the patterns of change in the tables and graphs that the expression or equation represents

- Solve linear and quadratic equations using symbolic reasoning

- Use algebraic reasoning to validate generalizations and conjectures

When you encounter a new problem, it is a good idea to ask yourself questions. In this Unit, you might ask questions such as:

What expression or equation represents the pattern or relationship in a context?

Can you write an equivalent expression for a given expression to provide new information about a relationship?

What operations can transform a given equation or expression into an equivalent form that can be used to answer a question?

How can symbolic reasoning help confirm a conjecture?

Common Core State Standards
Mathematical Practices and Habits of Mind

In the *Connected Mathematics* curriculum you will develop an understanding of important mathematical ideas by solving problems and reflecting on the mathematics involved. Every day, you will use "habits of mind" to make sense of problems and apply what you learn to new situations. Some of these habits are described by the *Common Core State Standards for Mathematical Practices* (MP).

MP1 Make sense of problems and persevere in solving them.

When using mathematics to solve a problem, it helps to think carefully about

- data and other facts you are given and what additional information you need to solve the problem;

- strategies you have used to solve similar problems and whether you could solve a related simpler problem first;

- how you could express the problem with equations, diagrams, or graphs;

- whether your answer makes sense.

MP2 Reason abstractly and quantitatively.

When you are asked to solve a problem, it often helps to

- focus first on the key mathematical ideas;

- check that your answer makes sense in the problem setting;

- use what you know about the problem setting to guide your mathematical reasoning.

MP3 Construct viable arguments and critique the reasoning of others.

When you are asked to explain why a conjecture is correct, you can

- show some examples that fit the claim and explain why they fit;

- show how a new result follows logically from known facts and principles.

When you believe a mathematical claim is incorrect, you can

- show one or more counterexamples—cases that don't fit the claim;

- find steps in the argument that do not follow logically from prior claims.

Notes _____

_____

MP4 Model with mathematics.

When you are asked to solve problems, it often helps to

- think carefully about the numbers or geometric shapes that are the most important factors in the problem, then ask yourself how those factors are related to each other;
- express data and relationships in the problem with tables, graphs, diagrams, or equations, and check your result to see if it makes sense.

MP5 Use appropriate tools strategically.

When working on mathematical questions, you should always

- decide which tools are most helpful for solving the problem and why;
- try a different tool when you get stuck.

MP6 Attend to precision.

In every mathematical exploration or problem-solving task, it is important to

- think carefully about the required accuracy of results: is a number estimate or geometric sketch good enough, or is a precise value or drawing needed?
- report your discoveries with clear and correct mathematical language that can be understood by those to whom you are speaking or writing.

MP7 Look for and make use of structure.

In mathematical explorations and problem solving, it is often helpful to

- look for patterns that show how data points, numbers, or geometric shapes are related to each other;
- use patterns to make predictions.

MP8 Look for and express regularity in repeated reasoning.

When results of a repeated calculation show a pattern, it helps to

- express that pattern as a general rule that can be used in similar cases;
- look for shortcuts that will make the calculation simpler in other cases.

You will use all of the Mathematical Practices in this Unit. Sometimes, when you look at a Problem, it is obvious which practice is most helpful. At other times, you will decide on a practice to use during class explorations and discussions. After completing each Problem, ask yourself:

- What mathematics have I learned by solving this Problem?
- What Mathematical Practices were helpful in learning this mathematics?

Notes _____

_____

_____

Unit Project

Finding the Surface Area of Rod Stacks

In this Unit Project, you will find different ways to find the surface area of colored rod stacks.

Part 1: Staircase Stacks

1. Choose a rod length to use to make a staircase stack. Use one of the unit rods to determine the dimensions of your chosen rod.

2. Stack several rods of this length as shown. Each rod is one unit high and one unit wide and is staggered one unit.

stacked rods   **unit rod**

   Find the surface area of one rod, a stack of two rods, a stack of three rods, and so on. Describe a pattern that you see in the surface areas of the stacks you made.

3. Write an equation that shows the relationship between the surface area A and the number of rods n in the stack. Explain.

4. Repeat Exercises 1–3 for two other rod lengths.

5. Find a student who used rods of the same length for Exercises 1–3 and whose expression for area from Exercise 3 looks different from yours. Are your expressions equivalent? Explain.

Notes

6. a. Make a table with columns for rod length and surface area equation. Complete the table for rod lengths 2 through 10. You will need to find students who used rods that you did not use.

   b. Do the equations in your table represent linear, quadratic, or exponential relationships? Explain.

   c. Write an equation for the surface area A of any stack of n rods of length ℓ.

   d. Use your equation from part (c) to find the surface area of a stack of 50 rods of length 10.

Part 2: Finding the Surface Area of a Rectangular Prism

Suppose rods of length 4 are stacked to form a rectangular prism as shown below right.

7. What are the dimensions of the prism?

8. Find an equation for the surface area of the prism.

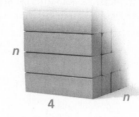

9. Suppose the prism is 10 rods high and 10 rods wide. What is the surface area of the prism?

10. How would the equation change if the rod length were a length other than 4?

11. Is the relationship between the surface area and the number of rods in a prism stack linear, quadratic, exponential, or none of these? Explain.

Write a report about the results you found for rod stacks and rod prisms. Explain how you found the equations for surface area in each case. Use diagrams to show what you did and what you found.

Notes _____

Investigation 1

PLANNING

▶ INVESTIGATION
OVERVIEW

GOALS AND
STANDARDS

Making Sense of Symbols: Equivalent Expressions

▼ Investigation Overview

Investigation Description

Students have an opportunity to generate and justify, in their own ways, the equivalence of two or more symbolic expressions for the same situation. They are encouraged to think about problems in a variety of ways, leading to different, yet equivalent, expressions. Equivalency is discussed in terms of graphs, tables, and the validity of the reasoning each expression or equation represents. In addition, the structures of the problems reintroduce the important properties of numbers, especially the Distributive Property. By the end of this Investigation, students will have developed a strong sense of the Distributive Property independent of a specific context.

Investigation Vocabulary

- Commutative Property of Addition
- Commutative Property of Multiplication
- Distributive Property
- equivalent expressions
- expanded form
- factored form

Mathematics Background

- Making Sense of Symbols
- Equivalent Expressions

Planning Chart

Content	ACE	Pacing	Materials	Resources
Problem 1.1	1, 2, 18–24	1 day	**Labsheet 1.1** Pool Problem unit squares or tiles (optional)	**Teaching Aid 1.1** Tiling Pools
Problem 1.2	3, 4, 25–34, 58	1 day	**Labsheet 1ACE:** Exercise 3 (accessibility)	
Problem 1.3	5, 6, 35–52, 59	1 day	**Labsheet 1.3** The Community Pool Problem	**Teaching Aid 1.3** The Community Pool Problem
Problem 1.4	7–17, 53–57, 60	1 day		**Teaching Aid 1.4** Different Dimensions
Mathematical Reflections		½ day		
Assessment: **Check Up 1**		½ day		• Check Up 1

Goals and Standards

Goals

Equivalence Develop understanding of equivalent expressions and equations.

- Model situations with symbolic statements

- Recognize when two or more symbolic statements represent the same context

- Use the properties of real numbers, such as the Distributive Property, to write equivalent expressions

- Determine if different symbolic expressions are mathematically equivalent

- Interpret the information that equivalent expressions represent in a given context

- Determine the equivalent expression or equation that is most helpful in answering a particular question about a relationship

- Use algebraic equations to describe the relationship among the volumes of cylinders, cones, and spheres that have the same height and radius

- Solve linear equations involving parentheses

- Determine if a linear equation has a finite number of solutions, an infinite number of solutions, or no solution

- Develop understanding and some fluency with factoring quadratic expressions

- Solve quadratic equations by factoring

- Recognize how and when to use symbols, rather than tables or graphs, to display relationships, generalizations, and proofs

Mathematical Reflections

Look for evidence of student understanding of the goals for this Investigation in their responses to the questions in *Mathematical Reflections*. The goals addressed by each question are indicated below.

1. What does it mean to say that two expressions are equivalent?

Goals

- Model situations with symbolic statements

- Recognize when two or more symbolic statements represent the same context

- Interpret the information that equivalent expressions represent in a given context

- Determine the equivalent expression or equation that is most helpful in answering a particular question about a relationship

- Recognize how and when to use symbols, rather than tables or graphs, to display relationships, generalizations, and proofs

2. Explain how you can use the Distributive Property to write equivalent expressions.

Goal

- Use the properties of real numbers, such as the Distributive Property, to write equivalent expressions

3. Explain how you can use the Distributive and Commutative properties to show that two or more expressions are equivalent.

Goals

- Determine if different symbolic expressions are mathematically equivalent
- Recognize how and when to use symbols, rather than tables or graphs, to display relationships, generalizations, and proofs

Standards

Common Core Content Standards

8.EE.C.7 Solve linear equations in one variable. *Problems 1, 2, and 4*

8.EE.C.7b Solve linear equations with rational number coefficients, including equations whose solutions require expanding expressions using the Distributive Property and collecting like terms. *Problems 1, 2, and 4*

8.F.A.3 Interpret the equation $y = mx + b$ as defining a linear function, whose graph is a straight line; give examples of functions that are not linear. *Problems 1 and 3*

N-Q.A.1 Use units as a way to understand problems and to guide the solution of multi-step problems; choose and interpret units consistently in formulas; choose and interpret the scale and the origin in graphs and data displays. *Problem 1*

A-SSE.A.1 Interpret expressions that represent a quantity in terms of its context. *Problems 1, 2, 3, and 4*

A-SSE.A.1a Interpret parts of an expression, such as terms, factors, and coefficients. *Problems 3 and 4*

A-SSE.A.1b Interpret complicated expressions by viewing one or more of their parts as a single entity. *Problems 2, 3, and 4*

A-SSE.A.2 Use the structure of an expression to identify ways to rewrite it. *Problems 1, 3, and 4*

A-SSE.B.3 Choose and produce an equivalent form of an expression to reveal and explain properties of the quantity represented by the expression. *Problems 2, 3, and 4*

A-CED.A.1 Create equations and inequalities in one variable and use them to solve problems. *Problems 1 and 2*

A-REI.B.3 Solve linear equations and inequalities in one variable, including equations with coefficients represented by letters. *Problems 1 and 2*

F-IF.C.9 Compare properties of two functions each represented in a different way (algebraically, graphically, numerically in tables, or by verbal descriptions). *Problem 1*

F-BF.A.1a Determine an explicit expression, a recursive process, or steps for calculation from a context. *Problem 2*

Facilitating the Mathematical Practices

Students in *Connected Mathematics* classrooms display evidence of multiple Common Core Standards for Mathematical Practice every day. Here are just a few examples of when you might observe students demonstrating the Standards for Mathematical Practice during this Investigation.

Practice 1: **Make sense of problems and persevere in solving them.**

Students are engaged every day in solving problems and, over time, learn to persevere in solving them. To be effective, the problems embody critical concepts and skills and have the potential to engage students in making sense of mathematics. Students build understanding by reflecting, connecting, and communicating. These student-centered problem situations engage students in articulating the "knowns" in a problem situation and determining a logical solution pathway. The student-student and student-teacher dialogues help students not only to make sense of the problems, but also to persevere in finding appropriate strategies to solve them. The suggested questions in the Teacher Guides provide the metacognitive scaffolding to help students monitor and refine their problem-solving strategies.

Practice 3: **Construct viable arguments and critique the reasoning of others.**

In Problem 1.2, students determine if the equations that represent the number of tiles are equivalent. Some students may use sketches to interpret the numbers and variables that make up the equations. Others may substitute values of s into each expression to show equivalence. Through the process of their choice, they will notice that Hank's equation is not equivalent to the other equations. The students who choose the sketching method will critique that he counted the corner tiles twice. The students who choose to test values of s into each expression will critique that $4(s + 2) \neq 4s + 4$ because $4(1 + 2) = 12$ and $4(1) + 4 = 8$.

Students identify and record their personal experiences with the Standards for Mathematical Practice during the Mathematical Reflections at the end of the Investigation.

Tiling Pools
Writing Equivalent Expressions

▼ **Problem Overview**

> *Focus Question* What expression(s) represents the number of border tiles needed to surround a square pool with side length *s*?

Problem Description

In *Moving Straight Ahead* and *Thinking With Mathematical Models*, students explored ways in which relationships can be expressed in tables, graphs, and equations. For the most part, the contextual clues or the patterns in the tables or graphs were so influential in the construction of the symbolic rule that only one version of the rule appeared. In this Problem, students are deliberately presented with a situation in which contextual clues can be interpreted in several different ways to produce equivalent symbolic expressions. Students write equations to represent the number of border tiles that surround a square pool of side length *s*. They justify the equivalence of two or more symbolic expressions for the same situation.

Problem Implementation

Students can work in pairs and then share their work with another pair. Have students show their work with drawings on poster paper to use in the Summarize. You might also provide unit squares or tiles for students who need a more concrete approach.

Materials

• **Labsheet 1.1:** Pool Problem
• **Teaching Aid 1.1:** Tiling Pools

unit squares or tiles (optional)

Vocabulary

• equivalent expressions

Mathematics Background

- Making Sense of Symbols
- Equivalent Expressions

At a Glance and Lesson Plan

- At a Glance: Problem 1.1 Say It With Symbols
- Lesson Plan: Problem 1.1 Say It With Symbols

▼ Launch

Launch Video

This animation shows a pool installer talking to a truck driver about the number of tiles required to surround a square pool. During the conversation, they are loading the tiles onto the truck. They lose count as they talk. The animation ends by posing the question in the introduction to the Problem. Visit Teacher Place at mathdashboard.com/cmp3 to see the complete video.

You can show this animation to introduce the Problem. Then continue with Presenting the Challenge.

Connecting to Prior Knowledge

Pose the situation and questions concerning the two different expressions for the perimeter of a rectangle. Ask students to justify why both expressions for the rectangle's perimeter, $2(L + W)$ and $2L + 2W$, are correct and why Alberto used parentheses in his equation. Students may offer examples or talk generally about the dimensions and perimeter of any rectangle.

Suggested Questions

If necessary, direct the conversation to focus on the method each expression represents.

- Describe the method each student is using to compute the perimeter. (Mika notes that the perimeter is the length of all four sides, $L + W + W + L$ or $2L + 2W$. Alberto notes that if you add $L + W$ as you go around the rectangle, you are halfway around, so all you need to do is multiply by 2 to get $2(L + W)$.)

- Could Alberto have written $2L + W$? (No, because you would only be counting the length twice and the width once. The parentheses are needed to show that you must add length and width, then multiply the sum by 2.)

• Are $3(x + 5)$ and $3x + 5$ equivalent? Explain. (No, because the Distributive Property states that $3(x + 5) = 3x + 15$ and $3x + 15 \neq 3x + 5$.)

Remind students that these expressions for the perimeter of a rectangle, $2(L + W)$ and $2L + 2W$, are equivalent expressions.

Presenting the Challenge

To introduce the Problem, you might construct a model of a square pool with sides of length *s* units using transparent square tiles, draw a square pool on the board, or display **Teaching Aid 1.1: Tiling Pools**. Explain to the students that the pool has sides of length *s* feet and you want to make a border around the pool from 1-foot-square tiles.

Put some tiles around the pool. Try to keep the Problem open by using *s* for the side length. If you use a specific value, students may start making tables, which is not the intended direction of this Problem. By keeping the Problem open with length *s*, students will use interesting geometric patterns in the border and pool to write several different expressions for the number of tiles. During the Explore, if students have difficulty noticing the patterns, you can suggest trying specific cases for the size of the pool.

Suggested Questions

• Is there an efficient way to calculate the number of border tiles needed for a square pool, no matter what the lengths of the sides of the pool are? (Yes; you can write an equation to represent the number of border tiles *N* needed for a square pool with side length *s*.)

Pass out **Labsheet 1.1: Pool Problem**.

▼ Explore

Providing for Individual Needs

Having students articulate how they visualize the situation will help them to make the transition to interpreting the reasoning represented by the symbols. Different ways of reasoning about the Problem lead to different strategies, which in turn result in different equations. Encourage students to find more than one way to reason about the situation. (Problem 1.2 presents several ways of thinking about this situation, some of which your students will discover.)

Some students may need help using parentheses in their equations. If you see students who cannot communicate their ideas in writing, you might talk with them about the use of parentheses. Students will work more with this idea in Problem 1.4. The primary objective of this Problem is that students be able to justify to their classmates that the expressions they develop to represent the number of tiles are equivalent. It is essential that students articulate their reasoning.

Look for interesting ways that students are thinking about the Problem. Also look for the interesting ways they show that two expressions for the number of border tiles are equivalent.

Planning for the Summary

What evidence will you use in the summary to clarify and deepen understanding of the Focus Question?

What will you do if you do not have evidence?

▼ Summarize

Orchestrating the Discussion

Have the class examine the posters from each pair of students and then allow them time to ask questions about each piece of work.

Suggested Questions

For each equation, ask the class:

- Can you explain the reasoning that was used to arrive at this equation? (Possible answer: This poster shows that they wrote their equation by looking at the tiles on the sides, and then the corners. They have s tiles for each side and 1 tile for each corner, which is how they wrote $N = s + s + s + s + 1 + 1 + 1 + 1 = 4s + 4$.)

- How do the parts of the equation relate to the elements of the Problem? (Possible answer: On this poster, they wrote $N = 4(s + 1)$. They put a side together with a corner. Then, they multiplied the sum by 4 because there are 4 sides and 4 corners.)

For any equations that the class cannot decipher, ask the students who wrote them to use diagrams to explain their thinking and how the parts of the equation relate to the elements of the Problem. Students' explanations might be noted on the board where they can be amended if necessary. Students may be reasoning from numerical examples or from a geometric sketch. Verbal and graphical arguments are sufficient at this stage. Students' equations may include some of the following:

$N = 4s + 4$

$N = s + s + s + s + 4$

$N = 2s + 2(s + 2)$

$N = 4(s + 2) - 4$

$N + (s + 2)^2 - s^2$

$N = 4(s + 1)$

$N = 8 + 4(s - 1)$

Don't try to get all of these equations at this time. This question is revisited in Problem 1.2, where students are asked to draw pictures that represent the thinking captured in several different expressions, to show that the expressions are equivalent.

The following are some of the ways students may have reasoned about the number of border tiles. It is acceptable if students do not offer all these ideas. They will explore several methods in the next Problem.

They may have considered the four sides first and then added the corner tiles, resulting in the equation $N = 4s + 4$.

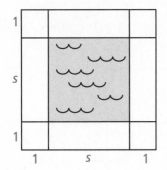

$$N = 4\left(1 \boxed{}_s\right) + 4\left(1 \boxed{}_1\right)$$

They may have thought about adding the four long strips along the sides and then subtracting the four corner tiles that are counted twice, resulting in the equation $N = 4(s + 2) - 4$.

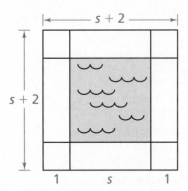

$$N = 4\left(1 \boxed{}_{s+2}\right) - 4\left(1 \boxed{}_1\right)$$

They may have reasoned that the number of border tiles is equal to the difference between the areas of the two squares, resulting in the equation $N = (s + 2)^2 - s^2$.

Even though students agree that the reasoning behind this equation is valid, some may question whether it is equivalent to the other equations since it looks quadratic. The other equations have all been linear. In fact, if the expression $(s + 2)^2 - s^2$ is simplified, it is equivalent to $4s + 4$. (In Problem 1.4, students will show this equivalence using the Distributive Property.) When you discuss the tables and graphs for each of these equations, students will also see that the graph and table of this equation are the same as for the other equations.

They may have divided the border into four rectangles with dimensions $s + 1$ and 1, resulting in the equation $N = 4(s + 1)$.

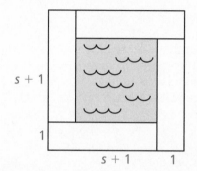

$$N = 4 \left(1 \; \boxed{} \atop s + 1 \right)$$

Some students may have made tables and seen the following pattern in their table: To find the number of border tiles, add 1 to the side length and then multiply by 4, or $N = 4(s + 1)$.

s	1	2	3	4	5	6	7	8	9
N	8	12	16	20	24	28	32	36	40

Other students may use a table to arrive at the equation $N = 4s + 4$ by noting that the table represents a linear relationship whose slope is 4. Students may reason backward in the table to find the y-intercept, which is 4, and then write the equation $N = 4s + 4$.

Some students may observe this pattern in the table: For $s = 1$, $N = 8$. For $s = 2$, $N = 8 + 4$. For $s = 3$, $N = 8 + 4 + 4$. For $s = 4$, $N = 8 + 4 + 4 + 4$. Thus, for any s, N is equal to 8 plus $(s - 1)$ fours, or $N = 8 + 4(s - 1)$. In other words, they used 8 as a starting point and successively added 4. The number of 4's added to get N for any value of s is one less than s.

Students may wonder is there is an infinite number of equivalent expressions. The reasoning behind this is exhibited in the Mathematical Practice section of this Investigation (Student Edition).

Be sure to look at tables and graphs for the equations that are generated in class.

- If the graphs and tables are the same, are the equations equivalent? (Students may be surprised that equations that appear quite different can have identical graphs and tables. Making graphs for different, but equivalent, equations reinforces what students have learned about equivalent representations. You might ask students how they could predict the shape of the graph from the equations or the tables.)

  See **Equivalent Equations** in the Mathematics Background for more information about equivalent expressions.

The summary of this Problem can lead into the Launch of Problem 1.2.

- Are there other ways to show that these expressions for the number of tiles are equivalent, without using tables or graphs? (Some students may suggest checking the equivalence for a few values of s and argue that if two answers are correct, the expressions must be equivalent. This is discussed in the next Problem.)

Be sure to discuss whether the equations are linear or nonlinear. You might extend to discussing whether the equations are linear, quadratic, or exponential. Use a few of the equations to make the connection between the numbers and variables in the equation and how they relate to various components of the table and graph.

Reflecting on Student Learning

Use the following questions to assess student understanding at the end of the lesson.

- What evidence do I have that students understand the Focus Question?
  - Where did my students get stuck?
  - What strategies did they use?
  - What breakthroughs did my students have today?
- How will I use this to plan for tomorrow? For the next time I teach this lesson?
- Where will I have the opportunity to reinforce these ideas as I continue through this Unit? The next Unit?

ACE Assignment Guide

- **Applications:** 1, 2
- **Connections:** 18–24

PROBLEM
1.2

Thinking in Different Ways
Determining Equivalence

▼ Problem Overview

> *Focus Question* How can you determine if two or more expressions are equivalent?

Problem Description

This Problem serves as a summary for Problem 1.1. It provides several equations that students have used to represent the relationships between the number of border tiles and the side length of a square pool. Students show equivalence by relating the equations to related geometric models, tables, and graphs. Later, in Problem 1.4, students revisit the Distributive Property and use it and other properties of operations to show equivalence of symbolic expressions.

Problem Implementation

Students can work in groups of 3–4.

Materials

• **Labsheet 1ACE:** Exercise 3 (accessibility)

Using Technology

If students have access to a graphing calculator, they may find it helpful for Problem 1.2. They can use the calculator to make tables and graphs of expressions to explain their equivalence.

Vocabulary

There are no new glossary terms introduced in this Problem.

Mathematics Background

• Equivalent Expressions

At a Glance and Lesson Plan

• At a Glance: Problem 1.2 Say It With Symbols
• Lesson Plan: Problem 1.2 Say It With Symbols

▼ Launch

Connecting to Prior Knowledge

Some of this Problem may have been discussed in the Summarize of Problem 1.1. If so, have students use the equations for the number of border tiles from ACE Exercise 4, or direct the students to Question B of this Problem. Take note of the equation in Question A that is not equivalent to the others. Students will need to discuss this in Question B.

Suggested Questions

• If a pair of values for (s, N) such as (4, 20) satisfies two different expressions, are the expressions equivalent? (Some students may think that one pair is enough, but this is not true. Collect some responses and return to this question in the Summarize.)

If your students didn't discuss the equations in Question A, ask them about Takashi's picture of $N = 4s + 4$.

• What equation do you think Takashi wrote to relate N and s? (Possible answers might include equations such as Stella's or Jeri's equations in Question A.)

Presenting the Challenge

Tell the class that students from Takashi's class generated other equations for the Tiling Pool Problem. Explain to students that they will be drawing pictures to illustrate the thought process behind these equations.

Explore

Providing for Individual Needs

Encourage students to think about whether checking one value of *s* for two expressions is sufficient to show equivalence.

Suggested Questions

- How many values do you need to try before you are convinced that the two expressions are equivalent? (In the case of linear expressions, you need at least two values to show equivalence.)

Note: Only three of the expressions in Question A are equivalent. Hank's is not equivalent. Students may reason geometrically that Hank forgot to remove the four corner pieces, or they may see that after substituting a value for *s* into Hank's and another student's expression, the number of tiles is not the same. For the other three expressions, even though the value of 10 produces the same value for *N* in each expression, it doesn't mean that the expressions are equivalent. This discussion should come out in the Summarize.

Some students may try to find other expressions. Keep these in mind and use them during the Summarize to test various conjectures that occur.

Planning for the Summary

What evidence will you use in the summary to clarify and deepen understanding of the Focus Question?

What will you do if you do not have evidence?

▼ Summarize

Orchestrating the Discussion

Suggested Questions

- Is one value enough to check in order to prove that two expressions are equivalent? (no)

If students say no, then you might use the following questions.

- Are $2s + 2(s + 2)$ and $4s + 4$ equivalent? (Yes, $2s + 2(s + 2)$ and $4s + 4$ are equivalent. Both of these expressions represent a linear relationship. The graph of each relationship is a straight line. Substitute two different values for *s* into each expression. If $s = 3$, then *N*, or the value of each expression, equals 16. Similarly, if $s = 5$, then $N = 24$. This means that the points (3, 16) and (5, 24) lie on both lines. And since two points determine exactly one line, the two expressions must be the same.)

- What are other ways of showing that the two expressions are equivalent? (You can use tables, graphs, or valid reasoning behind the symbols.)

If students say yes, then write the equations $N = 2s + 1$ and $N = s + 2$ on the board.

- Find N if $s = 1$. ($N = 3$ in each case.)
- Find N if $s = 3$. ($N = 7$ in the first equation, and $N = 5$ in the second equation. So the two expressions $2s + 1$ and $s + 2$ are not equivalent.)

Look at the graphs of both equations on the same axes. Ask students to analyze why the equations were equivalent when $s = 1$.

- Why did we get the same value for N when we had $s = 1$? (That is where the two lines intersect. So the coordinate pair $(1, 3)$ is the same for both equations.)

Write two more expressions on the board: $N = 4(s + 2) - 4$ and $N = 4(s + 1)$.

- Suppose you try two values of s, and the N-value is the same in both cases. Is this sufficient to show that two expressions are equivalent? Suppose you try $s = 5$ and $s = 10$. (The answer is yes, but this may be a bit subtle for students. If so, ask the next two questions.)
- What kind of relationship does each equation in this Problem represent? (They are all linear.)
- So if you know that two distinct points, $(5, 24)$ and $(10, 44)$, lie on the graphs of two linear equations, what can you say about the graphs? (Some students may know that two points determine exactly one straight line. If two points lie on the graphs of two linear equations, then the graphs of the linear equations are the same line, so the equations must be equivalent.)

It is also valuable to use the unique rate of change for a linear situation. Ask:

- How else could you show that checking two points is sufficient for showing that two linear expressions are equivalent? (If you know that an expression represents a linear situation, then it only takes two points to determine its rate of change. For the two points above, the rate of change is 4, so in the table below, the next value of N is $12 + 4$, and the next value is $12 + 4 + 4$. Since $(1, 8)$ and $(2, 12)$ lie on the lines that represent the expressions in parts (1), (2), and (4) from Question A, no matter which equation you pick, the rate and the set of points generated are the same. Since the rate of change is the same, each equation will generate the same set of values for (s, N).)

s	1	2	3	4
N	8	12	$12 + 4$	$12 + 4 + 4$

For any complicated expressions that students come up with for the number of border tiles, you may want to come back to them after Problem 1.4 to see if they can use the Distributive and Commutative properties as a way to justify equivalence. For example, students may have found the expressions in ACE Exercise 4. After Problem 1.4, this ACE exercise could be revisited in class.

Reflecting on Student Learning

Use the following questions to assess student understanding at the end of the lesson.

- What evidence do I have that students understand the Focus Question?
  - Where did my students get stuck?
  - What strategies did they use?
  - What breakthroughs did my students have today?
- How will I use this to plan for tomorrow? For the next time I teach this lesson?
- Where will I have the opportunity to reinforce these ideas as I continue through this Unit? The next Unit?

ACE Assignment Guide

- **Applications:** 3, 4
- **Connections:** 25–34
- **Extensions:** 58
- **Labsheet 1ACE:** Exercise 3 (accessibility)

This labsheet may be helpful for students who need more practice interpreting a model to write equivalent equations.

The Community Pool Problem

Interpreting Expressions

▼ Problem Overview

> *Focus Question* What information does an expression represent in a
> given context?

Problem Description

In this Problem, a context of the area of a community pool is presented as a
symbolic statement. A diagram of the indoor part of the pool is given in terms
of x. Students interpret an equation for the area A that represents the area of
a community pool, which has an indoor section and an outdoor section.

$$A = \frac{\pi x^2}{2} + x^2 + 8x + \frac{\pi x^2}{4}$$

Students determine which part of the equation represents the area for the indoor
part of the pool. Then, they use the remaining part of the equation to draw a
diagram of the outside part of the pool.

Problem Implementation

Students can work in groups of 3–4.

Materials

- **Labsheet 1.3:** The Community Pool Problem
- **Teaching Aid 1.3:** The Community Pool Problem

Vocabulary

There are no new glossary terms introduced in this Problem.

Mathematics Background

- Equivalent Expressions

At a Glance and Lesson Plan

• At a Glance: Problem 1.3 Say It With Symbols

• Lesson Plan: Problem 1.3 Say It With Symbols

▼ Launch

Launch Video

This animation shows a designer with an assistant working on shapes for an indoor/outdoor pool for the community. As they discuss the different possibilities for the outdoor portion, they realize that they have an expression that specifies the entire area of the pool. With this information, they can select the correct shape of the outdoor portion. Visit Teacher Place at mathdashboard.com/cmp3 to see the complete video.

You can show this animation to introduce the Problem, and afterward continue by Presenting the Challenge and explaining the goal of the Problem.

Connecting to Prior Knowledge

In the last Problem, students looked at equations that were generated by other students and discussed the patterns and reasoning of each equation. In this Problem, they will look at an equation for the area of a community pool and use it to make decisions about the shape of the pool.

Presenting the Challenge

Display **Teaching Aid 1.3: The Community Pool Problem** and distribute **Labsheet 1.3: The Community Pool Problem**. Try to keep the Problem open enough that a variety of interesting strategies emerge. You might ask students to describe the shape of the indoor part of the pool. Be sure that they know that the outdoor part of the pool is not shown.

Explain to students that the goal is to identify the parts of the equation that represent the areas of the indoor and outdoor parts of the pool. Then, they will use this information to sketch possible shapes of the outdoor part of the pool.

▼ Explore

Providing for Individual Needs

Students are generally comfortable with the area of a circle after taking the Grade 6 and Grade 7 CMP classes. If a student is unsure of the formula, ask another student for the formula for the area of a circle. You may also ask someone in the class to describe why this formula works. Students, who have developed the area of a circle in *Filling and Wrapping* and then used it in later Units, usually remember the formula or can quickly recall it with a little prompting.

Suggested Questions

Students may need some prompting to find the part of the expression that describes the area of the rectangle.

- What are the dimensions of the rectangle? (4x and something else)

- What is the something else? How can you find it? Draw the missing dimension. (Students may now make the connection that the missing dimension is the diameter of a circle whose radius is *x*. So, the missing dimension is 2x and the area of the pool is 2x times 4x, or $8x^2$.)

For Question C, if students are struggling with the interpretation, ask:

- How are $\frac{\pi x^2}{8}$ and $\frac{\pi x^2}{4}$ related? (One is half the other, since $\frac{\pi x^2}{8}$ can be represented by an eighth of a circle and $\frac{\pi x^2}{4}$ can be represented by a quarter of a circle.)

Going Further

Ask students to reflect on the original equation $A = x^2 + \frac{\pi x^2}{2} + 8x + \frac{\pi x^2}{4}$. Challenge students to determine the type of relationship that the equation for the area represents.

- Does the equation for the area of the pool represent a linear, exponential, or quadratic relationship, or none of these? (The equation is quadratic. Students might enter the equation on a graphing calculator to see the pattern of change in the table or the graph. Some may know it is quadratic from the power of 2 in the equation.)

Planning for the Summary

What evidence will you use in the summary to clarify and deepen understanding of the Focus Question?

What will you do if you do not have evidence?

● ▼ Summarize

Orchestrating the Discussion

Go over Questions A and B. Students will be intrigued at all the ways that the outdoor pool can be drawn. Some might represent x^2 as a square, and others might represent it as a rectangle with dimensions $\frac{x}{2}$ and $2x$. This rectangle will match one side of the rectangular portion of the indoor part of the pool. Some will add a quarter of a circle to the square or rectangle. Others may split the quarter circle into two equal eighths of a circle.

Suggested Questions

- Describe how each shape might be useful for different water activities. (Possible answer: The square and quarter circle shape can be used for lap swimming and water volleyball. The square and two eighths of a circle can be used for water basketball or for separate activities such as basketball, diving, and aerobic exercises.)

For Question C, allow students time to discuss why certain expressions are equivalent for the outside part of the pool. Introduce two ways of thinking about the outside pool design, which may or may not have been addressed already.

- How might Stella and Jeri have drawn the outdoor part of the pool? How do you know that their expressions are equivalent to the original expression for the outside of the pool? (At this time, students may use geometric reasoning and say that they are all equivalent because the expressions represent the same area of the outside of the pool. They may also make a table or a graph. Some students may reason symbolically by matching and comparing parts of the expressions. If students check two values for x in the expressions, you will want to come back to this idea after Question D. You may also want to see whether students think two points are enough to check for equivalence of quadratics. They are not, but leave the question open for now. This idea comes up in Problem 4.2.)

For Question D, you could ask:

- Describe the shape of the graph of the equation $A = \frac{\pi x^2}{2} + x^2 + 8x^2 + \frac{\pi x^2}{4}$ or $A = \left(\frac{3\pi}{4} + 9\right)x^2$. (It is a parabola whose minimum point is on the y-axis at $(0, 0)$. The coefficient $\left(\frac{3\pi}{4} + 9\right)$ is a number approximately equal to 11.36. This fits between the parabolas of $y = 11x^2$ and $y = 12x^2$. The line of symmetry is the y-axis and the x-intercept is $(0, 0)$.

Reflecting on Student Learning

Use the following questions to assess student understanding at the end of the lesson.

- What evidence do I have that students understand the Focus Question?
  - Where did my students get stuck?
  - What strategies did they use?
  - What breakthroughs did my students have today?
- How will I use this to plan for tomorrow? For the next time I teach this lesson?
- Where will I have the opportunity to reinforce these ideas as I continue through this Unit? The next Unit?

ACE Assignment Guide

- **Applications:** 5, 6
- **Connections:** 35–52
- **Extensions:** 59

PROBLEM
1.4

Diving In
Revisiting the Distributive Property

▼ Problem Overview

> *Focus Question* How can you use the Distributive and Commutative
> properties to show that two expressions are equivalent?

Problem Description

This Problem revisits the Distributive and Commutative properties and applies them
to rewriting expressions to show that two or more expressions are equivalent.

Problem Implementation

Students can work in pairs.

Materials
• **Teaching Aid 1.4:** Different Dimensions

Vocabulary

• Commutative Property of Addition
• Commutative Property of Multiplication
• Distributive Property
• expanded form
• factored form

Mathematics Background

• Equivalent Expressions

At a Glance and Lesson Plan

• At a Glance: Problem 1.4 Say It With Symbols
• Lesson Plan: Problem 1.4 Say It With Symbols

▼ Launch

Connecting to Prior Knowledge

Display **Teaching Aid 1.4: Different Dimensions** and review the Distributive Property. If your students have studied the Grade 8 Unit *Frogs, Fleas, and Painted Cubes*, this should be a brief discussion. Students also studied the Distributive Property in several Grade 6 and Grade 7 Units.

Suggested Questions

- Find two equivalent expressions for the area of each rectangle.

  (Pool 1: $30(x + 10)$ and $30x + 300$

  Pool 2: $25x + x^2$ and $x(25 + x)$

  Pool 3: $(x + 2)(x + 3)$ and $x^2 + 2x + 3x + 6 = x^2 + 5x + 6$

  Pool 4: $ab + ac$ and $a(b + c)$)

- Explain how these illustrate the Distributive Property. (At this time, write an expression like $30(x + 10)$ or $(x + 2)(x + 3)$ on the board.

$$30(x + 10) = 30x + 300$$

$$(x + 2)(x + 3) = (x + 2)x + (x + 2)3 =$$

$$(x + 2)x + (x + 2)3 = x^2 + 2x + 3x + 6 = x^2 + 5x + 6)$$

- Describe how you can use the Distributive Property to show that two expressions are equivalent. (If the expression is in factored form, you can write it in expanded form. Likewise, if it is in expanded form, then you can write it in factored form. You can also use it to combine like terms.)

You may want to write the Distributive Property and the Commutative Property for Addition and Multiplication on the board. Ask the class to give examples of each.

Presenting the Challenge

- Tell students that they will be using the Distributive and Commutative properties to rewrite expressions. They will also use the properties to determine whether two expressions are equivalent, including some of the expressions from Problem 1.2.

Explore

Providing for Individual Needs

Look for students who need a further discussion on the Distributive and Commutative properties. This is an opportunity for you to assess their level of understanding.

For students who are struggling with correctly applying the symbolic statement of the Distributive Property, relate the expressions to how students may have thought of multiplication as grouping in elementary grades. $3(x + 5)$ can be thought of as 3 groups of $(x + 5)$, or $(x + 5) + (x + 5) + (x + 5) = 3x + 15$. $2(3x - 10)$ can be thought of as 2 groups of $(3x - 10)$, or $(3x - 10) = (3x - 10) = 6x - 20$. This can help students who forget to multiply the coefficient by all the terms inside the parentheses.

After the groups complete Questions A and B, have a class discussion on strategies for using the properties. It is important that throughout this Unit you continue to make sure that students are using the Distributive Property correctly in the Explore. Have students work on the rest of the Problem.

Suggested Questions

For Question C, ask:

- What is an equivalent expression for $(s + 2)^2$? (Students may need help recognizing that $(s + 2)^2$ can be written as $(s + 2)(s + 2)$.)

While students are working on Question C, this is a good opportunity to remind students about the Order of Operations.

- What is the order of steps that correctly simplifies Sal's expression $2s + 2(s + 2)$? (First, perform the multiplication using the Distributive Property. Then, combine $2s + 2s$, getting a final expression of $4s + 4$.)

Make sure that students understand the directions for Question E. Explain that you must place the parentheses before simplifying the expression to the left of the equal sign.

Planning for the Summary

What evidence will you use in the summary to clarify and deepen understanding of the Focus Question?

What will you do if you do not have evidence?

▼ Summarize

Orchestrating the Discussion

Go over Questions C–E. For Question C, you could include other equations that occurred in your class for Problem 1.1 to check students' understanding.

Suggested Questions

For Question D, if students do not use linearity in their answer, ask:

- Suppose you set *y* equal to one of the expressions. What relationship does each equation (or expression) represent? (The relationship associated with the equation is a linear relationship.)

- What must be true about equivalent linear expressions? (Each expression represents a quantity that is the dependent variable. The rate of change between the independent variable and implied dependent variable, or slope of the line, for each equation must be the same. They also have identical graphs.)

- How could you use this information to show which linear expression is not equivalent? (The expression that does not have the same slope or *y*-intercept as the other three is not equivalent. Its graph and table will also be different.)

After students have shared their reasoning for Question E, challenge them to find another way to write the expression $6p + 2 - 2p$ using parentheses and to give a different resulting expression. Ask students to share their final expression and have the rest of the class guess how they placed the parentheses. For example, a student may give $12 - 6p$. For this result, the parentheses would have to occur as follows: $6(p + 2 - 2p)$.

Reflecting on Student Learning

Use the following questions to assess student understanding at the end of the lesson.

- What evidence do I have that students understand the Focus Question?
  - Where did my students get stuck?
  - What strategies did they use?
  - What breakthroughs did my students have today?
- How will I use this to plan for tomorrow? For the next time I teach this lesson?
- Where will I have the opportunity to reinforce these ideas as I continue through this Unit? The next Unit?

ACE Assignment Guide

- **Applications:** 7–17
- **Connections:** 53–57
- **Extensions:** 60

▼ Mathematical Reflections

Possible Answers to Mathematical Reflections

1. Two expressions are equivalent when they are symbolic representations for the same situation. For all values of the variable, they should give the same result. Likewise, the expressions should have the same table and graph.

2. You can write equivalent expressions in factored form, the product of two or more factors, or expanded form, the sum of two or more terms, by the Distributive Property. For example, the expression $2x(x + 5)$ is in factored form. Using the Distributive Property, you can rewrite it in expanded form: $2x^2 + 10x$. The expression $6x^2 - 9x$ is in expanded form. Using the Distributive Property, you can rewrite it in factored form: $3x(2x - 3)$.

3. To show that two expressions are equivalent, apply the Distributive and Commutative properties to one of the expressions until it is identical to the other expression. If the two expressions are not equivalent, then this procedure will result in a contradiction. For example, the expressions $-2(x - 3)$ and $5 - 2x$ are not equivalent. If you apply the Distributive Property to the first expression, $-2(x - 3) = -2x + 6$. Then, if you apply the Commutative Property, $-2x + 6 = 6 + -2x$ and $6 - 2x \neq 5 - 2x$.

Possible Answers to Mathematical Practices Reflections

Students may have demonstrated all of the eight Common Core Standards for Mathematical Practice during this Investigation. During the class discussion, have students provide additional Practices that the Problem cited involved and identify the use of other Mathematical Practices in the Investigation.

One student observation is provided in the Student Edition. Here is another sample student response.

> In Problem 1.3, we used the part of the expression for the area of a pool to draw the shape of the pool that was hidden. We found that there were many different ways of interpreting the expression in a drawing, but they all had the required area.
>
> **MP4: Model with mathematics.**

Notes

Investigation 1

Making Sense of Symbols: Equivalent Expressions

When you want to communicate an idea in words, you can express it in many ways. For example, all the statements below communicate the same information about Mika and Alberto.

- Alberto is older than Mika.
- Mika is younger than Alberto.
- Alberto was born before Mika.
- Mika was born after Alberto.

- Can you think of other ways to express the same idea?

You have written symbolic expressions and equations with variables to represent situations. Since you can usually think about a situation in more than one way, you can often express the situation in symbols in more than one way.

Common Core State Standards

8.EE.C.7 Solve linear equations in one variable.

8.EE.C.7b Solve linear equations with rational number coefficients, including equations whose solutions require expanding expressions using the distributive property and collecting like terms.

8.F.A.3 Interpret the equation $y = mx + b$ as defining a linear function, whose graph is a straight line; give examples of functions that are not linear.

Also A-SSE.A.1, A-SSE.A.1a, A-SSE.A.1b, A-SSE.A.2, A-SSE.B.3, A-CED.A.1, A-REI.B.3, F-IF.C.9, F-BF.A.1a

Investigation 1   **Making Sense of Symbols: Equivalent Expressions**   7

Consider the perimeter *P* of a rectangle with length *L* and width *W*.

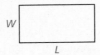

Alberto says the perimeter of the rectangle above is $P = 2(L + W)$. Mika says the perimeter is $P = 2L + 2W$.

- Why do you think Alberto used parentheses in his equation?
- Are both equations correct ways to represent perimeter? Explain.

Since $2(L + W)$ and $2L + 2W$ represent the same quantity (the perimeter of a rectangle), they are **equivalent expressions.** In this Investigation, you will explore situations in which a quantity can be described with different but equivalent expressions.

- How can you determine if two expressions are equivalent?

1.1 Tiling Pools
Writing Equivalent Expressions

In-ground pools are often surrounded by borders of tiles. The Custom Pool Company gets orders for square pools of different sizes. For example, the pool below has side lengths of 5 feet and is surrounded by square border tiles. All Custom Pool border tiles measure 1 foot on each side.

? How many border tiles do you need to surround a square pool with side length *s*?

Notes _____

STUDENT PAGE

Problem 1.1

In order to calculate the number of tiles needed for a project, the Custom Pool manager wants an equation relating the number of border tiles to the size of the pool.

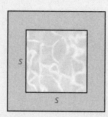

border tile

1 ft
1 ft

A 1. Write an expression for the number of border tiles needed to surround a square pool with sides of length *s* feet.

2. Write a different but equivalent expression for the number of tiles needed to surround the square pool.

3. Explain why your two expressions for the number of border tiles are equivalent.

B 1. Use each expression in Question A to write an equation for the number of border tiles *N*. Make a table and a graph for each equation.

2. Based on your table and graph, are the two expressions for the number of border tiles in Question A equivalent? Explain.

C Is the relationship between the side length of the pool and the number of border tiles linear or nonlinear? Explain.

ACE Homework starts on page 15.

Investigation 1 **Making Sense of Symbols: Equivalent Expressions** 9

Notes _____

1.2 Thinking in Different Ways
Determining Equivalence

When Takashi reported his ideas about an equation relating N and s in Problem 1.1, he made the following sketch.

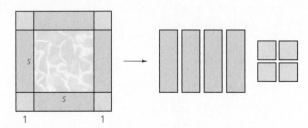

- What equation do you think Takashi wrote to relate N and s?

Problem 1.2

A Four students in Takashi's class came up with different equations for counting the number of border tiles. For each equation, make a sketch that shows how the student might have been thinking about the border of the pool.

1. Stella's equation: $N = 4(s + 1)$
2. Jeri's equation: $N = s + s + s + s + 4$
3. Hank's equation: $N = 4(s + 2)$
4. Sal's equation: $N = 2s + 2(s + 2)$

B Use each equation in Question A to find the number of border tiles needed for a square pool with a side length of 10 feet. Can you conclude from your results that all the expressions for the number of tiles are equivalent? Explain your reasoning.

C Which of the expressions for the number of border tiles in Question A represent Takashi's sketch? Explain.

ACE Homework starts on page 15.

Notes

1.3 The Community Pool Problem
Interpreting Expressions

In this Problem, you will interpret symbolic statements and use them to make predictions.

A community center is building a pool, part indoor and part outdoor. A diagram of the indoor part of the pool is shown. The indoor shape is made from a half-circle with radius x and a rectangle with length $4x$.

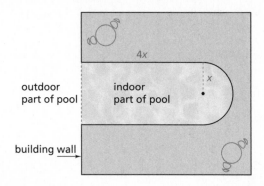

Problem 1.3

The exact dimensions of the pool are not available, but the area A of the whole pool is given by the equation:

$$A = x^2 + \frac{\pi x^2}{2} + 8x^2 + \frac{\pi x^2}{4}$$

A Which part of the expression for the area of the pool represents

1. the area of the indoor part? Explain.

2. the area of the outdoor part? Explain.

B **1.** Make a sketch of the outdoor part. Label the dimensions.

2. If possible, draw another shape for the outdoor part of the pool. If not, explain why not.

continued on the next page >

Notes

Problem 1.3 *continued*

C Stella and Jeri each rewrote the expression for the area of the outdoor part of the pool to help them make a sketch.

Stella $x^2 + \frac{\pi x^2}{8} + \frac{\pi x^2}{8}$ **Jeri** $\left(\frac{1}{2}x\right)(2x) + \frac{\pi x^2}{4}$

1. Explain the reasoning that each person may have used to write their expression.

2. Decide if these expressions are equivalent to the original expression in Question A, part (2). Explain your reasoning.

D Does the equation for the area of the pool represent a linear or nonlinear function? Explain.

A C E Homework starts on page 15.

1.4 Diving In
Revisiting the Distributive Property

In Problems 1.1 and 1.2, you found patterns that could be represented by several different but equivalent symbolic expressions, such as:

$$4s + 4$$
$$4(s + 1)$$
$$s + s + s + s + 4$$
$$2s + 2(s + 2)$$

You can show the equivalence of these expressions with arrangements of the border tiles. You can also show that these expressions are equivalent by using properties of numbers and operations.

An important property is the **Distributive Property:**

For any real numbers a, b, and c:

$$a(b + c) = ab + ac \quad \text{and} \quad a(b - c) = ab - ac$$

For example, this property guarantees that $4(s + 1) = 4s + 4$ for any s.

We say that $a(b + c)$ and $4(s + 1)$ are in **factored form** and $ab + ac$ and $4s + 4$ are in **expanded form.**

Notes

The next problem revisits the Distributive Property.

Swimming pools are sometimes divided into sections that are used for different purposes. A pool may have a section for swimming laps and a section for diving, or a section for experienced swimmers and a section for small children.

Below are diagrams of pools with swimming and diving sections. The dimensions are in meters.

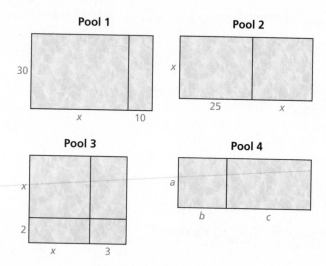

- For each pool, what are two different but equivalent expressions for the total area?

- How do these diagrams and expressions illustrate the Distributive Property? Explain.

The Distributive Property, as well as the Commutative Property and other properties for numbers, are useful for writing equivalent expressions. The **Commutative Property** states that for any real numbers a and b:

$$a + b = b + a \quad \text{and} \quad ab = ba$$

These properties were discussed in previous Units.

Investigation 1   **Making Sense of Symbols: Equivalent Expressions**   13

Notes _____

Problem 1.4

Ⓐ Use the Distributive Property to write each expression in expanded form.

1. $3(x + 5)$

2. $2(3x - 10)$

3. $2x(x + 5)$

4. $(x + 2)(x + 5)$

Ⓑ Use the Distributive Property to write each expression in factored form.

1. $12 + 24x$

2. $x + x + x + 6$

3. $x^2 + 3x$

4. $x^2 + 4x + 3$

Ⓒ The following expressions all represent the number of border tiles for a square pool with side length s.

$$4(s + 1)$$
$$2s + 2(s + 2)$$
$$(s + 2)^2 - s^2$$

$$s + s + s + s + 4$$
$$4(s + 2) - 4$$
$$2[2(s + 2) - 2]$$

Use the Distributive and Commutative properties to show that these expressions are equivalent.

Ⓓ Three of the following expressions are equivalent. Explain which expression is not equivalent to the other three.

1. $2x - 12x + 10$

2. $10 - x$

3. $10(1 - x)$

4. $\dfrac{20(-x + 1)}{2}$

Ⓔ Copy each equation. Insert one set of parentheses in the expression to the left of the equal sign so that it is equivalent to the expression to the right of the equal sign.

1. $6p + 2 - 2p = 4p + 12$

2. $6p + 2 - 2p = 6p$

Ⓐ Ⓒ Ⓔ Homework starts on page 15.

Notes _____

_____

_____

Applications

1. **a.** How many 1-foot-square border tiles do you need to surround a pool that is 10 feet long and 5 feet wide?

   b. Write an expression for the number of border tiles needed to surround a pool *L* feet long and *W* feet wide.

   c. Write a different but equivalent expression for the number of tiles needed in part (b). Explain why your expressions are equivalent.

2. A square hot tub has sides of length *s* feet. A tiler makes a border by placing 1-foot-square tiles along the edges of the tub and triangular tiles at the corners, as shown. The tiler makes the triangular tiles by cutting the square tiles in half along a diagonal.

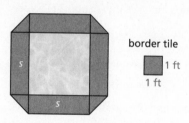

border tile

1 ft
1 ft

   a. Suppose the hot tub has sides of length 7 feet. How many square tiles does the tiler need for the border?

   b. Write an expression for the number of square tiles *N* needed to build this border for a square tub with sides of length *s* feet.

   c. Write a different but equivalent expression for the number of tiles *N*. Explain why your expressions are equivalent.

   d. Is the relationship between the number of tiles and side length linear or nonlinear? Explain.

Notes

3. A rectangular pool is *L* feet long and *W* feet wide. A tiler makes a border by placing 1-foot-square tiles along the edges of the pool and triangular tiles on the corners, as shown. The tiler makes the triangular tiles by cutting the square tiles in half along a diagonal.

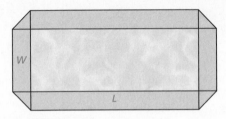

a. Suppose the pool is 30 feet long and 20 feet wide. How many square tiles does the tiler need for the border?

b. Write two expressions for the number of square tiles *N* needed to make this border for a pool *L* feet long and *W* feet wide.

c. Explain why your two expressions are equivalent.

4. Below are three more expressions students wrote for the number of border tiles needed to surround the square pool in Problem 1.2.

$$4\left(\frac{s}{2} + \frac{s}{4}\right) + 4 \qquad 2(s + 0.5) + 2(s + 1.5) \qquad 4\left[\frac{s + (s + 2)}{2}\right]$$

a. Use each expression to find the number of border tiles *N* if *s* = 0.

b. Do you think the expressions are equivalent? Explain.

c. Use each expression to find the number of border tiles if *s* = 12. Has your answer to part (b) changed? Explain.

d. What can you say about testing specific values as a method for determining whether two or more expressions are equivalent?

5. A square surrounds a circle with a radius *r*. Each expression represents the area of part of this figure. Describe the shape or region each area represents.

a. $4r^2 - \pi r^2$

b. $4r^2 - \frac{\pi r^2}{4}$

Notes _____

_____

_____

6. The dimensions of a pool are shown below.

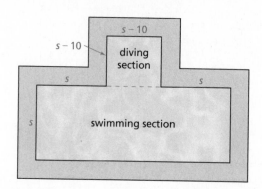

Each expression represents the surface area for part of the pool.

   i. $s(3s - 10)$ **ii.** $(s - 10)^2$

  iii. $2s^2 + s(s - 10)$ **iv.** $s^2 - 20s + 100$

a. Which expression(s) could represent the area of the diving section?

b. Which expression(s) could represent the area of the swimming section?

c. If you chose more than one expression for parts (a) and (b), show that they are equivalent.

d. Write an equation that represents the total surface area A of the pool.

e. What kind of relationship does the equation in part (d) represent?

For Exercises 7–9, complete parts (a)–(c).

a. For each expression, write an equation of the form $y = expression$. Make a table and a graph of the two equations. Show x values from -5 to 5 on the graph.

b. Based on your table and graph, tell whether you think the two expressions are equivalent.

c. If you think the expressions are equivalent, use the properties you have learned in this Investigation to verify their equivalence. If you think they are not equivalent, explain why.

7. $-3x + 6 + 5x$ **8.** $10 - 5x$ **9.** $(3x + 4) + (2x - 3)$
     $6 + 2x$ $5x - 10$ $5x + 1$

Investigation 1   Making Sense of Symbols: Equivalent Expressions   **17**

Notes _____

_____

_____

10. Use the Distributive Property to write each expression in expanded form.

    a. $3(x + 7)$ **b.** $5(5 - x)$

    c. $2(4x - 8)$ **d.** $(x + 4)(x + 2)$

11. Use the Distributive Property to write each expression in factored form.

    a. $2x + 6$ **b.** $14 - 7x$

    c. $2x - 10x$ **d.** $3x + 4x$

12. Use the Distributive and Commutative properties to determine whether each pair of expressions is equivalent for all values of x.

    a. $3x + 7x$ and $10x$ **b.** $5x$ and $5x - 10x$

    c. $4(1 + 2x) - 3x$ and $5x + 4$ **d.** $5 - 3(2 - 4x)$ and $-1 + 12x$

13. Here is one way Maleka proved that $2(s + 2) + 2s$ is equivalent to $4s + 4$.

$$
\begin{aligned}
(1) \quad 2(s + 2) + 2s &= 2s + 4 + 2s \\
(2) \qquad\qquad\qquad &= 2s + 2s + 4 \\
(3) \qquad\qquad\qquad &= (2 + 2)s + 4 \\
(4) \qquad\qquad\qquad &= 4s + 4
\end{aligned}
$$

What properties of numbers and operations justify each step?

14. Find three equivalent expressions for $6x + 3$.

For Exercises 15–17, copy the statement. Insert parentheses on the left side of the equation, if necessary, to make the statement true for all values of p.

    15. $7 + 5p - p = 11p$ **16.** $7 + 5p - p = 7$ **17.** $7 + 5p - p = 7 + 4p$

Notes _____

_____

_____

Connections

In Exercises 18–23, each expression represents the area of a rectangle. Draw a divided rectangle for each expression. Label the lengths and areas. For Exercises 18–20, write an equivalent expression in expanded form. For Exercises 21–23, write an equivalent expression in factored form.

18. $x(x + 6)$ **19.** $x(x - 6)$ **20.** $x(5 + 1)$

21. $x^2 + 4x$ **22.** $x^2 - 2x$ **23.** $3x + 4x$

24. A circular pool with a radius of 4 feet has a 1-foot border.

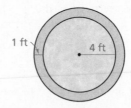

1 ft   4 ft

     a. What is the area of the circular pool?

     b. What is the area of the border?

     c. Write an expression for the area of a circular pool with a radius of r feet.

     d. Write an expression for the area of a 1-foot border around a circular pool with a radius of r feet.

25. **Multiple Choice** Which of the following expressions is equivalent to $m + m + m + m + m$?

     A. $m + 5$ **B.** $5m$ **C.** m^5 **D.** $5(m + 1)$

26. **Multiple Choice** Which of the following expressions is equivalent to $a - b$, where a and b are any numbers?

     F. $b - a$ **G.** $a + b$ **H.** $-a + b$ **I.** $-b + a$

Notes

27. Percy wants to write an equation for the number of tiles needed to surround a square pool with sides of length s feet. He makes a table for pools with sides of length 1, 2, 3, 4, and 5 feet. Then he uses the patterns in his table to write the equation $N = 8 + 4(s - 1)$.

Border Tiles

Side Length	1	2	3	4	5
Number of Tiles	8	12	16	20	24

a. What patterns does Percy see in his table?

b. Is Percy's expression for the number of tiles equivalent to $4(s + 1)$, Stella's expression in Problem 1.2? Explain.

Draw and label a rectangle whose area is represented by the expression. Then write an equivalent expression in expanded form.

28. $(x + 1)(x + 4)$ **29.** $(x + 5)(x + 6)$ **30.** $3x(5 + 2)$

For Exercises 31–33, draw and label a rectangle whose area is represented by the expression. Then write an equivalent expression in factored form.

31. $x^2 + x + 2x + 2$ **32.** $x^2 + 7x + 10$ **33.** $x^2 + 14x + 49$

34. Two expressions for the number of border tiles for the pool below are given. Sketch a picture that illustrates each expression.

$$2(s + 0.5) + 2(s + 1.5) \qquad 4\left[\frac{s + (s + 2)}{2}\right]$$

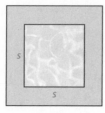

border tile

1 ft
1 ft

Notes

Find the sum or difference.

35. $\frac{5}{7} - \frac{1}{3}$ **36.** $\frac{5}{2} + \frac{1}{3}$

37. $\frac{1}{2}x + \frac{1}{2}x$ **38.** $\frac{2}{3}x - \frac{1}{2}x$

Find the sum, difference, product, or quotient.

39. 2×14 **40.** $-2 - (-14)$ **41.** $-2 \div (-14)$

42. $-6 \times (-11)$ **43.** $-6 + 11$ **44.** $6 - 11$

45. $-18(3x)$ **46.** $\frac{-24x}{-8}$ **47.** $-18x \div 3$

Find the greatest common factor for each pair of numbers.

48. 35 and 40   **49.** 36 and 12

50. 100 and 25   **51.** 42 and 9

52. Below is a diagram of Otter Middle School's outdoor track. The shape of the interior region (shaded green) is a rectangle with a half-circle at each end.

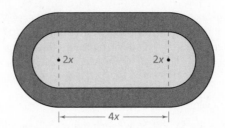

    a. Find an expression that represents the area of the interior region.

    b. Find the perimeter of the interior region as if you wanted to put a fence around it. Explain how you found your answer.

    c. Write an expression equivalent to the one in part (b).

Notes _____

_____

53. For Problem 1.2, Percy wrote the expression $8 + 4(s - 1)$ to represent the number of border tiles needed to surround a square pool with side length s.

   a. Is this expression equivalent to the other expressions? Explain.

   b. Four students used Percy's expression to calculate the number of border tiles needed for a pool with a side length of 6 feet. Which student performed the calculations correctly?

Stella	Hank
$8 + 4(6 - 1) = 8 + 24 - 1$ $ = 31 \text{ tiles}$	$8 + 4(6 - 1) = 8 + 4(5)$ $ = 8 + 20$ $ = 28 \text{ tiles}$

Takashi	Jackie
$8 + 4(6 - 1) = 12 + (6 - 1)$ $ = 12 + 5$ $ = 17 \text{ tiles}$	$8 + 4(6 - 1) = 12(6 - 1)$ $ = 12(5)$ $ = 60 \text{ tiles}$

54. Meiko invests D dollars in a money-market account that earns 10% interest per year. She does not plan on taking money out during the year. She writes the expression $D + 0.10D$ to represent the amount of money in the account at the end of one year.

   a. Explain why this expression is correct.

   b. Write an equivalent expression in factored form.

   c. Suppose Meiko invested $1,500. How much money will she have in her account at the end of one year?

Notes _____

_____

_____

For Exercises 55 and 56, use this information: The ski club is planning a trip for winter break. They write the equation $C = 200 + 10N$ to estimate the cost in dollars C of the trip for N students.

55. Duncan and Corey both use the equation to estimate the cost for 50 students. Duncan says the cost is $10,500, and Corey says it is $700.

    a. Whose estimate is correct? Show your work.

    b. How do you think Duncan and Corey found such different estimates if they both used the same equation?

56. a. Suppose 20 students go on the trip. What is the cost per student?

    b. Write an equation for the cost per student S when N students go on the trip.

    c. Use your equation to find the cost per student when 40 students go on the trip.

57. Below are two students' calculations for writing an equivalent expression for $10 - 4(x - 1) + 11 \times 3$.

    a. Which student performed the calculations correctly?

    b. What mistakes did the other student make?

Sarah

$$10 - 4(x - 1) + 11 \times 3 = 10 - 4x + 4 + 11 \times 3$$
$$= 10 - 4x + 4 + 33$$
$$= 10 - 4x + 37$$
$$= 10 + 37 - 4x$$
$$= 47 - 4x$$

Emily

$$10 - 4(x - 1) + 11 \times 3 = 10 - 4x + 4 + 11 \times 3$$
$$= 10 - 4x + 15 \times 3$$
$$= 25 - 4x \times 3$$
$$= 25 - 12x$$

Notes

Extensions

For Exercises 58 and 59, write an equation for the number of
1 foot-by-1 foot tiles N needed to surround each pool based on the
width w of the border. The diagrams below show each pool surrounded
by a border of widths 1, 2, and 3.

58.

  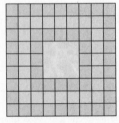

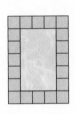 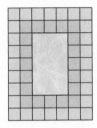 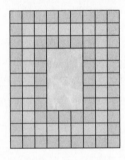

59.

60. The expression puzzles below all start with the original expression
$2n - 3 + 4n + 6n + 1$. Each one ends with a different expression.

Expression Puzzles

Puzzle	Original Expression	Desired Result
1	$2n - 3 + 4n + 6n + 1$	$12n - 5$
2	$2n - 3 + 4n + 6n + 1$	$12n + 3$
3	$2n - 3 + 4n + 6n + 1$	$12n - 2$
4	$2n - 3 + 4n + 6n + 1$	$n + 1$

a. Solve each puzzle by inserting one set of parentheses in the
original expression so that it is equivalent to the desired result.

b. Show that your expression is equivalent to the desired result.
Justify each step.

Notes

Mathematical Reflections 1

In this Investigation, you found different but equivalent expressions to represent a quantity in a relationship. The following questions will help you summarize what you have learned.

Think about these questions. Discuss your ideas with other students and your teacher. Then write a summary of your findings in your notebook.

1. **What** does it mean to say that two expressions are equivalent?

2. **Explain** how you can use the Distributive Property to write equivalent expressions.

3. **Explain** how you can use the Distributive and Commutative properties to show that two or more expressions are equivalent.

Notes _____

Common Core Mathematical Practices

As you worked on the Problems in this Investigation, you used prior knowledge to make sense of them. You also applied Mathematical Practices to solve the Problems. Think back over your work, the ways you thought about the Problems, and how you used Mathematical Practices.

Hector described his thoughts in the following way:

In Problem 1.1, we found many different but equivalent expressions to represent the number of unit tiles needed to surround a pool. When the teacher asked if there were more, Jon said there were an infinite number.

Jon showed how you could multiply the term $4n$ in the expression $4n + 4$ by 3 and then divide by 3 to get $\frac{3(4n)}{3} + 4$. He then showed how you could multiply $4n$ by 4 and then divide by 4 to get $\frac{4(4n)}{4} + 4$. Both expressions are equivalent to $4n + 4$. You could do this with any number, so there are an infinite number of equivalent expressions.

Common Core Standards for Mathematical Practice
MP7 Look for and make use of structure.

• What other Mathematical Practices can you identify in Hector's reasoning?

• Describe a Mathematical Practice that you and your classmates used to solve a different Problem in this Investigation.

Notes _____

Investigation

2

PLANNING

INVESTIGATION
OVERVIEW

GOALS AND
STANDARDS

Combining Expressions

▼ Investigation Overview

Investigation Description

In this Investigation, students combine expressions to write new expressions either by adding or subtracting expressions or by substituting an equivalent expression for a given quantity in an expression or equation. They also explore the relationship among the volumes of cylinders, cones, and spheres that have the same height and radius. They describe these relationships with algebraic equations that lead to formulas for the volumes. They use the properties of real numbers to write equivalent expressions as they continue to connect symbolic expressions with real-world contexts.

Investigation Vocabulary

There are no new glossary terms introduced in this Investigation.

Mathematics Background

- Equivalent Expressions
- Combining Expressions
- Solving Equations

Planning Chart

Content	ACE	Pacing	Materials	Resources
Problem 2.1	1–5, 17–21, 40	1 day	**Labsheet 2ACE:** Exercise 1 (accessibility) graphing calculators (optional)	
Problem 2.2	6–9, 22–31	1 day	poster paper markers graphing calculators (optional)	
Problem 2.3	10–12, 32–34, 41–43	1 day	graphing calculators (optional) equal dimension plastic geometric cones, cylinders, and spheres (optional)	• Pouring and Filling
Problem 2.4	13–16, 35–39	1 day	graphing calculators (optional)	
Mathematical Reflections		½ day		
Assessment: Partner Quiz		1 day		• Partner Quiz • Partner Quiz (optional)

Goals and Standards

Goals

Equivalence Develop understanding of equivalent expressions and equations.

- Model situations with symbolic statements

- Recognize when two or more symbolic statements represent the same context

- Use the properties of real numbers, such as the Distributive Property, to write equivalent expressions

- Determine if different symbolic expressions are mathematically equivalent

- Interpret the information that equivalent expressions represent in a given context

- Determine the equivalent expression or equation that is most helpful in answering a particular question about a relationship

- Use algebraic equations to describe the relationship among the volumes of cylinders, cones, and spheres that have the same height and radius

- Solve linear equations involving parentheses

- Determine if a linear equation has a finite number of solutions, an infinite number of solutions, or no solution

- Develop understanding and some fluency with factoring quadratic expressions

- Solve quadratic equations by factoring

- Recognize how and when to use symbols, rather than tables or graphs, to display relationships, generalizations, and proofs

Functions Develop understanding of specific functions such as linear, exponential, and quadratic functions.

- Develop proficiency in identifying and representing relationships, expressed in problem contexts, with appropriate functions, and use these relationships to solve problems

- Analyze equations to determine the patterns of change in the related tables and graphs

- Relate parts of a symbolic statement or expression to the underlying properties of the relationship they represent and to the context of the problem

- Determine characteristics of a graph (intercepts, maxima and minima, shape, etc.) of an equation by looking at its symbolic representation

Mathematical Reflections

Look for evidence of student understanding of the goals for this Investigation in their responses to the questions in *Mathematical Reflections*. The goals addressed by each question are indicated below.

1. Describe a situation in which it is helpful to add expressions to form a new expression. Explain how you can combine the expressions.

    Goals

    *   Model situations with symbolic statements
    *   Recognize when two or more symbolic statements represent the same context
    *   Use the properties of real numbers, such as the Distributive Property, to write equivalent expressions
    *   Determine the equivalent expression or equation that is most helpful in answering a particular question about a relationship

2. Describe a situation in which it is helpful to substitute an equivalent expression for a quantity in an equation.

    Goals

    *   Determine if different symbolic expressions are mathematically equivalent
    *   Interpret the information that equivalent expressions represent in a given context
    *   Recognize when two or more symbolic statements represent the same context
    *   Determine the equivalent expression or equation that is most helpful in answering a particular question about a relationship

3. What are the advantages and disadvantages of working with one equation rather than two or more equations in a given situation?

    Goal

    *   Relate parts of a symbolic statement or expression to the underlying properties of the relationship they represent and to the context of the problem

4. Write an expression that represents the volume of each three-dimensional figure. Explain your reasoning.

    a. cylinder

    b. cone

    c. sphere

    Goals

    *   Use algebraic equations to describe the relationship among the volumes of cylinders, cones, and spheres that have the same height and radius

- Relate parts of a symbolic statement or expression to the underlying properties of the relationship they represent and to the context of the problem
- Recognize how and when to use symbols, rather than tables or graphs, to display relationships, generalizations, and proofs

Standards

Common Core Content Standards

8.EE.C.7 Solve linear equations in one variable. *Problems 1 and 2*

8.EE.C.7b Solve linear equations with rational number coefficients, including equations whose solutions require expanding expressions using the distributive property and collecting like terms. *Problems 1 and 2*

8.F.A.1 Understand that a function is a rule that assigns to each input exactly one output. The graph of a function is the set of ordered pairs consisting of an input and the corresponding output. *Problems 2, 3, and 4*

8.F.A.2 Compare properties of two functions each represented in a different way (algebraically, graphically, numerically in tables, or by verbal descriptions). *Problem 3*

8.F.A.3 Interpret the equation $y = mx + b$ as defining a linear function, whose graph is a straight line; give examples of functions that are not linear. *Problems 1 and 2*

8.G.C.9 Know the formulas for the volumes of cones, cylinders, and spheres and use them to solve real-world and mathematical problems. *Problems 3 and 4*

N-Q.A.1 Use units as a way to understand problems and to guide the solution of multi-step problems; choose and interpret units consistently in formulas; choose and interpret the scale and the origin in graphs and data displays. *Problems 1, 2, 3, and 4*

N-Q.A.2 Define appropriate quantities for the purpose of descriptive modeling. *Problems 3 and 4*

A-SSE.A.1 Interpret expressions that represent a quantity in terms of its context. *Problems 1, 2, 3, and 4*

A-SSE.A.1a Interpret parts of an expression, such as terms, factors, and coefficients. *Problems 1, 2, 3, and 4*

A-SSE.A.1b. Interpret complicated expressions by viewing one or more of their parts as a single entity. *Problems 1, 2, 3, and 4*

A-SSE.A.2 Use the structure of an expression to identify ways to rewrite it. *Problems 1, 2, and 3*

A-SSE.B.3 Choose and produce an equivalent form of an expression to reveal and explain properties of the quantity represented by the expression. *Problems 1, 2, and 3*

A-CED.A.1 Create equations and inequalities in one variable and use them to solve problems. *Problems 2, 3, and 4*

A-REI.B.3. Solve linear equations and inequalities in one variable, including equations with coefficients represented by letters. *Problems 2, 3, and 4*

F-IF.C.9 Compare properties of two functions each represented in a different way (algebraically, graphically, numerically in tables, or by verbal descriptions). *Problems 1 and 3*

F-BF.A.1 Write a function that describes a relationship between two quantities. *Problems 1, 2, 3, and 4*

F-BF.A.1a Determine an explicit expression, a recursive process, or steps for calculation from a context. *Problems 1, 2, and 3*

Facilitating the Mathematical Practices

Students in *Connected Mathematics* classrooms display evidence of multiple Common Core Standards for Mathematical Practice every day. Here are just a few examples of when you might observe students demonstrating the Standards for Mathematical Practice during this Investigation.

Practice 1: **Make sense of problems and persevere in solving them.**

Students are engaged every day in solving problems and, over time, learn to persevere in solving them. To be effective, the problems embody critical concepts and skills and have the potential to engage students in making sense of mathematics. Students build understanding by reflecting, connecting, and communicating. These student-centered problem situations engage students in articulating the "knowns" in a problem situation and determining a logical solution pathway. The student-student and student-teacher dialogues help students not only to make sense of the problems, but also to persevere in finding appropriate strategies to solve them. The suggested questions in the Teacher Guides provide the metacognitive scaffolding to help students monitor and refine their problem-solving strategies.

Practice 4: **Model with mathematics.**

In Problem 2.1, students explore situations that can be modeled using mathematical expressions. The first situation is a walkathon that involves three students who walk the same distance together. Students model, from the individual pledges for each student to a combined expression, the total pledges for the three. Problem 2.2 also involves expressions to model profit and the number of visitors. These two separate expressions are used to make a model for profit based on the probability of rain. In Problem 2.3, students revisit volume formulas for cylinders, cones, and spheres to predict the amount of material required to make candles. Again, they develop expressions to model each situation, and then they use the models to predict the amounts of material required for each situation.

Students identify and record their personal experiences with the Standards for Mathematical Practice during the Mathematical Reflections at the end of the Investigation.

PROBLEM 2.1

Walking Together
Adding Expressions

▼ Problem Overview

> *Focus Question*   What are the advantages and disadvantages of using one equation rather than two or more equations to represent a situation?

Problem Description

This Problem revisits a walkathon from *Moving Straight Ahead*. Students add several expressions and apply the distributive and commutative properties to write equivalent expressions. Some of the expressions contain parentheses, which students have not had much experience with. This is an opportunity to assess student understanding of the Distributive Property.

Problem Implementation

Students can work in small groups of 2–4.

Materials

• **Labsheet 2ACE:** Exercise 1 (accessibility)

Using Technology

graphing calculators (optional)

Vocabulary

There are no new glossary terms introduced in this Problem.

Mathematics Background

• Equivalent Expressions

At a Glance and Lesson Plan

- At a Glance: Problem 2.1 Say It With Symbols
- Lesson Plan: Problem 2.1 Say It With Symbols

▼ Launch

Connecting to Prior Knowledge

In the last Investigation, students made and identified equivalent expressions.

Suggested Questions

- How did you show that these expressions were equivalent? (If each expression represents a relationship, then equivalent expressions have the same graphs and tables. We also validated that the expression connected to patterns in the Problem, such as the patterns among the border tiles. We also used using the Distributive and Commutative Properties.)

In this Problem, students continue to create expressions.

Presenting the Challenge

Remind students about the walkathon from *Moving Straight Ahead*. The same three students with the same amount of money from their sponsors are involved. Giving students information about the number of sponsors will be new. You could write the following information on the board:

Leanne: $10 from each of her sponsors

Gilberto: $2 from each sponsor for each kilometer that he walks

Alana: $5 plus $.50 from each sponsor for each kilometer that she walks

Each student will walk the same number of miles, x, but each student has a different number of sponsors: 16 for Leanne, 7 for Gilberto, and 11 for Alana.

Suggested Questions

- How could you calculate the total amount of money the three students will collect? (Just take the kilometers and calculate the amount that each student collects from his/her sponsor and add them together.)

Using student suggestions, find total amounts for different numbers of kilometers. Have students guide the calculations and justify the steps.

Challenge your students to write an equation to calculate the total amount of money collected by Leanne, Gilberto, and Alana for any number of kilometers they walk.

Explore

Providing for Individual Needs

As you observe your students, look for ways that they are combining the total amounts. Be sure to share these in the Summarize.

As students write an equation, ask them how they know it is correct. Suggest that they try to use their equation to compute the money for the number of kilometers you used in the Launch.

Suggested Questions

If students have difficulty getting started with Question A, ask:

- How much will Leanne raise per kilometer from each of her sponsors? ($10 total)

- How many sponsors does Leanne have? (16)

- So, how much will she raise for walking x kilometers? ($160)

- How much will Gilberto raise per kilometer from each of his sponsors? ($2)

- So, how much will he raise walking x kilometers from each of his sponsors? ($2x$)

- How many sponsors does Gilberto have? (7)

- So, how much will he raise for walking x kilometers? (($2x$)(7) or $14x$)

- How much will Alana raise from each of her sponsors? ($5 + 0.5x$)

- How many sponsors does Alana have? (11)

- So, how much will she raise for walking x kilometers? (($5 + 0.5x$)(11))

- Now, write an expression that shows the total amount for all three. (Most students can at least write the sum of the previous three expressions to get one expression. Some may recognize that they can apply the Distributive Property to Alana's total.)

For Question B, if students are having trouble, you can ask:

- What would be an equivalent expression for Alana's total? (If they don't remember the Distributive Property, don't push too hard. It will come up in the Summarize.)

As you observe how students are solving the Problem, listen to how students talk about the expressions. How do they talk about the expressions? Do they recognize like terms? You may have talked to them about like terms in Investigation 1. If not, use the expression $2x + 10x$ to illustrate why the expression is equivalent to $12x$ using an area model or the pouches used in Moving Straight Ahead. Do they recognize that $9x$ and 3 cannot be combined since they are not like terms? So, $9x + 3$ is the simplest form possible, meaning that all the operations that can be performed have been performed. The language of "like terms" is not necessary at this time and can be introduced at your discretion.

- Do students understand the implication of the parentheses?
- Do students relate to the expressions in terms of some invented context?
- Do students suggest various ways to manipulate the expressions?

Come back to these ideas in the Summarize.

Planning for the Summary

What evidence will you use in the summary to clarify and deepen understanding of the Focus Question?
What will you do if you do not have evidence?

▼ Summarize

Orchestrating the Discussion

Have students share their equations for the total amount that the walkathon team will raise.

Suggested Questions

- What ways do you know for checking whether two expressions are equivalent? (Students will probably suggest making graphs, tables, or substituting a few values into each expression. They may describe some of their own rules, as well as their present understanding of the Distributive Property.)

Encourage students to use explanations like the following:

- When there are several quantities in parentheses to be added and a factor outside the parentheses, each quantity must be multiplied by the factor outside the parentheses.

- When there are a certain number of *x*'s and another number of *x*'s, they can be combined by adding the numbers or the coefficients of *x*.

- When you add or multiply two quantities, it does not matter which one you start with. You can add or multiply in any order.

Note: For vocabulary, you might insert words such as *term* in place of *quantity* without disrupting the flow of ideas.

- Pick one of your expressions to find the total amount the team will raise. Use the expression to find the total amounts if the students walk 5 kilometers and if they walk 8 kilometers. ($224.75, $230.60)

- Which expression did you use, and why? (Discuss the advantages and disadvantages of each expression for finding the total amount of money raised.)

- What are the advantages and disadvantages of using one expression rather than two or more expressions to represent a situation? (More simplified expressions are usually easier to use for calculating specific values of the variable because there are fewer arithmetic operations to perform. However, they often contain less information about the context than more complex expressions.)

Be sure to discuss Question C. It is important to keep the concepts of linear, exponential, and quadratic equations current. Since the expressions for the total amount of money are not in the form $y = mx + b$, you need to check to see if students can recognize that this is still a linear situation.

- Does the equation for total money raised represent a linear function? How can you tell? (Some students may write the equation in $y = mx + b$ form. Some may use a table or graph. Some may recognize that the highest exponent of x is 1.)

- What is the slope? y-intercept? (Note that slope is the sum of the coefficients of x or the sum of the slopes from the individual sums. The y-intercept is the amount of money that Alana and Leanne collected without having to walk.)

Check for Understanding

You can use the following to assess students' understanding. Write a few expressions on the board. Several of these expressions should be equivalent.

- Identify the expressions that are equivalent in the list.

    $2x + 3 + 7x$

    $2x(3 + 7x)$

    $9x + 32x + 10x$

    $2(x + 3) + 7x$

    $2x(3 + 7x)$

    $3(3x + 1)$

    $7x + 2x + 3$

    ($2x + 3 + 7x$, $7x + 2x + 3$, and $3(3x + 1)$ are equivalent. $2x(3 + 7x)$, $9x + 32x + 10x$, and $2(x + 3) + 7x$ are not equivalent, and none of them are equivalent to $2x + 3 + 7x$, $7x + 2x + 3$, and $3(3x + 1)$.)

Presenting a short list of expressions, such as the one shown above, makes an effective class opener. This practice gives students an opportunity to talk about the meaning of the symbols and how to determine equivalence. It also helps students connect new knowledge to the interpretation of the expressions. That experience helps students move into a world of symbols independent of context. You could also provide two or three linear expressions and ask students to add or subtract two of them.

Reflecting on Student Learning

Use the following questions to assess student understanding at the end of the lesson.

- What evidence do I have that students understand the Focus Question?
  - Where did my students get stuck?
  - What strategies did they use?
  - What breakthroughs did my students have today?
- How will I use this to plan for tomorrow? For the next time I teach this lesson?
- Where will I have the opportunity to reinforce these ideas as I continue through this Unit? The next Unit?

ACE Assignment Guide

- **Applications:** 1–5
- **Connections:** 17–21
- **Extensions:** 40
- **Labsheet 2ACE:** Exercise 1
This Labsheet provides scaffolding for Exercise 1.

Predicting Profit
Substituting Expressions

▼ Problem Overview

Focus Question   What are some ways that you can combine one or more expressions (or equations) to create a new expression (or equation)?

Problem Description

In this Problem, an equation for profit is given based on the number of visitors. A second equation relates the number of visitors to the probability of rain. So, the expression for the number of visitors based on the probability of rain can be substituted for the variable representing the number of visitors in the profit equation. This substitution gives a new equation for profit based on the probability of rain.

Students simplify the new equation to find an equivalent expression for profit. They relate the numbers and variables of each equation to the situation to see what information is represented by the equation. This is a two-stage process. Given the probability of rain, students can find the profits using this new equation, or they can first find the number of visitors and then substitute this number into the original profit equation. The equations are used to predict the profit for a given probability of rain and conversely to predict the probability given a daily profit.

Problem Implementation

Students can work in pairs and then share their work with another pair.

Materials

poster paper
markers

Using Technology

You may want to allow students to use graphing calculators to make tables and graphs of the expressions and equations in this Problem.

Vocabulary

There are no new glossary terms introduced in this Problem.

Mathematics Background

• Combining Expressions
• Solving Equations

At a Glance and Lesson Plan

• At a Glance: Problem 2.2 Say It With Symbols
• Lesson Plan: Problem 2.2 Say It With Symbols

▼ Launch

Connecting to Prior Knowledge

In the last Problem, you combined three expressions by adding them together.

Suggested Questions

• What information did each expression represent? (Each expression represented the amount of money a walker received from a sponsor for walking x kilometers.)

• What information did the sum of the expressions represent? (The sum of the expressions represented the total amount of money received by the walkers.)

• Is it possible to find the total amount another way? (Yes; by finding out how much each walker raised and finding the sum.)

• Which method do you prefer? (Answers will vary. They are equivalent. There are fewer calculations when you use a simpler version of the expression for the total.)

Presenting the Challenge

Tell the story about the amusement park. Write the two equations: one that predicts profit, $P = 2.50V - 500$, and one that predicts the number of visitors, $V = 600 - 500R$.

It is worth having a brief conversation about the meaning of the numbers and variables in the equations.

● **Suggested Questions**

- What information do the numbers and variables represent in this situation? (The revenue is 2.50V and cost is 500 in the profit equation. In the second equation, 600 is the number of visitors if the probability of rain is 0%. For every 1% increase in the probability of rain, the number of visitors decreases by 500.)

Note: This is an opportunity to address the role of units in solving a problem. In the equation $P = 2.50V - 500$, 2.50V represents \$2.50 profit per visitor for V visitors, while the expression $2.50V - 500$ represents the profit in dollars after deducting the expenses. The unit that would represent a solution to this equation would be dollars. In the second equation, the number of visitors is determined based on the probability of rain.

When students combine the equations, they have an equation for profit in dollars given the percent probability of rain. One way to think about this is by keeping track of the units in the equation $P = 2.50(600 - 500R) - 500$.

$$P \text{ in dollars} = \$2.50 \text{ per visitor } (600 \text{ visitors} - 500R \text{ visitors}) - \$500$$
$$= 2.50(600 - 500R) - \$500$$

The result yields the profit in dollars, so dollars is the unit.

Problem 3.1 and Problem 4.1 directly address the Algebra 1 Standard N-Q.3, which refers to dimension analysis in science. At this stage of development, students use the context and their intuition to make sense of the units as they move through the Problem. In high school, student sophistication will evolve as more complex situations are encountered in science courses such as chemistry and physics.

Challenge students to find one equation that will predict the profit based on the probability of rain.

▼ # Explore

Providing for Individual Needs

Question A, part (1) is mostly a review. Students need to use the second equation that predicts the number of visitors based on the given probability. Once they have the number of visitors, then they use the profit equation to find profit. Answering these questions will give students an intuitive feel for the combining needed when finding profit in terms of the probability of rain.

Check to see whether students are evaluating the expressions using the Distributive Property, the Commutative Property, and the Order of Operations. This is also a good time to check to see that students are using percents correctly in calculations.

If students are having difficulty writing one equation for profit that is based on the probability of rain in Question B, use their work from Question A to help them find the new equation for profit based on the probability of rain.

Suggested Questions

- What is the probability of rain? (25% or $\frac{1}{4}$ or 0.25)

- How can you use the probability to find the number of visitors? (Substitute probability for R in the visitor equation.)

- How can you use the number of visitors to find the profit? (Substitute the number of visitors for V in the profit equation.)

For Questions B and C, distribute poster paper to a few students to display how they found different expressions for profit. Ask them to show why the two expressions for profit are equivalent.

Look for ways that students solve the new equation for profit to find the probability of rain given a specific profit in Question C, part (2). Be sure to have students share these strategies in the Summarize. They can put their solutions on poster paper.

Planning for the Summary

What evidence will you use in the summary to clarify and deepen understanding of the Focus Question?

What will you do if you do not have evidence?

▼ Summarize

Orchestrating the Discussion

Use the Summarize to clarify any misconceptions or weaknesses that you have observed in the Explore.

Ask students to explain how the expressions for profit are equivalent.

Suggested Questions

- Why does $2.50(600 - 500R) - 500 = 1,000 - 1,250R$? (Have students demonstrate each step.)

Writing the equation $P = 2.50(600 - 500R) - 500$ in the form $P = 1,000 - 1,250R$ provides an opportunity to talk about the slope and intercept of the equation and what each means in this context.

- Describe the relationship that this equation represents. (The equation represents a linear relationship. The slope of the line is represented by $-1,250$. That means that for every percent increase in chance of rain, profit decreases by $1,250.)

Have students share their strategies for Question C, part (2). Use a symbolic method to review what it means to solve an equation and to review the properties of equality. If no one suggests it, use the new equation $P = 2.50(600 - 500R) - 500$ to demonstrate how to solve the equation for R given a specific value of P, say 600. Ask the class to provide each step in the solution and a justification for each step. For example, if $600 = 2.50(600 - 500R) - 500$, then $R = 32\%$.

Review Opportunity You can use this opportunity to review other methods for solving an equation.

- Describe how you can use a table to find the solution when $P = 325$. What does the solution mean in terms of the original equation $P = 2.5(600 - 500R) - 500$? (Enter the equation $y = 2.50(600 - 500x) - 500$ and generate a table of values. Find 325 in the y column. Then find the corresponding x-value for that row. When students do this, they will have to use hundredths for their x-values in order to get the correct answer, which is 0.15 or 15%.)

- Describe how you can use a graph to find the solution. What does the solution mean in terms of the original equation? (Find the point on the line of the equation with $y = 325$ and read off the value on the x-axis, or whose coordinates are $(R,325)$.)

Question D gives you a chance to see whether students can connect these complicated equations to linear relationships and to the information given about the patterns of change and y-intercept.

Students will find it interesting to discuss why the number of visitors is −250 if the probability of rain is 100%.

- What is the range for the values of the probability? (0–100% or 0.0 to 1.0)
- What is the range for the profits? ($1,000 to −$250)

Finally, ask:

- Describe why and how you combined the two equations into one equation. (The two equations were combined to simplify the number of arithmetic operations needed to find the answer. These were combined by substituting one expression for a variable in another equation.)

- Compare the work you did in this Problem of creating a new equation to the work in Problem 2.1 for creating new equations. (In this Problem, two equations were combined by substituting one expression for a variable in another equation. In Problem 2.1, adding three expressions together made the single equation. In both instances, the equations were simplified using the Distributive Property.)

This summary should help prepare students for solving equations in the next Investigation.

Reflecting on Student Learning

Use the following questions to assess student understanding at the end of the lesson.

- What evidence do I have that students understand the Focus Question?
  - Where did my students get stuck?
  - What strategies did they use?
  - What breakthroughs did my students have today?
- How will I use this to plan for tomorrow? For the next time I teach this lesson?
- Where will I have the opportunity to reinforce these ideas as I continue through this Unit? The next Unit?

ACE Assignment Guide

- **Applications:** 6–9
- **Connections:** 22–31

PROBLEM
2.3

Making Candles
Volumes of Cylinders, Cones, and Spheres

▼ Problem Overview

> *Focus Question* What equations represent the relationships among the
> volumes of cylinders, cones, and spheres?

Problem Description

In this Problem, students experiment with the volumes of cylinders, cones, and
spheres, which have the same radius and a height equal to two times the radius.
They first find the volume of a cylinder by comparing the cylinder to a prism. The
volume for both the prism and cylinder is the area of the base times the height.

Next, students compare the volumes of the three shapes by using an activity,
Pouring and Filling, that allows them to fill and empty the containers with water.
Alternatively, they could use plastic containers and physically pour the water
into the containers. From this experiment, they find relationships among the
shapes that can be represented as equations. With these equations, they write an
expression for the volume of a cone and an expression for the volume of a sphere..

Problem Implementation

Students can work in pairs and then share their work with another pair.

Have poster paper available for students to record all of their observations about
the relationships among the volumes of the three shapes.

Note: If your students studied volumes of cylinders, cones, and spheres in the
Filling and Wrapping Unit in Grade 7, then you can quickly review the formulas. It
is still worth having them explore the relationships among the volumes using the
applet or plastic containers. It provides a rich opportunity to generate a variety of
expressions. You may want to do Question A first, which develops the formula for
a cylinder, do a quick summary, and then let the class explore Questions B and C.

Materials

equal dimension plastic geometric cones, cylinders, and spheres (optional)

Using Technology

Pouring and Filling can be used to illustrate the volume relationships used in this
Problem. Also, you may want to allow students to use graphing calculators to
make tables and graphs of the expressions and equations in this Problem.

Vocabulary

There are no new glossary terms introduced in this Problem.

Mathematics Background

- Equivalent Expressions
- Combining Expressions

At a Glance and Lesson Plan

- At a Glance: Problem 2.3 Say It With Symbols
- Lesson Plan: Problem 2.3 Say It With Symbols

▼ Launch

Launch Video

This animation can be shown prior to Presenting the Challenge. The animation depicts a candle-manufacturing situation in which an order changes from one candle shape to another. The problem is that the candles for the order had already been made. In the animation, an employee melts the candles and reforms them to fulfill the changed order. This shows the relationship between the volumes of cylinders, cones, and spheres. Visit Teacher Place at mathdashboard.com/cmp3 to see the complete video.

Connecting to Prior Knowledge

In the last two Problems, you used the context of walkathons and amusement parks to generate equivalent equations. Then these equations were used to answer questions. In this Problem, you will continue to generate expressions to explore the relationships among volumes of cylinders, cones, and spheres.

Presenting the Challenge

Tell the story about Rocky Middle School and the plans for the charity event. The school plans to make and sell candles that come in three shapes—cylinders, cones, and spheres—at the event. The candles have the same height and radius. The school needs to know how much wax to buy.

Suggested Questions

- How can you find the volume of a cylinder? (Students may know how to find the volume of a cylinder by finding the number of unit cubes that are in the base and multiplying by the height from work done in the Grade 7 Unit *Filling and Wrapping*. If students do not know how to find the volume of a cylinder, proceed with the following questions.)

Display the picture of a rectangular prism and cylinder. Ask the class about the similarities of finding the volumes of each. You can remind students of the experiment that they did in *Filling and Wrapping*, where they created prisms with polygonal bases. It is better if you have plastic rectangular and cylindrical containers that you can fill to demonstrate.

- What happened to the shape as the number of sides of the base of the polygon increased? (The prism became more round or more cylindrical. The base approaches the shape of a circle.)

- How can you find the volume of a prism? Will the same method work for a cylinder? (To find the volume of a prism, find how many cubes fit on the area of the base and multiply it by the height. Yes.)

▼ Explore

Providing for Individual Needs

Encourage students to find several relationships among the three shapes for volume. Using the relationships, ask students to find equivalent expressions for the volumes of the shapes in terms of the dimensions r and h. Students may use the Distributive and Commutative Properties.

Urge them to find an expression that represents the volume of a cone and sphere. For many students, the visual image of using three cones to fill a cylinder helps them to express the volume of a cone as $\frac{1}{3}\pi r^2 h$. The same is true for a sphere. They are likely to say that the volume of a sphere is $\frac{2}{3}$ the volume of a cylinder and write $\frac{2}{3}\pi r^2 h$. This is sufficient since the height to find the volume of any sphere is equal to $2r$. You could ask them to write the formula for the volume of a sphere in terms of its radius, $V = \frac{4}{3}\pi r^3$, and justify their reasoning.

For students who relate to visual representations, creating a chart of the relationships in their notes can be a valuable reference. You might encourage students to show both a picture and an equation for each relationship, as in the chart on the next page.

Relationships Among the Volumes of Cylinders, Cones, and Spheres

(cone = cylinder)	$V_{cone} = \frac{1}{3}\pi r^2 h$ or $\frac{2}{3}\pi r^3$
(sphere = cylinder)	$V_{sphere} = \frac{2}{3}\pi r^2 h$ or $\frac{4}{3}\pi r^3$
(cone + sphere = cylinder)	$V_{cone} + V_{sphere} = \pi r^2 h$ or $V_{cylinder}$
(cone = sphere)	$V_{cone} = \frac{1}{2}V_{sphere}$
(sphere = 2 cones)	$V_{sphere} = 2V_{cone}$
(cylinder = 3 cones)	$V_{cylinder} = 3V_{cone}$
(cylinder = sphere + half)	$V_{cylinder} = 1\frac{1}{2}V_{sphere}$
(sphere = cylinder − cone)	$V_{sphere} = V_{cylinder} - V_{cone}$

Question C provides an opportunity to review ratios since the ratio of the volume of a cone to a sphere to a cylinder is 1 : 2 : 3.

Planning for the Summary

What evidence will you use in the summary to clarify and deepen understanding of the Focus Question?

What will you do if you do not have evidence?

Summarize

Orchestrating the Discussion

Have the groups put up the relationships they found among the shapes. Give the class time to look at each poster. Encourage them to leave a sticky note on the poster if they have a question or comment.

Have each group respond to the questions or comments in turn. They may need access to the applet or the containers to demonstrate their reasoning.

Pick one or two equations and ask the class to write a simpler equivalent equation, or come up with another relationship in words and ask the class to write a symbolic equation.

Suggested Questions

- The volume of a cylinder minus the volume of a sphere is equal to the volume of a cone. Write a symbolic equation for this statement. ($\pi r^2 h - \frac{2}{3}\pi r^2 h = V_{cone}$)

- Write a simpler expression for the volume of the cone in this relationship. (Students can use the Distributive Property. $V_{cone} = \left(1 - \frac{2}{3}\right)\pi r^2 h$ or $\frac{1}{3}\pi r^2 h$)

- What does this equation tell you? (It tells the formula for finding the volume of a cone.)

- State in words what relationship $\pi r^2 h - \frac{1}{3}\pi r^2 h = V_{sphere}$ represents. (The volume of a cylinder minus the volume of a cone is equal to the volume of a sphere.)

- How can you use the formula for the volume of a prism to help you recall the formula for the volume of a cylinder? (The volume of a prism is the area of the base times the height. The same relationship applies to the volume of a cylinder. To find the volume of a prism or a cylinder, find how many cubes fit on the area of the base and multiply it by the height.)

- How can you use the formula for the volume of a cylinder to help you recall the formula for the volume of a cone? A sphere? (Knowing the volume of a cylinder, the volume of a cone is $\frac{1}{3}$ the volume of a cylinder and the volume of a sphere is $\frac{2}{3}$ the volume of a cylinder when $h = 2r$.)

Reflecting on Student Learning

Use the following questions to assess student understanding at the end of the lesson.

- What evidence do I have that students understand the Focus Question?
  - Where did my students get stuck?
  - What strategies did they use?
  - What breakthroughs did my students have today?
- How will I use this to plan for tomorrow? For the next time I teach this lesson?
- Where will I have the opportunity to reinforce these ideas as I continue through this Unit? The next Unit?

ACE Assignment Guide

- **Applications:** 10–12
- **Connections:** 32–34
- **Extensions:** 41–43

Selling Ice Cream
Solving Volume Problems

▼ Problem Overview

> *Focus Question* What formulas are useful in solving problems involving volumes of cylinders, cones, and spheres?

Problem Description

In this Problem, students apply their knowledge about the relationships among cylinders, cones, and spheres to answer an interesting question. Rocky Middle School is selling ice cream at the charity event in addition to the candles. The school buys ice cream in large, cylinder-shaped containers. It sells ice cream in two ways, by the scoop and in glass cups filled and topped with ice cream. The glass cups are cone-shaped, and they are topped with half a scoop of ice cream. In the Problem, students find how many cartons of ice cream the school should order. This Problem provides an application for students to use all three volume formulas as well as the relationship among the volumes.

Problem Implementation

Students can work in groups of 2–4.

Note: It might be helpful to have an empty ice cream carton from an ice cream store or one like it to display during the Launch.

Materials

There are no additional materials for this Problem.

Assessments

• Partner Quiz

Using Technology

You may want to allow students to use graphing calculators to make tables and graphs of the expressions and equations in this Problem.

Vocabulary

There are no new glossary terms introduced in this Problem.

Mathematics Background

- Equivalent Expressions
- Combining Expressions

At a Glance and Lesson Plan

- At a Glance: Problem 2.4 Say It With Symbols
- Lesson Plan: Problem 2.4 Say It With Symbols

▼ Launch

Connecting to Prior Knowledge

In the last Problem, you developed formulas for finding the volumes of cylinders, cones, and spheres. You also found some interesting relationships among the volumes.

In this Problem, you will have a chance to apply these formulas to solve some interesting problems.

Presenting the Challenge

Continue the story about Rocky Middle School and the charity event. In addition to selling candles, the school is selling ice cream and needs to determine how many cartons of ice cream to order.

▼ Explore

Providing for Individual Needs

If your students are having difficulty applying the formulas, ask:

Suggested Questions

- How many scoops of ice cream does the school need? (100)
- How do you find how much ice cream is in 100 scoops? (Find the volume of one scoop and multiply by 100.)

- How will this information help you determine how many cartons of ice cream to buy? (You need to compare the volume of 100 scoops to the volume of one carton.)

- How do you find how much ice cream is needed for the souvenir cup? (Find the volume of the cone and half the volume of the sphere and add them together.)

Planning for the Summary

What evidence will you use in the summary to clarify and deepen understanding of the Focus Question?

What will you do if you do not have evidence?

▼ Summarize

Orchestrating the Discussion

Collect answers to the Questions. Ask students to explain how they found their answers.

You might end this Investigation by having groups of students write application problems involving the volumes of cylinders, cones, and spheres. These problems could be exchanged among groups and solved, or they could be posted around the room to show a variety of applications and solutions using the volume formulas.

Reflecting on Student Learning

Use the following questions to assess student understanding at the end of the lesson.

- What evidence do I have that students understand the Focus Question?
  - Where did my students get stuck?
  - What strategies did they use?
  - What breakthroughs did my students have today?
- How will I use this to plan for tomorrow? For the next time I teach this lesson?
- Where will I have the opportunity to reinforce these ideas as I continue through this Unit? The next Unit?

ACE Assignment Guide

- **Applications:** 13–16
- **Connections:** 35–39

▼ Mathematical Reflections

Possible Answers to Mathematical Reflections

1. Answers will vary. If you have two or more equations for the amount of money each person collects for walking n kilometers, you can use the Distributive and Commutative properties to find the total amount t of money collected by the group. For example, if

    Leanne: 16(10)

    Gilberto: 7(2n)

    Alana: 11(5 + 0.5n); then the total
                 $16(10) + 7(2n) + 11(5 + 0.5n) = 33.5n + 215.$

2. Answers will vary. If you have two equations and they have a variable in common, like V, the number of visitors in Problem 2.2, where $P = 2.50V - 500$ and $V = 600 - 500R$, you can combine the equations into one by taking the expression $600 - 500R$ for V and substituting it into the equation $P = 2.50V - 500$. The equation becomes $P = 2.50(600 - 500R) - 500$. By combining them into one equation, if you know the probability of rain and want to predict the profit, you only have to do one calculation instead of two separate calculations.

3. The advantage of working with one equation is that you only have to solve one equation. If you have to find more than one data point, such as in the example above, then finding the profit when the probability of rain is 10%, 20%, 30%, etc., is done with one equation, not two. After tabulating the coordinate points, you can graph the equation or make a table in your calculator and find all the profit values at once. A disadvantage of combining two equations into one equation is that you may not be able to see the individual patterns that are involved in the separate equations, and you may lose a sense of context for the problem. For example, the equation $V = 600 - 500R$ tells you that when the probability of rain is 0, there will be 600 visitors and that, as the probability of rain increases, the number of visitors decreases. If profit is written in terms of the probability of rain, you lose the information about the number of visitors.

4. a. The volume of a cylinder can be represented by the expression $\pi r^2 h$. πr^2 represents the number of unit cubes needed to fit on the bottom layer and h represents the number of layers needed to fill the cylinder.

    b. The volume of a cone can be represented by the expression $\frac{1}{3}\pi r^2 h$. The volume of a cone is $\frac{1}{3}$ the volume of a cylinder with the same height and radius.

    c. The volume of a sphere can be represented by the expression $\frac{2}{3}\pi r^2 h$. The volume of a sphere is $\frac{2}{3}$ the volume of a cylinder with the same height and radius. The volume of a sphere can also be represented by the expression $\frac{4}{3}\pi r^3$ since the height of a sphere is two times its radius.

Possible Answers to Mathematical Practices Reflections

Students may have demonstrated all of the eight Common Core Standards for Mathematical Practice during this Investigation. During the class discussion, have students provide additional Practices that the Problem cited involved and identify the use of other Mathematical Practices in the Investigation.

One student observation is provided in the Student Edition. Here is another sample student response.

> We used clear plastic cylinders, cones, and spheres that had the same radius and height to determine the relationship among the volumes of the three solids in Problem 2.3. We used water to fill the various containers. In our group, we found that it took one cone and one sphere to fill a cylinder. We also found that the volume of the cone is $\frac{1}{3}$ the volume of a cylinder. Since we knew the formula for the volume of a cylinder, we were able to derive a formula for the volume of a cone and sphere.
>
> **MP5: Use appropriate tools. (or MP4)**

Notes

Combining Expressions

In the last Investigation, you found several ways to write equivalent expressions to describe a quantity. You also learned several ways to show that two expressions are equivalent. You will continue to answer these questions about two or more expressions:

- Are the expressions equivalent? Why?

- If expressions are equivalent, what information does each expression represent?

You will also look at ways to write new equations and to answer this question:

- What are the advantages and disadvantages of using one equation rather than two or more equations to represent a situation?

2.1 Walking Together
Adding Expressions

In *Moving Straight Ahead,* Leanne, Gilberto, and Alana enter a walkathon as a team. This means that they each will walk the same number of kilometers. The walkathon organizers offer a prize to the three-person team that raises the most money.

Common Core State Standards

8.F.A.3 Interpret the equation $y = mx + b$ as defining a linear function, whose graph is a straight line; give examples of functions that are not linear.

8.G.C.9 Know the formulas for the volumes of cones, cylinders, and spheres and use them to solve real-world and mathematical problems.

Also 8.EE.C.7, 8.EE.C.7b, 8.F.A.1, 8.F.A.2, N-Q.A.1, N-Q.A.2, A-SSE.A.1, A-SSE.A.1a, A-SSE.A.1b, A-SSE.A.2, A-SSE.B.3, A-CED.A.1, A-REI.B.3, F-IF.C.9, F-BF.A.1, F-BF.A.1a

Notes _____

_____

The individual pledges for each student are as follows:

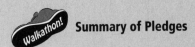

Summary of Pledges

Student	Number of Sponsors	Pledge
Leanne	16	$10, regardless of how far she walks
Gilberto	7	$2 per kilometer
Alana	11	$5 plus $.50 per kilometer

Problem 2.1

Ⓐ **1.** Write equations to represent the money M that each student will raise for walking x kilometers.

    a. $M_{Leanne} = $ ▨

    b. $M_{Gilberto} = $ ▨

    c. $M_{Alana} = $ ▨

2. Write an equation for the total amount of money M_{total} the three-person team will raise for walking x kilometers.

Ⓑ **1.** Write an expression that is equivalent to the expression for the total amount of money raised by the team in Question A, part (2). Explain why it is equivalent.

2. What information does this new expression represent about the situation?

3. Suppose each person walks 10 kilometers. Explain which expression(s) you would use to calculate the total amount of money raised.

Ⓒ Is the relationship between kilometers walked and total money raised linear or nonlinear? Explain.

ⒶⒸⒺ Homework starts on page 34.

Notes _____

_____

_____

2.2 Predicting Profit
Substituting Expressions

The manager of the Water Town amusement park uses data collected over the past several years to write equations that will help her make predictions about the daily operations of the park.

The daily concession-stand profit in dollars P depends on the number of visitors V. The manager writes the equation below to model this relationship:

$$P = 2.50V - 500$$

She uses the equation below to predict the number of visitors V based on the probability of rain R.

$$V = 600 - 500R$$

- What information might each of the numbers in the equations represent?

- What units should you use with the expression $-500R$? The expression $600 - 500R$?

 Can you write an equation to represent profit in terms of the probability of rain? What units would you use with this equation? Explain.

Problem 2.2

A **1.** Suppose the probability of rain is 25%. What profit can the concession stand expect? Explain.

2. What is the probability of rain if the profit expected is $625? Explain your reasoning.

B **1.** Write an equation you can use to predict the concession-stand profit P based on the probability of rain R.

2. Use your equation to predict profit when the probability of rain is 25%. Compare your answer with your result in Question A, part (1).

continued on the next page >

Investigation 2 **Combining Expressions** 29

Notes _____

Problem **2.2** *continued*

C 1. Write an equivalent expression for the profit in Question B. Explain why the two expressions are equivalent.

2. What probability of rain predicts a profit of $625? Compare your answer with your result in Question A, part (2).

3. Predict the profit when the probability of rain is 0%. Does your answer make sense? Explain.

4. Predict the profit when the probability of rain is 100%. Does your answer make sense?

D Do the equations in Questions B and C represent a linear or nonlinear function? Explain.

A C E Homework starts on page 34.

Did You Know?

The calculation of the quarterback rating in the National Football League (NFL™) uses a series of equations:

Completion Rating: $CR = 5\left(\dfrac{completions}{attempts}\right) - 1.5$

Yards Rating: $YR = \dfrac{\dfrac{yards}{attempts} - 3}{4}$

Touchdown Rating: $TR = 20\left(\dfrac{touchdowns}{attempts}\right)$

Interception Rating: $IR = \dfrac{19 - 2\left(\dfrac{interceptions}{attempts}\right)}{8}$

OVERALL RATING $= 100\left(\dfrac{CR + YR + TR + IR}{6}\right)$

Notes _____

_____

_____

2.3 Making Candles
Volumes of Cylinders, Cones, and Spheres

Rocky Middle School is sponsoring a charity event. They plan to make and sell candles at the outdoor market in the city.

Andy's committee is in charge of designing the candles. They designed three different shapes of candles: a sphere, a cone, and a cylinder. The molds for the three types of candles have the same radius and height.

❓ What is the relationship among the volumes of these three candles?

Problem 2.3

A Isaiah tried to figure out how much wax to buy to make the cylindrical candle, but he forgot the formula for the volume of a cylinder. Noah claims that to find the volume of a rectangular prism, you need to know the number of unit cubes in one layer of the prism and the prism's height. He thinks the same idea works for finding the volume of a cylinder.

1. Is Noah correct? Write an expression to find the volume of a rectangular prism.

2. Will this method work for finding the volume of a cylinder? Explain why or why not.

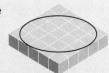

continued on the next page >

Notes _____

_____

Problem 2.3 *continued*

B Andy decided to explore the relationship among the volumes of the three candle designs. He used plastic containers in the shape of a cylinder, cone, and sphere. The containers have the same height h and inside radius r, which means that the inside diameter of the sphere is equal to the height. Andy tried to find relationships among the three containers.

1. Write the relationships among the three containers in words and then as algebraic equations.

2. Use the relationships in part (1) to write an expression for finding the volume of

   a. a cone with height h and radius r.

   b. a sphere with radius r.

C The price of each candle is based on the cost of wax plus markup for profit. If the cylindrical candle sells for $12, what should the prices of the other two candles be?

D Andy decides to sell cylindrical candles with a radius of 3 inches and a height of 1.25 feet.

   1. How much liquid wax does Andy need to make the candle?

   2. Describe the dimensions of a rectangular candle that uses the same amount of wax.

ACE Homework starts on page 34.

Notes _____

_____

_____

2.4

Selling Ice Cream
Solving Volume Problems

Rocky Middle School also plans to sell ice cream at the charity event.
They expect to sell about 100 scoops of ice cream. The ice cream comes in
cylindrical cartons. Ester's committee must decide how many cartons to
buy for the event.

Problem 2.4

Ⓐ Use the formulas from Problem 2.3 and the following information.

- A carton of ice cream has a radius of 11 centimeters and a
  height of 30 centimeters.

- A scoop of ice cream has a radius of 3 centimeters.

How many cartons of ice cream should Ester order to make
100 scoops?

Ⓑ Ester finds 50 souvenir glass cups left over from the last charity event. The
cup is cone-shaped and has a height of 16 centimeters and a radius of
3 centimeters. The cup is filled and then topped with half a scoop of ice cream.

1. How much ice cream do you need to make 50 cups?

2. If the 50 cups are in addition to the 100 scoops from Question A, how
   many more cartons of ice cream must Ester order?

Ⓐ Ⓒ Ⓔ Homework starts on page 34.

STUDENT PAGE

Notes

Applications

1. The student council is organizing a T-shirt sale to raise money for a local charity. They make the following estimates of expenses and income:

   - Expense of $250 for advertising
   - Income of $12 for each T-shirt
   - Expense of $4.25 for each T-shirt
   - Income of $150 from a sponsor

   a. Write an equation for the income I for selling n T-shirts.

   b. Write an equation for the expenses E for selling n T-shirts.

   c. Suppose the student council sells 100 T-shirts. What is their profit?

   d. Write an equation for the profit P made for selling n T-shirts.

For Exercises 2–5, use the following information: In *Variables and Patterns,* several students were planning a bike tour. They estimated the following expenses and incomes.

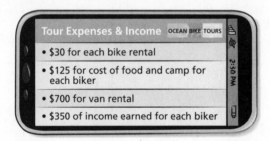

2. **a.** Write an equation for the total expenses E for n bikers.

   b. Write an equation for the total income I for n bikers.

   c. Write an equation for the profit P for n bikers.

   d. Find the profit for 25 bikers.

   e. Suppose the profit is $1,055. How many bikers went on the trip?

   f. Does the profit equation represent a linear, quadratic, or exponential function, or none of these? Explain.

Notes

3. **Multiple Choice** Suppose someone donates a van at no charge. Which equation represents the total expenses?

   A. $E = 125 + 30$

   B. $E = 125n + 30n$

   C. $E = 155$

   D. $E = 155 + n$

4. **Multiple Choice** Suppose students use their own bikes. Which equation represents the total expenses? (Assume they will rent a van.)

   F. $E = 125n + 700$

   G. $E = 125 + 700 + n$

   H. $E = 825n$

   J. $E = 350n + 125n + 700$

5. **Multiple Choice** Suppose students use their own bikes. Which equation represents the profit? (Assume they will rent a van.)

   A. $P = 350 - (125 + 700 + n)$

   B. $P = 350n - 125n + 700$

   C. $P = 350n - (125n + 700)$

   D. $P = 350 - 125n - 700$

For Exercises 6–8, recall the equations from Problem 2.2,
$P = 2.50V - 500$ and $V = 600 - 500R$.

6. Suppose the probability of rain is 50%. What profit can the concession stand expect to make?

7. What is the probability of rain if the profit expected is $100?

8. The manager estimates the daily employee-bonus fund B (in dollars) from the number of visitors V using the equation $B = 100 + 0.50V$.

   a. Suppose the probability of rain is 30%. What is the daily employee-bonus fund?

   b. Write an equation that relates the employee-bonus fund B to the probability of rain R.

   c. Suppose the probability of rain is 50%. Use your equation to calculate the employee-bonus fund.

   d. Suppose the daily employee-bonus fund is $375. What is the probability of rain?

STUDENT PAGE

Notes _____

9. A park manager claims that the profit P for a concession stand depends on the number of visitors V, and that the number of visitors depends on the day's high temperature T (in degrees Fahrenheit). The following equations represent the manager's claims:

$$P = 4.25V - 300$$
$$V = 50(T - 45)$$

   a. Suppose 1,000 people visit the park one day. Predict the high temperature on that day.

   b. Write an expression for profit based on temperature.

   c. Write an expression for profit that is equivalent to the one in part (b). Explain what information the numbers and variables represent.

   d. Find the profit if the temperature is 70°F.

10. Explain what happens to the volume of a cylinder when

   a. the radius is doubled.

   b. the height is doubled.

11. Explain what happens to the volume of a cone when

   a. the radius is doubled.

   b. the height is doubled.

12. Explain what happens to the volume of a sphere when

   a. the radius is doubled.

   b. the radius is tripled.

   c. the radius is quadrupled (multiplied by 4).

Notes _____

_____

_____

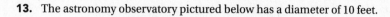

13. The astronomy observatory pictured below has a diameter of 10 feet.

a. What is the area of the floor?

b. Write a general algebraic expression for the area of the floor.

c. The observatory is made of a 3-foot-tall cylinder and half of a sphere (also called a *hemisphere*). What is the volume of the space inside the observatory?

d. Write a general algebraic expression for the volume of the space inside the observatory.

14. The Jackson Middle School model rocket club drew the model rocket design below. The rocket is made from a cylinder and a cone. Write an expression to represent the volume of the rocket.

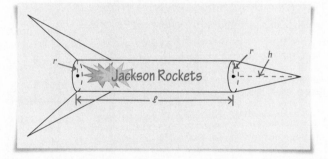

Notes _____

_____

_____

15. Ted made the model submarine shown below for his science class. Write an algebraic expression for the volume of Ted's submarine.

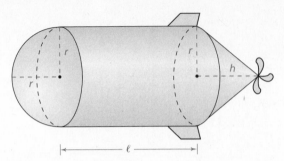

16. The pyramid and rectangular prism have the same base and height.

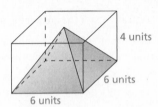

  a. Find the volume of the pyramid.

  b. Draw a pyramid with a volume of $\frac{1}{3}(8)$ cubic units.
  Hint: You might find it easier to draw the related prism first.

  c. Draw a pyramid with a volume of $\frac{1}{3}(27)$ cubic units.

  d. Find the height of a pyramid with a volume of $9x^3$ cubic units.

Notes

Connections

17. **Multiple Choice** Which statement is *false* when *a, b,* and *c* are different real numbers?

   F. $(a + b) + c = a + (b + c)$ **G.** $ab = ba$

   H. $(ab)c = a(bc)$ **J.** $a - b = b - a$

For Exercises 18–20, use the Distributive Property and sketch a rectangle to show the equivalence of the two expressions.

18. $x(x + 5)$ and $x^2 + 5x$

19. $(2 + x)(2 + 3x)$ and $4 + 8x + 3x^2$

20. $(x + 2)(2x + 3)$ and $2x^2 + 7x + 6$

21. A student's solution for $11x - 12 = 30 + 5x$ is shown below. Some steps are missing in the solution.

$$11x - 12 = 30 + 5x$$
$$11x = 42 + 5x$$
$$6x = 42$$
$$x = 7$$

   a. Copy the steps above. Fill in the missing steps.

   b. How can you check that $x = 7$ is the correct solution?

   c. Explain how you could use a graph or a table to solve the original equation for x.

Notes _____

_____

_____

STUDENT PAGE

22. In the following graph, line ℓ_1 represents the income for selling n soccer balls. Line ℓ_2 represents the expenses for manufacturing n soccer balls.

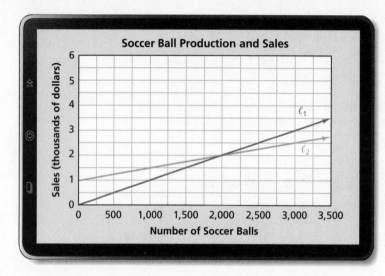

Soccer Ball Production and Sales

a. What is the start-up expense (the expense before any soccer balls are produced) for manufacturing the soccer balls?
Note: The vertical axis is in *thousands* of dollars.

b. What are the expenses and income for producing and selling 500 balls? 1,000 balls? 3,000 balls? Explain.

c. What is the profit for producing and selling 500 balls? 1,000 balls? 3,000 balls? Explain.

d. What is the break-even point? Give the number of soccer balls and the expenses.

e. Write equations for the expenses, income, and profit. Explain what the numbers and variables in each equation represent.

f. Suppose the manufacturer produces and sells 1,750 soccer balls. Use the equations in part (e) to find the profit.

g. Suppose the profit is $10,000. Use the equations in part (e) to find the number of soccer balls produced and sold.

Notes

For Exercises 23–28, use properties of equality to solve each equation. Check your solution.

23. $7x + 15 = 12x + 5$

24. $7x + 15 = 5 + 12x$

25. $-3x + 5 = 2x - 10$

26. $14 - 3x = 1.5x + 5$

27. $9 - 4x = \frac{3 + x}{2}$

28. $-3(x + 5) = \frac{2x - 10}{3}$

29. The writing club wants to publish a book of students' short stories, poems, and essays. A member of the club contacts two local printers to get bids on the cost of printing the books.

Bid 1: $100 plus $4 per book

Bid 2: $25 plus $7 per book

a. Make a table of values (*number of books printed, cost*) for each bid. Use your table to find the number of books for which the two bids are equal. Explain how you found your answer.

b. Make a graph of the two equations. Use your graph to find the number of books for which the two bids are equal. Explain.

c. For what numbers of books is Bid 1 less than Bid 2? Explain.

30. Use the information about printing costs from Exercise 29.

a. For each bid, find the cost of printing 75 books.

b. Suppose the cost cannot exceed $300. For each bid, find the greatest number of books that can be printed. Explain.

31. The writing club decides to request bids from two more printers.

Bid 3: $8 per book

Bid 4: $30 plus $6 per book

For what number of books does Bid 3 equal Bid 4? Explain.

Notes

Simplify each expression. Then explain how the expression could represent a volume calculation.

32. $3.14 \times 4.25^2 \times 5.5$

33. $\frac{1}{3} \times 3.14 \times 4.25^2 \times 5.5$

34. $\frac{4}{3} \times 3.14 \times 4.25^3$

35. $\frac{1}{3} \times 3.14 \times 4.25^2 \times 5.5 + \frac{4}{6} \times 3.14 \times 4.25^3$

36. $3.14 \times 4.25^2 \times 5.5 + \frac{4}{6} \times 3.14 \times 4.25^3$

37. $3.14 \times 4.25^2 \times 5.5 + \frac{1}{3} \times 3.14 \times 4.25^2 \times 3.5$

38. $3.14 \times 4.25^2 \times 5.5 - \frac{4}{6} \times 3.14 \times 4.25^3$

39. $3.14 \times 4.25^2 \times 5.5 - \frac{1}{3} \times 3.14 \times 4.25^2 \times 3.5$

Extensions

40. The Phillips Concert Hall staff estimates their concession stand profits P_C and admission profits P_A with the following equations, where x is the number of people attending (in hundreds):

$$P_C = 15x - 500$$
$$P_A = 106x - x^2$$

The concession-stand profits include revenue from advertising and the sale of food and souvenirs. The admission profits are based on the difference of ticket sales and cost.

a. Write an equation for the total profit for P in terms of the number of people x (in hundreds).

b. What is the maximum profit? How many people must attend in order to achieve the maximum profit?

Notes

For Exercises 41–43, suppose you slice the three-dimensional figure as indicated. Describe the shape of the face that results from the slice.

41. **a.** vertical slice

b. horizontal slice

42. **a.** vertical slice

b. horizontal slice

43. **a.** vertical slice

b. horizontal slice

Investigation 2   **Combining Expressions**   43

Notes

Mathematical Reflections 2

In this Investigation, you combined expressions or substituted an equivalent expression for a quantity to make new expressions. You wrote expressions to represent the relationships among the volumes of cylinders, cones, and spheres. You also used these expressions to make predictions. The following questions will help you summarize what you have learned.

Think about these questions. Discuss your ideas with other students and your teacher. Then write a summary of your findings in your notebook.

1. **Describe** a situation in which it is helpful to add expressions to form a new expression. Explain how you can combine the expressions.

2. **Describe** a situation in which it is helpful to substitute an equivalent expression for a quantity in an equation.

3. **What** are the advantages and disadvantages of working with one equation rather than two or more equations in a given situation?

4. Write an expression that represents the volume of each three-dimensional figure. **Explain** your reasoning.

   a. cylinder

   b. cone

   c. sphere

Notes _____

Common Core Mathematical Practices

As you worked on the Problems in this Investigation, you used prior knowledge to make sense of them. You also applied Mathematical Practices to solve the Problems. Think back over your work, the ways you thought about the Problems, and how you used Mathematical Practices.

Elena described her thoughts in the following way:

> We discovered an efficient way to find the profit in Problem 2.2. The profit P depends on the number of visitors V that attend the park. The equation $P = 2.50V - 500$ represents profit. The number of visitors depends on the probability of rain R. The equation $V = 600 - 500R$ represents the number of visitors.
>
> We substituted the expression for the number of visitors written in terms of the probability of rain $(600 - 500R)$ for V in the equation that represents profit. Using one equation reduced the number of calculations that we had to do.

Common Core Standards for Mathematical Practice
MP6 Attend to precision.

- What other Mathematical Practices can you identify in Elena's reasoning?
- Describe a Mathematical Practice that you and your classmates used to solve a different Problem in this Investigation.

Notes _____

Solving Equations

▼ # Investigation Overview

Investigation Description

In the two previous Investigations, students used the Distributive and Commutative properties to write equivalent expressions. In this Investigation, they continue to use these properties, as well as the properties of equality, to solve linear equations with parentheses and to solve quadratic equations by factoring.

Investigation Vocabulary

- properties of equality
- roots

Mathematics Background

- Solving Equations

Planning Chart

Content	ACE	Pacing	Materials	Resources
Problem 3.1	1–7, 35–38, 53–55	1 day	graphing calculators (optional)	**Teaching Aid 3.1** Solving Linear Equations
Problem 3.2	8–23, 39–41, 43–44, 56	1 day	**Labsheet 3ACE:** Exercise 9 (accessibility) graphing calculators (optional) poster paper markers	
Problem 3.3	24–26, 45–48, 57–58	1 day		**Teaching Aid 3.3A** Factoring Quadratic Equations **Teaching Aid 3.3B** Quadratic Expression Model
Problem 3.4	27–34, 42, 49–52, 59–63	1 day	poster paper markers	**Teaching Aid 3.4** Solving Quadratic Equations
Mathematical Reflections		½ day		
Assessment: Check Up 2		½ day		• Check Up 2

▼ Goals and Standards

Goals

Equivalence Develop understanding of equivalent expressions and equations.

- Model situations with symbolic statements

- Recognize when two or more symbolic statements represent the same context

- Use the properties of real numbers, such as the Distributive Property, to write equivalent expressions

- Determine if different symbolic expressions are mathematically equivalent

- Interpret the information that equivalent expressions represent in a given context

- Determine the equivalent expression or equation that is most helpful in answering a particular question about a relationship

- Use algebraic equations to describe the relationship among the volumes of cylinders, cones, and spheres that have the same height and radius

- Solve linear equations involving parentheses

- Determine if a linear equation has a finite number of solutions, an infinite number of solutions, or no solution

- Develop understanding and some fluency with factoring quadratic expressions

- Solve quadratic equations by factoring

- Recognize how and when to use symbols, rather than tables or graphs, to display relationships, generalizations, and proofs

Functions Develop an understanding of specific functions such as linear, exponential, and quadratic functions.

- Develop proficiency in identifying and representing relationships, expressed in problem contexts, with appropriate functions, and use these relationships to solve problems

- Analyze equations to determine the patterns of change in the related tables and graphs

- Relate parts of a symbolic statement or expression to the underlying properties of the relationship they represent and to the context of the problem

- Determine characteristics of a graph of an equation (intercepts, maxima and minima, shape, etc.) by looking at its symbolic representation

Mathematical Reflections

Look for evidence of student understanding of the goals for this Investigation in their responses to the questions in Mathematical Reflections. The goals addressed by each question are indicated below.

1. **a.** Describe some general strategies for solving linear equations, including those with parentheses. Give examples that illustrate your strategies.

   b. Describe how you can tell if a linear equation has a finite number of solutions, an infinite number of solutions, or no solutions.

   Goals

   - Solve linear equations involving parentheses
   - Determine if a linear equation has a finite number of solutions, an infinite number of solutions, or no solution

2. Describe some strategies for solving quadratic equations of the form $ax^2 + bx + c = 0$. Give examples.

   Goals

   - Develop understanding and some fluency with factoring quadratic expressions
   - Solve quadratic equations by factoring

3. How are the solutions of linear and quadratic equations related to graphs of the equations?

   Goals

   - Develop proficiency in identifying and representing relationships, expressed in problem contexts, with appropriate functions, and use these relationships to solve problems
   - Analyze equations to determine the patterns of change in the related tables and graphs
   - Relate parts of a symbolic statement or expression to the underlying properties of the relationship they represent and to the context of the problem
   - Determine characteristics of a graph of an equation (intercepts, maxima and minima, shape, etc.) by looking at its symbolic representation

Standards

Common Core Content Standards

8.EE.A.2 Use square root and cube root symbols to represent solutions to equations of the form $x^2 = p$ and $x^3 = p$, where p is a positive rational number. Evaluate square roots of small perfect squares and cube roots of small perfect cubes. Know that $\sqrt{2}$ is irrational. *Problem 4*

8.EE.C.7 Solve linear equations in one variable. *Problems 1, 2, and 3*

8.EE.C.7a Give examples of linear equations in one variable with one solution, infinitely many solutions, or no solutions. Show which of these possibilities is the case by successively transforming the given equation into simpler forms, until an equivalent equation of the form $x = a$, $a = a$, or $a = b$ results (where a and b are different numbers). *Problem 2*

8.EE.C.7b Solve linear equations with rational number coefficients, including equations whose solutions require expanding expressions using the distributive property and collecting like terms. *Problems 1, 2, 3, and 4*

8.EE.C.8 Analyze and solve pairs of simultaneous linear equations. *Problem 2*

8.EE.C.8a Understand that solutions to a system of two linear equations in two variables correspond to points of intersection of their graphs, because points of intersection satisfy both equations simultaneously. *Problem 2*

8.EE.C.8b Solve systems of two linear equations in two variables algebraically, and estimate solutions by graphing the equations. Solve simple cases by inspection. *Problem 2*

8.EE.C.8c Solve real-world and mathematical problems leading to two linear equations in two variables. *Problem 2*

8.F.A.1 Understand that a function is a rule that assigns to each input exactly one output. The graph of a function is the set of ordered pairs consisting of an input and the corresponding output. *Problems 1 and 2*

N-Q.A.1 Use units as a way to understand problems and to guide the solution of multi-step problems; choose and interpret units consistently in formulas; choose and interpret the scale and the origin in graphs and data displays. *Problem 2*

N-Q.A.2 Define appropriate quantities for the purpose of descriptive modeling. *Problem 2*

A-SSE.A.1 Interpret expressions that represent a quantity in terms of its context. *Problems 1, 2, 3, and 4*

A-SSE.A.1a Interpret parts of an expression, such as terms, factors, and coefficients. *Problems 1, 2, 3, and 4*

A-SSE.A.1b Interpret complicated expressions by viewing one or more of their parts as a single entity. *Problems 1, 2, 3, and 4*

A-SSE.A.2 Use the structure of an expression to identify ways to rewrite it. *Problems 1, 2, 3, and 4*

A-SSE.B.3 Choose and produce an equivalent form of an expression to reveal and explain properties of the quantity represented by the expression. *Problems 1, 2, 3, and 4*

A-SSE.B.3a Factor a quadratic expression to reveal the zeros of the function it defines. *Problems 3 and 4*

A-CED.A.1 Create equations and inequalities in one variable and use them to solve problems. *Problem 4*

A-CED.A.2 Create equations in two or more variables to represent relationships between quantities; graph equations on coordinate axes with labels and scales. *Problems 2 and 4*

A-REI.A.1 Explain each step in solving a simple equation as following from the equality of numbers asserted at the previous step, starting from the assumption that the original equation has a solution. Construct a viable argument to justify a solution method. *Problem 1*

A-REI.B.3 Solve linear equations and inequalities in one variable, including equations with coefficients represented by letters. *Problems 1, 2, 3, and 4*

A-REI.B.4 Solve quadratic equations in one variable. *Problems 3 and 4*

A-REI.B.4b Solve quadratic equations by inspection (e.g., for $x^2 = 49$), taking square roots, completing the square, the quadratic formula and factoring, as appropriate to the initial form of the equation. Recognize when the quadratic formula gives complex solutions and write them as $a \pm bi$ for real numbers a and b. *Problems 3 and 4*

A-REI.C.6 Solve systems of linear equations exactly and approximately (e.g., with graphs), focusing on pairs of linear equations in two variables. *Problem 2*

A-REI.D.10 Understand that the graph of an equation in two variables is the set of all its solutions plotted in the coordinate plane, often forming a curve (which could be a line). *Problems 2 and 3*

A-REI.D.11 Explain why the x-coordinates of the points where the graphs of the equations $y = f(x)$ and $y = g(x)$ intersect are the solutions of the equation $f(x) = g(x)$; find the solutions approximately, e.g., using technology to graph the functions, make tables of values, or find successive approximations. Include cases where $f(x)$ and/or $g(x)$ are linear, polynomial, rational, absolute value, exponential, and logarithmic functions. *Problems 2 and 3*

F-BF.A.1a Determine an explicit expression, a recursive process, or steps for calculation from a context. *Problem 4*

Facilitating the Mathematical Practices

Students in *Connected Mathematics* classrooms display evidence of multiple Common Core Standards for Mathematical Practice every day. Here are just a few examples of when you might observe students demonstrating the Standards for Mathematical Practice during this Investigation.

Practice 1: **Make sense of problems and persevere in solving them.**

Students are engaged every day in solving problems and, over time, learn to persevere in solving them. To be effective, the problems embody critical concepts and skills and have the potential to engage students in making sense of mathematics. Students build understanding by reflecting, connecting, and communicating. These student-centered problem situations engage students in articulating the "knowns" in a problem situation and determining a logical solution pathway. The student-student and student-teacher dialogues help students not only to make sense of the problems, but also to persevere in finding appropriate strategies to solve them. The suggested questions in the Teacher Guides provide the metacognitive scaffolding to help students monitor and refine their problem-solving strategies.

Practice 2: **Reason abstractly and quantitatively.**

In Problem 3.1, students interpret a linear equation in the context of the Problem. By examining the structure of the equation, they see that it shows the difference of two quantities, income and expenses. Similarly, without solving the equation for some value, they recognize that the only constant term is the fixed cost. For this reason, they can conclude that the school choir must sell more than $100 worth of greeting cards before making a profit.

Students identify and record their personal experiences with the Standards for Mathematical Practice during the Mathematical Reflections at the end of the Investigation.

Selling Greeting Cards
Solving Linear Equations

▼ Problem Overview

> *Focus Question* What strategies can you use to solve equations that
> contain parentheses?

Problem Description

The profit for selling greeting cards is given by an equation that involves
parentheses and negative signs. Students interpret various parts of the equation in
terms of the context of the Problem. Then, they solve the equation to determine
the profit for selling a certain number of boxes of greeting cards. In solving the
equation, they review a strategy for distributing a negative sign over a sum or
difference in a linear expression.

Problem Implementation

Students can work in groups of 2–3. You might ask each student to read
Question A, parts (1) and (2) on their own before moving into groups. You could
also summarize after Questions A and B. Then let them apply the strategies they
developed in Questions A and B to solve the equations in Question C.

Materials

• **Teaching Aid 3.1:** Solving Linear Equations

Using Technology

You may want to allow students to use graphing calculators to make tables
and graphs of the expressions and equations in this Problem. They will see that
the graphs of equivalent expressions are the same. They will also see that the
x-intercept is the solution to solving for x when $y = 0$.

Vocabulary

• properties of equality

Mathematics Background

• Solving Equations

At a Glance and Lesson Plan

• At a Glance: Problem 3.1 Say It With Symbols
• Lesson Plan: Problem 3.1 Say It With Symbols

▼ Launch

Launch Video

This animation shows Shawna and Hector making last-minute preparations before the greeting card sale. In their conversation, they talk about profit, costs, and breaking even. This provides the context for the Problem. Visit Teacher Place at mathdashboard.com/cmp3 to see the complete video.

After Connecting to Prior Knowledge, show this animation instead of telling the story about the school choir selling cards to raise money. Then you can continue with the Suggested Questions.

Connecting to Prior Knowledge

Use the questions in the Introduction to the Problem to review the strategies for solving linear equations. You may want to display **Teaching Aid 3.1: Solving Linear Equations** for the discussion. Ask the class to provide a reason for each step. For steps (1) and (2), the property of equality was used; it states that subtracting the same quantity from each side of the equation maintains equality. In (1), the quantity was $4x$; in (2), it was 25.

Suggested Questions

• Could you begin with a different first step? (Yes; students could have subtracted 100 or 25 from both sides.)

• How could you check that 25 is the correct solution? (by substituting 25 for x in the equation $100 + 4x = 25 + 7x$)

• Describe another method for finding the solution to the equation. (Graph the equations $y = 100 + 4x$ and $y = 25 + 7x$ in a graphing calculator and trace the graphs to find the x-coordinate of the intersection point. Make a table for the two equations and find the place in the table where the y-coordinates are the same. At this y-value, the corresponding x-coordinate gives the solution.)

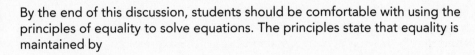

By the end of this discussion, students should be comfortable with using the principles of equality to solve equations. The principles state that equality is maintained by

- adding the same quantity to or subtracting the same quantity from each side of an equation;
- multiplying or dividing each side of an equation by the same nonzero quantity.

The following questions provide a quick review from *Moving Straight Ahead*.

- What does 7x mean? (7x means 7 times x, or x + x + x + x + x + x + x.)
- Why does 7x − 4x equal 3x? (Using the Distributive Property, 7x − 4x = x(7 − 4) = 3x.)
- Why does 3x divided by 3 equal x? (Since 3x = x + x + x or three groups of x, when you divide 3 times x into 3 groups, you get x in each group.)

Presenting the Challenge

Put the equation $P = 5s − (100 + 2s)$ on the board. Tell the story or show the Launch Video about the school choir selling cards to raise money.

Suggested Questions

- What affects the profit? (The number of boxes sold, which is the income; and the expenses, or costs. Profit = income − expenses.)

Try to keep the Problem open so the students can develop strategies for interpreting symbols in an equation.

▼ Explore

Providing for Individual Needs

If students aren't independently connecting parts of the equation to the context, point to various parts of the equation and ask what information each part represents.

Suggested Questions

For Question A, part (3), some students may need to be reminded of what break-even means.

- How do you find the break-even point? (The break-even point is when Income = Expenses, or in this case, when profit equals zero.)

Look at the ways students are solving the equation. Suggest to students who are solving using a table or graph to try solving without a table or graph.

Look for how students are distributing the negative sign. If you notice that they are not doing it correctly, suggest that they try substituting a value into the original expression for profit and their new equivalent expression to see if the expressions are equivalent. This will tell them that they do not have an equivalent expression. You might also remind students that subtraction can be thought of as adding the opposite quantity. For example, $5 - 3 = 5 + (-3)$. In this Problem, $5s - (100 + 2s)$ is the same as $5s + -1(100 + 2s)$.

This is a good time to check on students' use of the order of operations. In the expression $5s - 2(50 + s)$ from Question A, part (5), the multiplication of -2 by $50 + s$ is the first step in finding an equivalent expression. Students may need to be reminded again while they work on Question C. There are many opportunities in the ACE Exercises of this Unit to review or practice order of operations.

This Problem is another opportunity to see how students use the units associated with the context.

- What information does $5s$ represent? What units should be attached to this expression? ($5s$ represents the amount of money collected from selling s boxes of cards for $5 each.)

Repeat similar questions for $(100 + 2s)$.

Be sure to discuss the various strategies that students used and any misconceptions that might have occurred.

Planning for the Summary

What evidence will you use in the summary to clarify and deepen understanding of the Focus Question?
What will you do if you do not have evidence?

▼ Summarize

Orchestrating the Discussion

Discuss the answers to each question. Be sure students give a reason for each step, or have someone else give a reason for each step as a student presents his/her solution.

Suggested Questions

- In Question A, part (2), is there another way to solve the equation $200 = 5s - (100 + 2s)$? (Some will suggest using tables or graphs. Be sure to have a symbolic method illustrated. Most students will distribute the negative sign and then add the constant 100 to both sides or combine $5s$ and $-2s$. Some may subtract $5s$ from both sides of the equation as the first step. For some students, you may need to write the equation as $200 = 5s - 1(100 + 2s)$. This should help them understand the role of the minus sign in front of the parentheses and the need to apply the Distributive Property.)

Be sure to summarize the strategies for solving equations with parentheses. Take note of how students use the Order of Operations. Then let the class solve the equations in Question C. Call on different groups to show their solutions, including how they check to see if they were correct.

Pick one or two of the equations and ask:

- How could you use a graph or table to solve the equation? (Use a scientific calculator to make a graph and table for each equation.)

- Where is the solution on a graph or table? (The x-intercept on the graph of each equation is the value of x when $y = 0$. Similarly in a table, look for the row that shows $y = 0$. The associated value of x is the solution.)

Reflecting on Student Learning

Use the following questions to assess student understanding at the end of the lesson.

- What evidence do I have that students understand the Focus Question?
  - Where did my students get stuck?
  - What strategies did they use?
  - What breakthroughs did my students have today?
- How will I use this to plan for tomorrow? For the next time I teach this lesson?
- Where will I have the opportunity to reinforce these ideas as I continue through this Unit? The next Unit?

ACE Assignment Guide

- **Applications:** 1–7
- **Connections:** 35–38
- **Extensions:** 53–55

Comparing Costs
Solving More Linear Equations

▼ Problem Overview

> *Focus Question* What are strategies for finding a solution that is common to two-variable linear equations?

Problem Description

This Problem presents two linear equations with parentheses that represent the costs for tiles needed to surround a pool. Students are asked to find the number of tiles in which the costs are equal without using tables or graphs. This equation is somewhat more complicated than previous equations because it has parentheses on both sides of the equation. It is also an example of solving a system of two linear equations. More methods for solving such equations are discussed in *It's in the System*.

Problem Implementation

Students can work on this Problem in groups of 2–3.

You might have some groups put their work on larger poster paper.

Materials

• **Labsheet 3ACE:** Exercise 9 (accessibility)

poster paper

markers

Using Technology

Students may find it helpful to use a graphing calculator to graph the linear equations in this Problem. They can use it to compare the slopes of the graphs and to find the point of intersection.

Vocabulary

There are no new glossary terms introduced in this Problem.

Mathematics Background

• Solving Equations

At a Glance and Lesson Plan

• At a Glance: Problem 3.2 Say It With Symbols
• Lesson Plan: Problem 3.2 Say It With Symbols

▼ Launch

Launch Video

In this animation, a couple compares the costs for tiling from *Cover and Surround It* and *Tile and Beyond*. They make a table to compare the costs generated from the two equations given in the introduction to the Problem. The animation ends with the husband asking, "How can you use the equations to determine which company has the better deal?" Visit Teacher Place at mathdashboard.com/cmp3 to see the complete video.

After showing the animation, you can continue with the Launch by asking the Suggested Questions in Presenting the Challenge.

Connecting to Prior Knowledge

In the last Problem, students discussed the profit for selling boxes of greetings cards. The profit was given as an equation in terms of the number of boxes of greeting cards.

Suggested Questions

• How did this equation differ from those you saw in earlier Units? (It had parentheses and negative signs before the parentheses.)

In this Problem, students will explore two similar equations for the cost of tiles.)

Presenting the Challenge

Describe the Problem. Display the two equations for the cost of tiles.

Suggested Questions

• Do these equations make sense given the information about the two companies? (Students should be able to relate parts of the equation to the given information and recognize the Units as discussed in Problems 2.1 and 3.1.)

- What information does the constant number on each side of the equal sign represent? (For *Cover and Surround It*, $1,000 is the start-up cost, which includes the first 12 tiles. Similarly, for *Tile and Beyond*, $740 is the start-up cost, which includes the first 10 tiles.)

- What information does the number in front of the parentheses represent? (For *Cover and Surround It*, the 25 means that the cost of each tile is $25 for any number of tiles over 12. For *Tile and Beyond*, the cost per tile is $32 for any number of tiles over 10.)

▼ Explore

Providing for Individual Needs

Similar to the last Problem, solving linear equations with parentheses continues in this Problem. In this context, however, there are parentheses on both sides of the equal sign for determining when the costs of the two companies are equal.

If students make a graph for the two equations, check if they represent the situations accurately. For *Cover and Surround It*, they should have a horizontal line ($y = 1,000$) for tiles up to 12, which represents a fixed charge of $1,000 up to 12 tiles, then the graph of $1,000 + 25(N - 12)$ beyond the first 12 tiles. Similarly, for *Tile and Beyond*, they should have a horizontal line ($y = 740$) for tiles up to 10, which represents a fixed charge of $740 up to 10 tiles, then the graph of $740 + 32(N - 10)$ beyond the first 10 tiles.

Look for different ways that students might solve the Problem. See the first question in the Summarize.

Planning for the Summary

What evidence will you use in the summary to clarify and deepen understanding of the Focus Question?

What will you do if you do not have evidence?

● ▼ Summarize

Orchestrating the Discussion

Call on a group to present its work for Question A, parts (1) and (2). Have the rest of the class validate the group's work and/or ask the group questions.

Suggested Questions

- Did any group use a different first step? (Some may have subtracted 1,000 or 740 from both sides of the equation before distributing the number in front of the parentheses. Or, after subtracting one of the constant terms, they could divide both sides by the number in front of the parentheses. If this happens, be sure they divide correctly.)

- For the expression $740 + 32(N - 10)$ on the right side of the equation, can you add 740 and 32 as a first step? (No. Following the order of operations, multiplication comes before addition when finding an equivalent expression.)

- Describe how you could use a table or graph to solve this equation. (Make a table of values for each expression and look for the value of x that makes the values of the expressions equivalent. You could also graph each expression and find the point of intersection. The x-value of that point is the solution. If you have an overhead display for the graphing calculator, you could use it to illustrate how a table or graph might be used.)

- How can you determine the number of tiles for which the *Tile and Beyond* company is the cheaper of the two companies? (Some may suggest substituting a number that is less than the number of tiles for when the two costs are equal. Since the costs are equal when $N = 40$, check for $N = 39$. You will find that *Tile and Beyond* is cheaper than *Cover and Surround It*, so you can conclude that it is cheaper up to 39 tiles.)

If no one suggests using a graph, ask:

- How can you use a table or graph to decide which company is cheaper? (On a graph, look at the parts of the line graphs that are to the left and right of the point of intersection. The line that is the lowest will have costs that are the cheaper of the two. You might have students use the graph to explain why this is true and to determine the amount of money for which the lower company is cheaper. It is the difference in the vertical heights for any given value of N.)

Discuss the graphs of each equation. Each graph contains a horizontal line and a nonhorizontal line. See answer to Question A, part (3).

Check for Understanding

You could end by posing an equation to solve. It might have some fractions or decimals. For example,

$$10.5 - \frac{3}{2}\left(5 - 6x\right) = 12 + 3\left(5x - \frac{1}{2}x\right)$$
$$x = -2$$

Reflecting on Student Learning

Use the following questions to assess student understanding at the end of the lesson.

- What evidence do I have that students understand the Focus Question?
  - Where did my students get stuck?
  - What strategies did they use?
  - What breakthroughs did my students have today?
- How will I use this to plan for tomorrow? For the next time I teach this lesson?
- Where will I have the opportunity to reinforce these ideas as I continue through this Unit? The next Unit?

ACE Assignment Guide

- **Applications:** 8–23
- **Connections:** 39–41, 43–44
- **Extensions:** 56
- **Labsheet 3ACE:** Exercise 9

This Labsheet may be helpful for students who need more practice with the Order of Operations for solving linear equations.

PROBLEM
3.3   Factoring Quadratic Equations

▼ Problem Overview

> *Focus Question* What are some strategies for factoring a quadratic expression?

Problem Description

Students revisit factoring quadratic expressions, which was first introduced in *Frogs, Fleas, and Painted Cubes*. They will factor quadratic expressions of different forms. They will see expressions of the form $ax^2 + bx + c$ where b or c is equal to 0. They will also see expressions where a does not equal 1.

Problem Implementation

Students can work in pairs on this Problem.

Note: You might want to have a class discussion after each pair works on Question A. Then, let the class explore the rest of the Problem.

Materials

- **Teaching Aid 3.3A:** Factoring Quadratic Equations
- **Teaching Aid 3.3B:** Quadratic Expression Model

Vocabulary

- roots

Mathematics Background

- Solving Equations

At a Glance and Lesson Plan

- At a Glance: Problem 3.3 Say It With Symbols
- Lesson Plan: Problem 3.3 Say It With Symbols

▼ Launch

Connecting to Prior Knowledge

Write the equation $y = x^2 + 5x$ on the board.

Suggested Questions

- How would you describe the shape of the graph? (The graph is a parabola, opening upward. Students should be able to do this without making a sketch or using a calculator.)

- How can you use a table or graph to find the x-intercepts? (On a table, find the value of x when $y = 0$. On a graph, find the value of x where the graph intersects the x-axis.)

- What are the coordinates of the x-intercepts? ((0, 0) and (0, 5))

Explain to students that finding the x-intercepts is the same as solving the equation $0 = x^2 + 5x$ for x. This is called solving a quadratic equation for x when $y = 0$. Display **Teaching Aid 3.3A: Factoring Quadratic Equations**, which shows the connection between finding the x-intercepts of the graph of a quadratic equation and solving the equation if $y = 0$ using a table or graph.

Note: When students work with functions in algebra, they will apply what they know about the roots of polynomial equations to find the zeros of functions, which are also the x-intercepts of the graph of the functions. This concept is further developed in *Function Junction*.

- What is the factored form of $x^2 + 5x$? ($x(x + 5)$)

- What is the relationship between the factored form of $x^2 + 5x$ and the x-intercepts of the graph of $y = x^2 + 5x$? (The factored form of $x^2 + 5x$, which is $x(x + 5)$, is related to the x-intercepts. When y is zero, each x-intercept is the value for x that makes each factor equal to zero, in this case, $x = 0$ and $x + 5 = 0$, or $x = -5$. Therefore, 0 and -5 are the x-intercepts.)

If students don't suggest a relationship, ask them:

- How would you use an area model to get the factored form? (The dimensions of the rectangle are x and $x + 5$. The areas of the subparts of the rectangle are x^2 and $5x$.)

It is important for the students to understand that finding the x-intercepts using the factored form of a quadratic expression is the same as solving the equation $0 = ax^2 + bx + c$. To do this, we need to review how to factor a quadratic expression.

Display **Teaching Aid 3.3B: Quadratic Expression Model** and go over the questions.

- Does Trevor's area model match the expression $x^2 + 5x + 6$? (Yes; since the sum of the areas of the four rectangles are $x^2 + 3x + 2x + 6$, or $x^2 + 5x + 6$.)

- Find the factors of $x^2 + 5x + 6$. ($(x + 2)$ and $(x + 3)$)

- What are the x-intercepts of the equation for $y = x^2 + 5x + 6$? (-2 and -3)

- Describe the relationship between the x-intercepts of $y = x^2 + 5x + 6$ and the factored form of the expression $x^2 + 5x + 6$. (Students may recognize that the x-intercepts in this case are the additive inverse of the 2 and 3 in the factored form. The x-intercepts are the value of x when each of the factors $(x + 2)$ and $(x + 3)$ are set equal to zero.)

Put up another expression such as $x^2 + 7x + 12$ and ask the class to write it in factored form.

- Can you factor this expression without using the area model? (Students may explain that you can graph the expression and find the x-intercepts. The x-intercepts are -3 and -4, so the factored form is $(x + 3)(x + 4)$.)

- What clues in the area model will help you factor this expression? (Students should begin to notice that if m and n are the constant terms of the model dimensions, then $mn = 12$, the constant term of the expression, and $m + n = 7$, the coefficient of the x term. That is, a pair of corresponding factors of 12 must have a sum of 7. This is true because the coefficient of x is 1.)

- How could you use an area model to factor $2x^2 + 6x$? (The dimensions of the rectangle are either x and $2x + 6$, $2x$ and $x + 3$, or 2 and $x^2 + 3x$. The areas of the subparts of the rectangle are $2x^2$ and $6x$, or x^2, x^2, and $6x$. See area models below.)

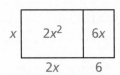   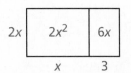

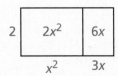   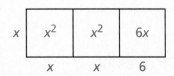

- What are the x-intercepts for the equation $y = 2x^2 + 6x$? ($2x^2 + 6x = 2x(x + 3)$, so the x-intercepts are 0 and -3.)

Presenting the Challenge

In this Problem, students will continue to refine their strategies for factoring quadratic expressions. Explain to them that being able to factor quadratic expressions gives insight on how to solve quadratic equations. This connection shows how the factored form relates to the graph of a quadratic function.

▼ Explore

Providing for Individual Needs

If students are having trouble factoring, suggest that they use an area model. When they are ready, have students check if they can adapt Jakai's method for Questions B and C.

Suggested Questions

• Will Jakai's method work? (His method works on any quadratic of the form $ax^2 + bc + c$ where $a = 1$. Students need to adjust Jakai's method if a is not equal to 1. They will have to consider the factors of a and c and find combinations that will equal the value of b.)

If you find that students need further assistance with Question B, parts (2) and (3), refer them to the first bullet of Jakai's method, which includes integer values in the factor pairs.

Some students may start working on Question D, and notice that Jakai's method does not apply here. Encourage them to use an area model to help find the factors.

Planning for the Summary

What evidence will you use in the summary to clarify and deepen understanding of the Focus Question?
What will you do if you do not have evidence?

▼ Summarize

Orchestrating the Discussion

Go over Questions B and C. In Question C, part (1d), $x^2 - 4$ is the difference of two squares. Its factored form is $(x + 2)(x - 2)$. An area model for this special quadratic was explored in Investigation 2 of *Frogs, Fleas, and Painted Cubes*. You might want to have a student present an area model for this expression.

Suggested Questions

You may also want to ask students:

- Will Jakai's method for factoring work for Question C, part (1d)? (Yes, but students may need help to realize that they need two numbers that multiply to -4 and add to zero since $x^2 - 4$ is equivalent to $x^2 + 0x - 4$. The factor pair that multiplies to -4 and adds to zero is 2 and -2.)

Write the expressions for Question D on the board.

- What is different about these expressions? (The coefficient of x^2 is not equal to 1.)

- Can you use Jakai's method? (Let the students try, but they will quickly see that Jakai's method does not take care of the coefficient of x^2.)

- Let's go back to an area model to see if we can adjust Jakai's method. (Students should see that factored pairs of c and factored pairs of a must combine to get b.)

For example, write $2x^2 + 7x + 6$ on the board.

- What are possibilities for factors of 2? (2 and 1)

- So we have $(2x + \blacksquare)(x + \blacksquare) = 2x^2 + 7x + 6$. What are possibilities for factors of 6? (6 and 1 or 2 and 3.)

- Now what are possibilities for $\blacksquare$ in $(2x + \blacksquare)(x + \blacksquare)$? $((2x + 6)(x + 1), (2x + 1)(x + 6), (2x + 2)(x + 3),$ or $(2x + 3)(x + 2))$

- How do we know which one is correct? (Use an area model or multiply each out using the Distributive Property.)

For Question D, part (1a) ask:

- What does each term have in common? (Each term has a common factor of 2.)

- Can you use this information to write an equivalent expression? (Yes; the Distributive Property allows you to write $2x^2 + 8x + 8$ as $2(x^2 + 4x + 4)$.)

- Is this in factored form? (Yes; but it is partially factored.)

- Can we predict the solutions or x-intercepts from this form? (No; but we can write $x^2 + 4x + 4$ in factored form as $(x + 2)(x + 2)$ using Jakai's method. So the complete factored form is $2(x + 2)(x + 2)$.)

For Question D, part (1a), you can tell the students that $(x + 2)(x + 2)$ can be written as $(x + 2)^2$. You could connect this expression, $2x^2 + 8x + 8$, to the graph of $y = 2x^2 + 8x + 8$ and to the graph of $y = x^2 + 4x + 4$, in order to introduce students to the idea that when a root is repeated for a quadratic, there is only one intercept. This comparison also illustrates the influence of the extra factor of 2; the two graphs have the same x-intercept, which are the minimums, but have different shapes.

Note: In the examples above we were only looking for whole-number factors. There may be a temptation to spend lots of time on factoring. Factoring quadratic expressions is a "guess and check" procedure. The examples are quite contrived, since picking whole numbers randomly for a, b, and c in the expression $ax^2 + bc + c$ will have a probability near zero of being factorable over the real numbers.

It is important to be clear that the relation between the factored and expanded forms depends on the Distributive Property. Understanding the Distributive Property is key to using factored and expanded form successfully in a variety of situations.

Check for Understanding

At this point, ask students to factor the following and summarize their strategies.

How could we factor the following?

- $x^2 + 7x + 12$ (Since $a = 1$, we can use Jakai's method: $(x + 3)(x + 4)$.)

- $3x^2 + 8x + 5$ (Since $a \neq 1$, we can't use Jakai's method. Use an area model or consider the combinations of the factor pairs for 3 and 5: $(3x + 5)(x + 1)$.)

- $2x^2 + 14x + 24$ (After the 2 is factored out, we can use Jakai's method: $2(x + 3)(x + 4)$. Have students compare this expression to the factors of $x^2 + 7x + 12$.)

Reflecting on Student Learning

Use the following questions to assess student understanding at the end of the lesson.

- What evidence do I have that students understand the Focus Question?
  - Where did my students get stuck?
  - What strategies did they use?
  - What breakthroughs did my students have today?
- How will I use this to plan for tomorrow? For the next time I teach this lesson?
- Where will I have the opportunity to reinforce these ideas as I continue through this Unit? The next Unit?

ACE Assignment Guide

- **Applications:** 24–26
- **Connections:** 45–48
- **Extensions:** 57–58

PROBLEM

3.4

Solving Quadratic Equations

▼ # Problem Overview

> $\mathit{Focus\ Question}$ What are some strategies for solving quadratic equations?

Problem Description

In this Problem, students explore the connections among a factored form of $ax^2 + bx + c$, the x-intercepts of the graph of the equation $y = ax^2 + bx + c$, and the solutions to $0 = ax^2 + bx + c$. They begin to develop some fluency with factoring quadratics, while applying this skill to solving quadratic equations.

Problem Implementation

Students can work in groups of 2–3.

Materials

• **Teaching Aid 3.4:** Solving Quadratic Equations

poster paper

markers

Vocabulary

There are no new glossary terms introduced in this Problem.

Mathematics Background

• Solving Equations

At a Glance and Lesson Plan

• At a Glance: Problem 3.4 Say It With Symbols

• Lesson Plan: Problem 3.4 Say It With Symbols

▼ Launch

Connecting to Prior Knowledge

Students will use their knowledge about factoring a quadratic expression to solve a quadratic equation.

Presenting the Challenge

Display **Teaching Aid 3.4: Solving Quadratic Equations** to show the equation from the Problem introduction, $0 = x^2 + 8x + 12$. Go over the questions.

Suggested Questions

- How can you solve the equation $0 = x^2 + 8x + 12$ by factoring? (First write $0 = x^2 + 8x + 12$ in factored form to get $(x + 2)(x + 6)$. This expression is the product of two linear factors.)

- When $0 = (x + 2)(x + 6)$, what must be true about one or both of the linear factors? (One or both of the factors must be equal to 0.)

- How can this information help you find the solutions to $0 = (x + 2)(x + 6)$? (Set $x + 2$ and $x + 6$ equal to 0, and then solve for x. The solutions are $x = -2$ and -6.)

- How can this information help you find the x-intercepts of $y = x^2 + 8x + 12$? (The information indicates that when $y = 0$, $x = -2$ and $x = -6$. This means that the x-intercepts of this graph are -2 and -6.)

The factoring parts are review for the students to understand how the product of two quantities could equal 0. They will connect the process of factoring a quadratic expression to solving a quadratic equation, $0 = ax^2 + bx + c$.

▼ Explore

Providing for Individual Needs

If a student has factored incorrectly, challenge the student to show that his or her factored expression is correct by multiplying it out using the Distributive Property or by trying three numerical values for the factored and expanded form to see if they are equivalent expressions.

You may want some pairs to put their work for an equation on large poster paper along with the graph and table showing alternate ways to solve the equations. Students can point out the connections among solutions for an equation, x-intercepts, line of symmetry, and maximum or minimum.

Planning for the Summary

What evidence will you use in the summary to clarify and deepen understanding of the Focus Question?

What will you do if you do not have evidence?

▼ Summarize

Orchestrating the Discussion

Go over each part of the Problem. Take time to connect solving quadratic equations to the bigger picture of quadratic relationships. Solving a quadratic equation, $0 = ax^2 + bx + c$, is the same as finding the x-intercepts of the graph of $y = ax^2 + bx + c$.

Discuss Question D, which introduces a context where it useful to solve a quadratic equation by factoring. Ask:

Suggested Questions

- What does solving $0 = 32t - 16t^2$ tell you about the pole vaulter's jump? About the graph of $y = 32t - 16t^2$? (The pole vaulter was on the ground at $t = 0$ and $t = 2$. The t-intercepts are at $t = 0$ and $t = 2$.)

- How do the solutions for the quadratic equation help you determine how high the pole vaulter jumped? Can you find this maximum point without actually making the graph? (The line of symmetry is halfway between the t-intercepts, so it must be at $t = 1$. Therefore, the maximum point must be $(1, y)$. Substituting 1 for t in $y = 32t - 16t^2$ gives $y = 16$. The maximum is at $(1, 16)$, and the maximum height of the pole vaulter's jump is 16 feet.)

Check for Understanding

Solve each of the following equations for x:

- $6 - 4(x + 4) = 2x$

  $(x = -\frac{5}{3})$

- $2x^2 - 18x + 28 = 0$

  $(x = 2 \text{ or } x = 7)$

- How could you use a graph or table to solve these equations? (Looking at a graph or table, find the values of x where $y = 0$.)

Reflecting on Student Learning

Use the following questions to assess student understanding at the end of the lesson.

- What evidence do I have that students understand the Focus Question?
  - Where did my students get stuck?
  - What strategies did they use?
  - What breakthroughs did my students have today?
- How will I use this to plan for tomorrow? For the next time I teach this lesson?
- Where will I have the opportunity to reinforce these ideas as I continue through this Unit? The next Unit?

ACE Assignment Guide

- **Applications:** 27–34
- **Connections:** 42, 49–52
- **Extensions:** 59–63

▼ Mathematical Reflections

Possible Answers to Mathematical Reflections

1. a. The goal of solving linear equations is to get x on one side of the equal sign and a constant on the other. Undo the operation on either side of the equation by adding, subtracting, multiplying, or dividing both sides by the same quantity. Some choices for proceeding are more helpful than others. Adding or subtracting first does not always lead to a simpler equation. When equations include parentheses, you want to replace the expressions with the equivalent expanded form.

Order of Operations is used when you are simplifying expressions on one side of the equal sign. For example, you can use the Order of Operations to solve the equation $42 = 6 + 2(x + 5)$. You can either subtract 6 from both sides or simplify the right side and replace it with the expression $6 + 2x + 10$, resulting in $42 = 6 + 2x$. Then, using the Commutative Property of Addition, you can replace the right side again with the expression $16 + 2x$. The equation is now $42 = 16 + 2x$. Subtracting 16 from both sides gives $26 = 2x$, which is equivalent to $x = 13$.

b. If the equation is simplified to have a variable on one side of the equal sign and a number on the other ($x = 1$), then it has a finite number of solutions. If the equation is simplified to have the same number on both sides of the equal sign ($0 = 0$), it is an identity. An identity equation is true for all values of the variable and has an infinite number of solutions. Last, if an equation is simplified to have different numbers on the left and right side of the equal sign ($1 = 2$), it has no solution since it leads to a contradiction. A contradiction is a false statement, so it has no solution. **Note:** In general, an equation is conditional if it has at least one solution but not all the values of the variable are a solution. An equation is a contradiction if it has no solutions. An equation is an identity if all the values for the variable are solutions.

2. You can make a table to find the value of x for which the expression is equal to zero. You can also make a graph of the equation and find the x-intercepts. You may be able to factor the quadratic expression by applying the Distributive Property or by drawing an area model to find the factors and then set each factor equal to 0 and solve for x. For example, in $x^2 + 5x + 6 = 0$, the Distributive Property helps you factor the expression to obtain $(x + 3)(x + 2) = 0$, so the solutions are $x = -3$ or $x = -2$.

3. The solution or root of a linear equation $0 = mx + b$ is the x-intercept of the graph of the associated linear equation $y = mx + b$. Similarly, the solutions or roots, to a quadratic equation $0 = ax^2 + bx + c$ are the x-intercepts of the graph of the associated graph of $y = ax^2 + bx + c$. To find the x-intercept of a linear equation or a quadratic equation, you could substitute 0 for y and solve for x.

Possible Answers to Mathematical Practices Reflections

Students may have demonstrated all of the eight Common Core Standards for Mathematical Practice during this Investigation. During the class discussion, have students provide additional Practices that the Problem cited involved and identify the use of other Mathematical Practices in the Investigation.

One student observation is provided in the Student Edition. Here is another sample student response.

> In Problem 3.2, we noticed that there are different ways for solving a linear equation. In the case of determining when the cost of the two companies are equal, the first step to the solution varied. You could apply the Distributive Property, or you could subtract the fixed cost from both sides of the equation. Graphs and tables are also helpful for solving this linear equation.
>
> **MP7: Look for and make use of structure.**

Investigation 3

Solving Equations

A problem often requires finding solutions to equations. In previous Units, you developed strategies for solving linear and quadratic equations. In this Investigation, you will use the properties of real numbers to extend these strategies.

3.1 Selling Greeting Cards
Solving Linear Equations

 The steps below show one way to solve $100 + 4x = 25 + 7x$ for x.

$$100 + 4x = 25 + 7x$$
$$(1) \quad 100 + 4x - 4x = 25 + 7x - 4x$$
$$(2) \quad 100 = 25 + 3x$$
$$(3) \quad 100 - 25 = 25 + 3x - 25$$
$$(4) \quad 75 = 3x$$
$$(5) \quad \frac{75}{3} = \frac{3x}{3}$$
$$(6) \quad 25 = x$$

Common Core State Standards

8.EE.C.7a Give examples of linear equations in one variable with one solution, infinitely many solutions, or no solutions . . .

8.EE.C.8b Solve systems of two linear equations in two variables algebraically, and estimate solutions by graphing the equations. Solve simple cases by inspection.

Also 8.EE.A.2, 8.EE.C.7, 8.EE.C.7b, 8.EE.C.8, 8.EE.C.8a, 8.EE.C.8c, 8.F.A.1, N-Q.A.1, N-Q.A.2, A-SSE.A.1, A-SSE.A.1a, A-SSE.A.1b, A-SSE.A.2, A-SSE.B.3, A-SSE.B.3a, A-CED.A.1, A-CED.A.2, A-REI.A.1, A-REI.B.3, A-REI.B.4, A-REI.B.4b, A-REI.C.6, A-REI.D.10, A-REI.D.11

Notes _____

_____

_____

- How could you explain Steps 1, 3, and 5 in the solution?

- The solution begins by subtracting $4x$ from each side of the equation. Could you begin with a different first step? Explain.

- How can you check that $x = 25$ is the correct solution?

- Can you describe another method for finding the solution to the equation?

The preceding example uses the **properties of equality** that you learned in the Grade 7 Unit *Moving Straight Ahead*.

- You can add or subtract the same quantity from each side of an equation to write an equivalent equation.

- You can multiply or divide each side of an equation by the same nonzero quantity to write an equivalent equation.

You can use these properties as well as the Distributive and Commutative properties to solve equations.

Problem 3.1

A The school choir is selling boxes of greeting cards to raise money for a trip. The equation for the profit in dollars P in terms of the number of boxes sold s is

$$P = 5s - (100 + 2s)$$

1. What information do the expressions $5s$ and $100 + 2s$ represent in the situation? What information do 100 and $2s$ represent?

2. Use the equation to find the number of boxes the choir must sell to make a $200 profit. Explain.

3. How many boxes must the choir sell to break even? Explain.

4. Write a simpler expression for profit. Explain how your expression is equivalent to the original expression for profit.

5. One of the choir members wrote the following expression for profit: $5s - 2(50 + s)$. Explain whether this expression is equivalent to the original expression for profit.

B Describe how to solve an equation that has parentheses such as $200 = 5s - (100 + 2s)$ without using a table or graph.

continued on the next page >

Notes

Problem **3.1** *continued*

C Solve each equation for x when $y = 0$. Check your solutions.

1. $y = 5 + 2(3 + 4x)$ **2.** $y = 5 - 2(3 + 4x)$

3. $y = 5 + 2(3 - 4x)$ **4.** $y = 5 - 2(3 - 4x)$

A C E Homework starts on page 55.

3.2 Comparing Costs
Solving More Linear Equations

Ms. Lucero wants to install tiles around her square swimming pool. She finds the following two advertisements for tile companies.

COVER *and* **SURROUND IT**

$1,000 for design and delivery

$25 per tile after 12 tiles

TILE and **Beyond**

- $740 for design and delivery
- $32 per tile after 10 tiles

The equations below show the estimated costs C (in dollars) of buying and installing N border tiles.

$$\text{Cover and Surround It: } C_C = 1{,}000 + 25(N - 12)$$

$$\text{Tile and Beyond: } C_T = 740 + 32(N - 10)$$

You can use *subscripts* to show different uses for a variable: C_C means cost for *Cover and Surround It*; C_T means cost for *Tile and Beyond*.

- Do the equations make sense, given the description above for each company's charges? Explain.

- Is the cost of *Tile and Beyond* always cheaper than the cost of *Cover and Surround It*? Explain.

Ms. Lucero wants to know when the costs of each company were equal.

- How can Ms. Lucero use the equation $C_C = C_T$ to answer her question?

Notes

Problem 3.2

Ⓐ 1. Without using a table or graph, find the number of tiles for which the two costs are equal.

2. How can you check that your solution is correct?

3. How can you use a graph or table to find the number of tiles for which the two costs are equal?

4. For what numbers of tiles is *Tile and Beyond* cheaper than *Cover and Surround It* ($C_T < C_C$)? Explain your reasoning.

Ⓑ Use the strategies that you developed in Problem 3.1 and in Question A to solve each equation for *x*. Check your solutions.

1. $3x = 5 + 2(3 + 4x)$

3. $10 + 3x = 2(3 + 4x) + 5$

2. $3x = 5 - 2(3 + 4x)$

4. $7 + 3(1 - x) = 5 - 2(3 - 4x)$

5. For what values of *x* is the inequality $10 + 3x > 2(3 + 4x) + 5$ true?

Ⓒ For each pair of equations,

- Find the values of *x* that make $y_1 = y_2$ without using a table or graph.
- State whether the linear equation $y_1 = y_2$ has a finite number of solutions, an infinite number of solutions, or no solutions.
- Graph the pair of equations.
- Use the graph to help explain your solution.

1. $y_1 = 3(2x - 5)$ and $y_2 = 2(3x - 1) + x$

2. $y_1 = 3(2x - 5)$ and $y_2 = 2(3x - 1) + 7$

3. $y_1 = 3(2x - 5)$ and $y_2 = 2(3x - 1) - 13$

Ⓐ Ⓒ Ⓔ Homework starts on page 55.

Notes

3.3 Factoring Quadratic Equations

Sometimes mathematical problems that appear to be different are actually the same. Finding the x-intercepts of the graph of $y = x^2 + 5x$ is the same as solving the equation $x^2 + 5x = 0$. The *solutions* to $x^2 + 5x = 0$ are also called the **roots** of the equation. In *Frogs, Fleas, and Painted Cubes*, you found the solutions or roots by using a table or graph of $y = x^2 + 5x$ as shown.

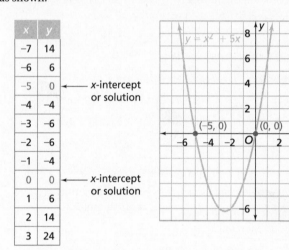

x	y
−7	14
−6	6
−5	0	← *x*-intercept or solution
−4	−4
−3	−6
−2	−6
−1	−4
0	0	← *x*-intercept or solution
1	6
2	14
3	24

- What is the factored form of $x^2 + 5x$?

- What is the relationship between the factored form of $x^2 + 5x$ and the x-intercepts of the graph of $y = x^2 + 5x$? Explain.

To factor the expression $x^2 + 5x + 6$, Trevor draws the area model shown.

- Does the model represent $x^2 + 5x + 6$?

- What are the factors of $x^2 + 5x + 6$?

- What are the x-intercepts of the graph of $y = x^2 + 5x + 6$?

- What is the relationship between the x-intercepts of the graph of $y = x^2 + 5x + 6$ and the factored form of $x^2 + 5x + 6$?

$3x$	6
x^2	$2x$

Notes

_____

_____

_____

Algebra provides important tools, such as factoring, that can help solve quadratic equations such as $x^2 + 5x = 0$ without using tables or graphs. Before using this tool, you need to review how to write quadratic expressions in factored form.

Problem 3.3

(A) Jakai suggests the method below to factor $x^2 + 8x + 12$.

> • Find factor pairs of 12, such as 1 and 12, 2 and 6, 3 and 4, −1 and −12, −2 and −6, and −3 and −4.
>
> • Find the factor pair whose sum is 8; 2 + 6 = 8.
>
> • Write the factored form: $(x + 2)(x + 6)$.

1. Use an area model to show why Jakai's method works for the expression $x^2 + 8x + 12$.

2. Could Jakai have used another factor pair, such as 1 and 12 or 3 and 4, to make an area model for the expression $x^2 + 8x + 12$? Explain.

(B) Use a method similar to Jakai's to write each expression in factored form. Show why each factored form is correct.

1. $x^2 + 5x + 4$ **2.** $x^2 - 5x + 4$

3. $x^2 - 3x - 4$ **4.** $x^2 + 4x + 4$

(C) 1. Examine the following expressions. How are they similar to and different from those in Question B?

    a. $x^2 + 4x$ **b.** $4x^2 + 32x$

    c. $6x^2 - 4x$ **d.** $x^2 - 4$

2. Will Jakai's method for factoring work on these expressions? If so, use his method to write them in factored form. If not, find another way to write each in factored form.

continued on the next page >

Investigation 3   **Solving Equations**   51

STUDENT PAGE

Notes

continued

D **1.** Examine the following expressions. How are they similar to and different from those in Question B?

    a. $2x^2 + 8x + 8$ **b.** $4x^2 + 4x + 1$ **c.** $2x^2 + 9x + 4$

2. Will Jakai's method work on these expressions? If so, write them in factored form. If not, find another way to write each in factored form. Explain why your expression is equivalent to the original expression.

ACE Homework starts on page 55.

3.4 Solving Quadratic Equations

In the last Problem, you explored ways to write quadratic expressions in factored form. In this Problem, you will use the factored form to find solutions to quadratic equations.

- If you know that the product of two numbers is zero, what can you say about the numbers?

- How can you solve the equation $0 = x^2 + 8x + 12$ by factoring?

First, write $x^2 + 8x + 12$ in factored form to get $(x + 2)(x + 6)$. This expression is the product of two linear factors.

- When $0 = (x + 2)(x + 6)$, what must be true about one or both of the linear factors?

- How can this information help you find the solutions to $0 = (x + 2)(x + 6)$?

- How can this information help you find the x-intercepts of the graph of $y = x^2 + 8x + 12$?

Notes _____

_____

_____

Problem 3.4

Ⓐ **1.** Write $x^2 + 10x + 24$ in factored form.

2. How can you use the factored form to solve $x^2 + 10x + 24 = 0$ for x?

3. Explain how the solutions to $0 = x^2 + 10x + 24$ relate to the graph of $y = x^2 + 10x + 24$.

Ⓑ Solve each equation for x without making a table or graph.

1. $0 = (x + 1)(2x + 7)$ **2.** $0 = (5 - x)(x - 2)$

3. $0 = x^2 + 6x + 9$ **4.** $0 = x^2 - 16$

5. $0 = x^2 + 10x + 16$ **6.** $0 = 2x^2 + 7x + 6$

7. How can you check your solution without using a table or a graph.

Ⓒ Solve each equation for x without making a table or graph. Check your answers.

1. $0 = x(9 - x)$ **2.** $0 = -3x(2x + 5)$

3. $0 = 2x^2 + 32x$ **4.** $0 = 18x - 9x^2$

Ⓓ You can approximate the height h of a pole-vaulter from the ground after t seconds with the equation $h = 32t - 16t^2$.

1. Suppose the pole-vaulter writes the equation $0 = 32t - 16t^2$. What information is the pole-vaulter looking for?

2. The pole-vaulter wants to clear a height of 17.5 feet. Will the pole-vaulter clear the desired height? Explain.

ⒶⒸⒺ Homework starts on page 55.

STUDENT PAGE

Notes

Did You Know?

You can find the solutions to many quadratic equations by using tables or graphs. Sometimes, however, these methods will only give approximate answers. For example, the solutions to the equation $x^2 - 2 = 0$ are $x = \sqrt{2}$ and $x = -\sqrt{2}$. Using a table or graph, you get only an approximation for $\sqrt{2}$.

You could try a factoring method similar to those used in this Investigation. However, the probability of being able to readily factor any quadratic expression $ax^2 + bx + c$, where a, b, and c are real numbers, is small.

François Viète

The Greeks used a geometric method to solve quadratic equations in around 300 B.C. There is evidence that mathematicians from India had methods for solving these equations in around 500 B.C., but their methods remain unknown.

For years, mathematicians tried to find a general solution to $ax^2 + bx + c = 0$. In a book published in 1591, François Viète was the first person to develop a formula for finding the roots of a quadratic equation. It is called the *quadratic formula* and is given below.

$$x = \frac{-b \pm \sqrt{b^2 - 4ac}}{2a}$$

This formula can be used to solve any quadratic equation. You will learn more about this formula in *Function Junction*.

Notes

 Applications | Connections | Extensions

Applications

1. The organizers of a walkathon discuss expenses and income. They make the following estimates:

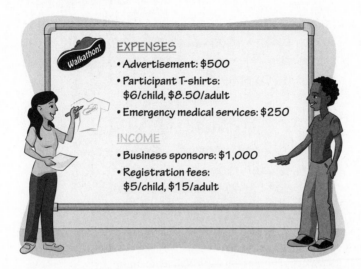

EXPENSES
- Advertisement: $500
- Participant T-shirts:
  $6/child, $8.50/adult
- Emergency medical services: $250

INCOME
- Business sponsors: $1,000
- Registration fees:
  $5/child, $15/adult

a. Suppose 30 adults and 40 children participate in the walkathon. Find the total income, the total expenses, and the profit. Show your work.

b. Write an equation showing the profit P in the form:

$P = $ (expression for income) $-$ (expression for expenses).

c. Write another expression for profit that is equivalent to the one in part (b).

d. Suppose 30 adults and 40 children participate. Use your equation from parts (b) or (c) to find the profit. Compare your answer to the profit you calculated in part (a).

e. Suppose 100 children participate and the profit is $1,099. How many adults participated? Show your work.

Notes

2. Marcel and Kirsten each try to simplify the following equation:

$$P = (1{,}000 + 5c + 15a) - (500 + 6c + 8.50a + 250)$$

They are both incorrect. Study the steps in their reasoning and identify their mistakes.

a.

Marcel

$P = (1{,}000 + 5c + 15a) - (500 + 6c + 8.50a + 250)$

$= 1{,}000 + 5c + 15a - 500 + 6c + 8.50a + 250$

$= 1{,}000 - 500 + 250 + 5c + 6c + 15a + 8.50a$

$= 750 + 11c + 23.50a$ ✗

b.

Kirsten

$P = (1{,}000 + 5c + 15a) - (500 + 6c + 8.50a + 250)$

$= 1{,}000 + 5c + 15a - 500 - 6c - 8.50a - 250$

$= 1{,}000 - 500 - 250 + 5c - 6c + 15a - 8.50a$

$= 250 + c + 6.50a$ ✗

3. According to the equation $V = 200 + 50(T - 70)$, the number of visitors V to a park depends on the day's high temperature T (in degrees Fahrenheit). Suppose 1,000 people visited the park one day. Predict that day's high temperature.

Solve each equation for x using the techniques that you developed in Problem 3.1. Check your solutions.

4. $10 + 2(3 + 2x) = 0$

5. $10 - 2(3 + 2x) = 0$

6. $10 + 2(3 - 2x) = 0$

7. $10 - 2(3 - 2x) = 0$

Notes

8. The two companies from Problem 3.2 decide to lower their costs for a Fourth of July sale. The equations below show the lower estimated costs C (in dollars) of buying and installing N border tiles.

   Cover and Surround It: $C_C = 750 + 22(N - 12)$

   Tile and Beyond: $C_T = 650 + 30(N - 10)$

   a. Without using a table or graph, find the number of tiles for which the cost estimates from the two companies are equal.

   b. How can you check that your solution is correct?

   c. Explain how a graph or table could be used to find the number of tiles for which the costs are equal.

   d. For what numbers of tiles is *Tile and Beyond* cheaper than *Cover and Surround It*? Explain your reasoning.

   e. Write another expression that is equivalent to the expression for *Tile and Beyond*'s cost estimate (C_T). Explain what information the variables and numbers represent.

9. The school choir from Problem 3.1 has the profit plan $P = 5s - (100 + 2s)$. The school band also sells greeting cards. The equation for the band's profit is $P = 4s - 2(10 + s)$. Find the number of boxes that each group must sell to have equal profits.

Solve each equation for x without using tables or graphs. Check your solutions.

10. $8x + 16 = 6x$

11. $8(x + 2) = 6x$

12. $6 + 8(x + 2) = 6x$

13. $4 + 5(x + 2) = 7x$

14. $2x - 3(x + 6) = -4(x - 1)$

15. $2 - 3(x + 4) = 9 - (3 + 2x)$

16. $2.75 - 7.75(5 - 2x) = 26$

17. $\frac{1}{2}x + 4 = \frac{2}{3}x$

Notes

For Exercises 18–23, solve each equation and state whether it has a finite number of solutions, an infinite number of solutions, or no solutions. Then explain how the solution is represented by the graph of two equations.

18. $3(2x - 5) = 5(x - 4)$

19. $3(2x - 5) = 6(x - 4) + 9$

20. $3(2x - 5) = 5(x - 4) + 5$

21. $3(2x - 5) = 5(x - 4) + x$

22. $3(2x - 5) = 5(x - 4) + x + 5$

23. $5 - 2(x - 1) = 2(3 - x) + 7$

24. Write each product in expanded form.

    a. $(x - 2)(x + 2)$

    b. $(x - 5)(x + 5)$

    c. $(x - 4)(x + 4)$

    d. $(x - 12)(x + 12)$

25. Write each quadratic expression in factored form.

    a. $x^2 + 5x + 4$

    b. $8 + x^2 + 6x$

    c. $x^2 - 7x + 10$

    d. $x^2 + 7x$

    e. $x^2 - 6 + 5x$

    f. $2x^2 - 5x - 12$

    g. $x^2 - 7x - 8$

    h. $x^2 - 5x$

26. Write each quadratic expression in factored form.

    a. $x^2 - 9$

    b. $x^2 - 36$

    c. $x^2 - 49$

    d. $x^2 - 400$

    e. $x^2 - 64$

    f. $x^2 - 144$

For Exercises 27–29, solve each equation for x. Check your solutions by using a calculator to make tables or graphs.

27. $x^2 + 1.5x = 0$

28. $x^2 + 6x + 8 = 0$

29. $8x - x^2 = 0$

30. The equation $H = -16t^2 + 8t$ describes the height of a flea's jump (in feet) after t seconds.

    a. Is the equation linear, quadratic, or exponential?

    b. Write an expression that is equivalent to $-16t^2 + 8t$.

    c. Without using a graph or a table, find the time when the flea lands on the ground. Explain how you found your answer.

Notes

31. Use an area model to factor each expression.

   a. $x^2 + 8x + 15$ **b.** $x^2 - 9$ **c.** $2x^2 + 5x + 3$

32. Use your answers to Exercise 31 to solve each equation.

   a. $x^2 + 8x + 15 = 0$ **b.** $x^2 - 9 = 0$ **c.** $2x^2 + 5x + 3 = 0$

In Exercises 33 and 34, each solution contains an error.

- Find the error, and correct the solution.

- How would you help a student who made this error?

33.

$$6x^2 - x = 1$$
Solution
$$6x^2 - x - 1 = 0$$
$$(3x - 1)(2x + 1) = 0$$
$$3x - 1 = 0 \text{ or } 2x + 1 = 0$$
$$x = \frac{1}{3} \text{ or } x = -\frac{1}{2} \quad \times$$

34.

$$24n^2 - 16n = 0$$
Solution
$$24n^2 - 16n = 0$$
$$24n^2 = 16n$$
$$n = \frac{16}{24} \text{ or } n = \frac{2}{3} \quad \times$$

Connections

35. In Problem 3.1, the equation for profit P, in terms of the number of boxes sold s, is $P = 5s - (100 + 2s)$. The number of boxes sold also depends on the number of choir members.

   a. Suppose each member sells 11 boxes. Write an equation that will predict profit from the number of choir members n.
      Hint: First find an expression for the number of boxes sold.

   b. Write an equivalent expression for profit in part (a). Explain what the variables and numbers represent.

   c. Suppose the choir has 47 members. What is the profit?

   d. Suppose the profit is $1,088. How many choir members are there?

   e. In part (d), how many boxes were sold?

Notes

36. The equations $N = 2s + 2(s + 2)$ and $N = 4(s + 2) - 4$ both represent the number of 1-foot square border tiles needed to surround a square pool with sides of length s feet.

    a. Suppose $N = 48$. Solve $N = 2s + 2(s + 2)$ for s.

    b. Suppose $N = 48$. Solve $N = 4(s + 2) - 4$ for s.

    c. How do your answers for parts (a) and (b) compare? Explain.

37. Multiple Choice If $\frac{3}{4}(x - 4) = 12$, what is the value of x?

    A. 6   **B.** 8   **C.** $18\frac{1}{3}$ **D.** 20

38. Multiple Choice What is the value of $x^2(7 - x) + 1$ when $x = 5$?

    F. 201   **G.** 75   **H.** 51   **J.** 28

39. In Problem 3.2, you found the number of tiles for which the cost estimates for the two companies were equal. What is the side length of the largest square pool that can be surrounded by that number of tiles? Explain your reasoning.

For Exercises 40 and 41, use the Distributive and Commutative properties to simplify each expression. Check that the original expression and your simplified expression are equivalent by testing several x values in both expressions.

    40. $2(9x + 15) - (8 + 2x)$ **41.** $(7x - 12) - 2(3x + 10)$

42. You can write quadratic expressions in factored and expanded forms. Which form would you use for each of the following? Explain.

    a. to determine whether a quadratic relationship has a maximum point or a minimum point

    b. to find the x- and y-intercepts of a quadratic relationship

    c. to find the line of symmetry for a quadratic relationship

    d. to find the coordinates of the maximum or minimum point for a quadratic relationship

Notes

_____

_____

Each figure in Exercises 43–47 has an area of 24 square meters. Find each labeled dimension.

43.

44.
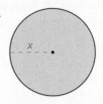

45.

46.
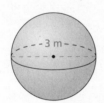

47.

48. An oil company ships oil in spherical tanks that are 3 meters in diameter. The company now wants to ship oil in cylindrical tanks that are 4 meters high but have the same volume as the spheres. What radius must the cylindrical tanks have?

Same Volume
Not drawn to scale

49. Write a quadratic equation that has

  a. one solution (one x-intercept)

  b. two solutions (two x-intercepts)

50. John wants to know if he can bounce a superball over his house. You can approximate the height h of the superball on one bounce with the equation $h = 48t - 16t^2$, where t is the number of seconds after the ball hits the ground.

  a. How long is the ball in the air?

  b. Suppose his house is 30 feet tall. Will the ball make it over his house? Explain.

STUDENT PAGE

Notes

51. Each team in a lacrosse league must play each of the other teams twice. The number of games g played in a league with n teams is $g = n^2 - n$. What are the x-intercepts for the graph of this equation? Explain what information they represent.

52. The height (in feet) of an arch above a point x feet from one of its bases is approximated by the equation $y = 0.2x(1,000 - x)$. What is the maximum height of the arch? Explain.

Extensions

For Exercises 53 and 54, find the value of c for which $x = 3$ is the solution to the equation.

53. $3x + c = 2x - 2c$ **54.** $3x + c = cx - 2$

55. Write two linear equations that have the solution $x = 3$. Are there more than two equations with a solution of $x = 3$? Explain.

56. Insert parentheses into the expression $13 = 3 + 5x - 2 - 2x + 5$ so that the solution to the equation is $x = 1$.

57. Write the following expressions in expanded form.

   a. $(x - 2)(x + 2)$ **b.** $(x - 12.5)(x + 12.5)$

   c. $\left(x - \sqrt{5}\right)\left(x + \sqrt{5}\right)$ **d.** $\left(x - \sqrt{2}\right)\left(x + \sqrt{2}\right)$

58. Factor.

   a. $x^2 - 100$ **b.** $x^2 - 1.44$

   c. $x^2 - 7$ **d.** $x^2 - 24$

59. Use the quadratic formula from the *Did You Know?* after Problem 3.4 to solve each equation.

   a. $x^2 - 6x + 8 = 0$ **b.** $-x^2 - x + 6 = 0$

   c. $10 - 7x + x^2 = 0$ **d.** $4x^2 - x = 0$

   e. $2x^2 - 12x + 18 = 0$ **f.** $3x + x^2 - 4 = 0$

Notes

60. The graphs of $y = 1.5x + 6$ and $y = -2x + 15$ are shown at the right. The scale on the x-axis is 1, and the scale on the y-axis is 3.

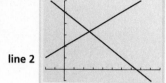

line 1

line 2

a. Is $y = 1.5x + 6$ or $y = -2x + 15$ the equation of line 1?

b. Find the coordinates of the point of intersection of the two lines.

c. How could you find the answer to part (b) without using a graph or a table?

d. What values of x satisfy the inequality $1.5x + 6 < -2x + 15$? How is your answer shown on the graph?

e. What values of x satisfy the inequality $1.5x + 6 > -2x + 15$? How is your answer shown on the graph?

61. Use the graph of $y = x^2 - 9x$ at the right. The scale on the x-axis is 1. The scale on the y-axis is 2.

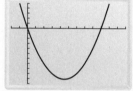

a. What are the coordinates of the x-intercepts?

b. How could you find the answer to part (a) without using a graph or a table?

c. What values of x satisfy the inequality $x^2 - 9x < 0$? How is your answer shown on the graph?

d. What values of x satisfy the inequality $x^2 - 9x > 0$? How is your answer shown on the graph?

e. What is the minimum y-value? What x-value corresponds to this minimum y-value?

Use what you have learned in this Investigation to solve each equation. Show your work and check your solutions.

62. $x^2 + 5x + 7 = 1$

63. $x^2 + 6x + 15 = 6$

STUDENT PAGE

Notes

Mathematical Reflections 3

In this Investigation, you learned methods for solving linear and quadratic equations. The following questions will help you summarize what you have learned.

Think about these questions. Discuss your ideas with other students and your teacher. Then write a summary of your findings in your notebook.

1. **a. Describe** some general strategies for solving linear equations, including those with parentheses. Give examples that illustrate your strategies.

   b. Describe how you can tell if a linear equation has a finite number of solutions, an infinite number of solutions, or no solutions.

2. **Describe** some strategies for solving quadratic equations of the form $ax^2 + bx + c = 0$. Give examples.

3. **How** are the solutions of linear and quadratic equations related to graphs of the equations?

Notes _____

_____

_____

Common Core Mathematical Practices

As you worked on the Problems in this Investigation, you used prior knowledge to make sense of them. You also applied Mathematical Practices to solve the Problems. Think back over your work, the ways you thought about the Problems, and how you used Mathematical Practices.

Sophie described her thoughts in the following way:

In Problem 3.4, we learned that the linear factors of a quadratic equation reveal the x-intercepts of its graph. First, we rewrite the quadratic equation in factored form. Then, we set the equation equal to 0. The solutions of the equation are the x-intercepts of its graph. Now we can use linear factors to help us sketch the graphs of quadratic equations.

Common Core Standards for Mathematical Practice
MP8 Look for and express regularity in repeated reasoning.

- What other Mathematical Practices can you identify in Sophie's reasoning?

- Describe a Mathematical Practice that you and your classmates used to solve a different Problem in this Investigation.

Notes

Looking Back at Functions

▼ Investigation Overview

Investigation Description

In this Investigation, students describe the underlying pattern of change represented by a symbolic equation. They also write symbolic equations to represent specific patterns of change found in a problem and to find answers to specific questions. The last Problem provides several problem situations. Students have to decide which function can be used to represent and solve the problem. This Investigation pulls together many of the algebraic ideas from the algebra strand together.

Investigation Vocabulary

There are no new glossary terms introduced in this Investigation.

Mathematics Background

- Equivalent Expressions
- Combining Expressions
- Solving Equations
- Predicting the Underlying Patterns of Change

Planning Chart

Content	ACE	Pacing	Materials	Resources
Problem 4.1	1–4, 25–28, 56	1 day	**Labsheet 4ACE:** Exercises 1 and 2 (accessibility) **Labsheet 4ACE:** Exercise 25 (accessibility) poster paper (optional) graphing calculators (optional)	
Problem 4.2	5–7, 29–39, 57	1 day	poster paper (optional) graphing calculators (optional)	
Problem 4.3	8–10, 40–51, 58	1 day	poster paper (optional) graphing calculators (optional)	**Teaching Aid 4.3** Check for Understanding
Problem 4.4	11–24, 52–55, 59, 60	1 day	**Labsheet 4.4** Function Matching poster paper (optional) graphing calculators (optional)	
Mathematical Reflections		½ day		

▼ Goals and Standards

Goals

Equivalence Develop understanding of equivalent expressions and equations.

- Model situations with symbolic statements
- Recognize when two or more symbolic statements represent the same context
- Use the properties of real numbers, such as the Distributive Property, to write equivalent expressions
- Determine if different symbolic expressions are mathematically equivalent
- Interpret the information that equivalent expressions represent in a given context
- **Determine the equivalent expression or equation that is most helpful in answering a particular question about a relationship**
- Use algebraic equations to describe the relationship among the volumes of cylinders, cones, and spheres that have the same height and radius
- Solve linear equations involving parentheses
- Determine if a linear equation has a finite number of solutions, an infinite number of solutions, or no solution
- Develop understanding and some fluency with factoring quadratic expressions
- Solve quadratic equations by factoring
- Recognize how and when to use symbols, rather than tables or graphs, to display relationships, generalizations, and proofs

Functions Develop understanding of equivalent expressions and equations.

- Develop proficiency in identifying and representing relationships, expressed in problem contexts, with appropriate functions, and use these relationships to solve problems
- Analyze equations to determine the patterns of change in the related tables and graphs
- Relate parts of a symbolic statement or expression to the underlying properties of the relationship they represent and to the context of the problem
- Determine characteristics of a graph (intercepts, maxima and minima, shape, etc.) of an equation by looking at its symbolic representation

Mathematical Reflections

Look for evidence of student understanding of the goals for this Investigation in their responses to the questions in *Mathematical Reflections*. The goals addressed by each question are indicated below.

1. Describe how you can tell whether an equation is a linear, exponential, or quadratic function. Include the factored or expanded form of the expression for *y*.

   Goal

   • Develop proficiency in identifying and representing relationships expressed in problem contexts with appropriate functions and use these relationships to solve the problem

2. Describe how you can determine specific features of the graph of a function from its equation. Include its shape, *x*- and *y*-intercepts, maximum and minimum points, and patterns of change.

   Goals

   • Determine characteristics of a graph (intercepts, maxima and minima, shape, etc.) of an equation by looking at its symbolic representation

   • Analyze equations to determine the patterns of change in the related tables and graphs

   • Relate parts of a symbolic statement or expression to the underlying properties of the relationship they represent and to the context of the problem

   • Determine the equivalent expression or equation that best applies to the answer of a particular question

3. Describe how you can recognize which function to use to solve an applied problem.

   Goals

   • Develop proficiency in identifying and representing relationships expressed in problem contexts with appropriate functions and use these relationships to solve the problem

   • Relate parts of a symbolic statement or expression to the underlying properties of the relationship they represent and to the context of the problem

   • Determine the equivalent expression or equation that best applies to the answer of a particular question

Standards

Common Core Content Standards

8.EE.C.7 Solve linear equations in one variable. *Problems 1 and 2*

8.EE.C.7b Solve linear equations with rational number coefficients, including equations whose solutions require expanding expressions using the distributive property and collecting like terms. *Problem 1*

8.F.A.1 Understand that a function is a rule that assigns to each input exactly one output. The graph of a function is the set of ordered pairs consisting of an input and the corresponding output. *Problems 1, 2, 3, and 4*

8.F.A.3 Interpret the equation $y = mx + b$ as defining a linear function, whose graph is a straight line; give examples of functions that are not linear. *Problems 1, 2, 3, and 4*

8.F.B.4 Construct a function to model a linear relationship between two quantities. Determine the rate of change and initial value of the function from a description of a relationship or from two (x, y) values, including reading these from a table or from a graph. Interpret the rate of change and initial value of a linear function in terms of the situation it models, and in terms of its graph or a table of values. *Problem 1, 2, 3, and 4*

8.F.B.5 Describe qualitatively the functional relationship between two quantities by analyzing a graph (e.g., where the function is increasing or decreasing, linear or nonlinear). Sketch a graph that exhibits the qualitative features of a function that has been described verbally. *Problem 4*

N-Q.A.1 Use units as a way to understand problems and to guide the solution of multi-step problems; choose and interpret units consistently in formulas; choose and interpret the scale and the origin in graphs and data displays. *Problems 1 and 2*

N-Q.A.2 Define appropriate quantities for the purpose of descriptive modeling. *Problem 1*

A-SSE.A.1 Interpret expressions that represent a quantity in terms of its context. *Problems 1 and 2*

A-SSE.A.1a Interpret parts of an expression, such as terms, factors, and coefficients. *Problems 1, 2, and 3*

A-SSE.A.1b Interpret complicated expressions by viewing one or more of their parts as a single entity. *Problems 1 and 2*

A-SSE.A.2 Use the structure of an expression to identify ways to rewrite it. *Problems 1 and 2*

A-SSE.B.3 Choose and produce an equivalent form of an expression to reveal and explain properties of the quantity represented by the expression. *Problems 1, 2, and 3*

A-SSE.B.3a Factor a quadratic expression to reveal the zeros of the function it defines. *Problems 2 and 4*

A-CED.A.1 Create equations and inequalities in one variable and use them to solve problems. *Problems 1, 2, 3, and 4*

A-CED.A.2 Create equations in two or more variables to represent relationships between quantities; graph equations on coordinate axes with labels and scales. *Problem 4*

A-REI.B.3 Solve linear equations and inequalities in one variable, including equations with coefficients represented by letters. *Problems 1 and 2*

A-REI.B.4 Solve quadratic equations in one variable. *Problem 4*

A-REI.B.4b Solve quadratic equations by inspection (e.g., for $x^2 = 49$), taking square roots, completing the square, the quadratic formula and factoring, as appropriate to the initial form of the equation. Recognize when the quadratic formula gives complex solutions and write them as $a \pm bi$ for real numbers a and b. *Problem 4*

F-IF.C.9 Compare properties of two functions each represented in a different way (algebraically, graphically, numerically in tables, or by verbal descriptions). *Problem 3*

F-BF.A.1 Write a function that describes a relationship between two quantities. *Problems 3 and 4*

F-BF.A.1a Determine an explicit expression, a recursive process, or steps for calculation from a context. *Problems 2 and 4*

F-LE.A.1 Distinguish between situations that can be modeled with linear functions and with exponential functions. *Problems 3 and 4*

F-LE.A.2 Construct linear and exponential functions, including arithmetic and geometric sequences, given a graph, a description of a relationship, or two input-output pairs (including reading these from a table). *Problem 3*

F-LE.B.5 Interpret the parameters in a linear or exponential function in terms of a context. *Problem 4*

Facilitating the Mathematical Practices

Students in *Connected Mathematics* classrooms display evidence of multiple Common Core Standards for Mathematical Practice every day. Here are just a few examples of when you might observe students demonstrating the Standards for Mathematical Practice during this Investigation.

Practice 1: **Make sense of problems and persevere in solving them.**

Students are engaged every day in solving problems and, over time, learn to persevere in solving them. To be effective, the problems embody critical concepts and skills and have the potential to engage students in making sense of mathematics. Students build understanding by reflecting, connecting, and communicating. These student-centered problem situations engage students in articulating the "knowns" in a problem situation and determining a logical solution pathway. The student-student and student-teacher dialogues help students not only to make sense of the problems, but also to persevere in finding appropriate strategies to solve them. The suggested questions in the Teacher Guides provide the metacognitive scaffolding to help students monitor and refine their problem-solving strategies.

Practice 6: **Attend to precision.**

Investigation 4 focuses students on the usage of functions to solve applied problems. In Problem 4.1, students analyze the measurement units associated with the terms of an equation to model pumping water from a pool over time. In Problem 4.2, students find the maximum area and profit. They can use tables and graphs to help identify the maximum. To find a maximum with a table, they must refine the precision of input values. For example, a minimum of $\left(-\frac{1}{2}, -\frac{1}{8}\right)$ would not be in the table of values unless the x-values were in increments of 0.5 or smaller. This is done to get the best possible estimate for the maximum. In Problem 4.4, in which students select appropriate functions as models for verbal descriptions, they can compare the outputs from a function to see if there is a match with the description. In Question B of Problem 4.4, they provide detailed descriptions of the graphs for the models. Here they give precise values for intercepts, maximums, and minimums, as well as patterns of change.

Students identify and record their personal experiences with the Standards for Mathematical Practice during the Mathematical Reflections at the end of the Investigation.

PROBLEM
4.1

Pumping Water
Looking at Patterns of Change

▼ Problem Overview

Focus Question How can you use an equation to answer particular questions about a function and the situation it represents?

Problem Description

This Problem uses linear equations not expressed in the form $y = mx + b$ to represent the amount of water w in a pool that is emptied after t hours. Students use the equations to answer questions about the rate at which water is being pumped out each hour, as well as the amount of water at the beginning of the pumping and the number of hours that it takes to empty the pool.

Problem Implementation

Students can work in pairs and share their work with another pair.

Materials

• **Labsheet 4ACE:** Exercises 1 and 2 (accessibility)
• **Labsheet 4ACE:** Exercise 25 (accessibility)

poster paper (optional)

Using Technology

You may want to allow students to use graphing calculators to make tables and graphs of the expressions and equations in this Problem.

Vocabulary

There are no new glossary terms introduced in this Problem.

Mathematics Background

• Equivalent Expressions
• Solving Equations

At a Glance and Lesson Plan

- At a Glance: Problem 4.1 Say It With Symbols
- Lesson Plan: Problem 4.1 Say It With Symbols

▼ Launch

Connecting to Prior Knowledge

In prior Problems, you looked at situations that could be modeled by specific functions and extended your knowledge about solving equations. In this Problem, you will apply your understanding to look at the context of a problem, which is represented by an equation. Pose the questions in the introduction, but do not expect students to have all the answers. These are intended to raise the issue of the appropriate unit to use as they work through the Problem. Come back to these at the end of the Summarize.

Presenting the Challenge

Describe the situation about water being pumped from Magnolia Middle School's pool. Write the equation on the board. Tell students that they are to find information about the amount of water in the pool and the rate at which it is being pumped out of the pool.

▼ Explore

Providing for Individual Needs

Some students may write $(t - 5)(-250)$ as an equivalent expression for the amount of water in the pool. This is correct, but encourage them to find another expression for the amount of water.

Suggested Questions

- Is there a way to write the equation in expanded form? If so, how?
  (Yes; $-250 + 1250$)

- Does the expanded form help you find the answers for Question A?
  (Yes; I can see that the pool starts with 1,250 gallons and water is being pumped out at a rate of 250 gallons each hour.)

Planning for the Summary

What evidence will you use in the summary to clarify and deepen understanding of the Focus Question?

What will you do if you do not have evidence?

▼ Summarize

Orchestrating the Discussion

For Questions A–D, ask different pairs of students to present their work. Ask the rest of the class if they agree and if they have any questions they want to ask the pair. The idea is to get the class to take charge of the learning.

For Question D, some students may have read the -450 as the rate per hour that the water is being pumped out. This will happen when students do not distribute the -450 to the 2, the coefficient of x inside the parentheses. Tables and graphs will be helpful to see the constant rate of 2 times -450 (or -900) gallons per minute. Some students will correctly apply the Distributive Property to write $w = 900t + 3{,}150$.

Make sure that all students understand how to use the Distributive Property to write the equations in the form $y = mx + b$.

Suggested Questions

- Which form of the equation, $w = -250(t - 5)$ or $w = -250t + 1{,}250$, would an engineer most likely use to represent this situation? Why? (Students might choose the second equation because it is in the familiar slope-intercept form, and tells immediately that the pool started with 1,250 gallons of water and empties at 250 gallons per hour. Some students may find plausible reasons for engineers to use the first equation; it is easier to solve for $w = 0$ since the factor $t - 5$ would have to be 0, leading to the solution $t = 5$. **Note:** When you start with the first equation, you will see if students recognize this form as a linear relationship between time and water remaining in the pool.)

- Without making a graph, describe the shape of the graph of the equation. Is this relationship linear? Exponential? Quadratic? Why? (The graph is linear with a slope of -250 and y-intercept of 1,250. The line is decreasing.)

- In Question A, part (1) and Question D, part (1), how is the information about the amount of water being pumped out related to the graph of the equation? (It is the slope of the line that represents the equation. The slope represents the constant rate of change relating the two variables, the amount of water and time. As time increases by 1 hour, the amount of water decreases by 250 gallons in Question A, part (1) and by 900 gallons in Question D, part (1).)

End by discussing the questions from the introduction.

- What information does the −250 represent? (The −250 must be the rate since it multiplies *t*. In this situation, it is the rate at which the water is removed per hour.)

- What units should you use for −250? (gallons per hour)

- What information does $(t − 5)$ represent? What units should you use for $(t − 5)$? ($(t − 5)$ looks like it represents number of hours. Subtracting 5 from the number of hours is not clear from the context. Students will find that an equivalent expression is more helpful.)

- What units should you use for $−250(t − 5)$? Explain. (Multiplying gallons per hour by the number of hours should give you the number of gallons.)

Reflecting on Student Learning

Use the following questions to assess student understanding at the end of the lesson.

- What evidence do I have that students understand the Focus Question?
  - Where did my students get stuck?
  - What strategies did they use?
  - What breakthroughs did my students have today?
- How will I use this to plan for tomorrow? For the next time I teach this lesson?
- Where will I have the opportunity to reinforce these ideas as I continue through this Unit? The next Unit?

ACE Assignment Guide

- **Applications:** 1–4
- **Connections:** 25–28
- **Extensions:** 56
- **Labsheet 4ACE:** Exercises 1 and 2 (accessibility)
- **Labsheet 4ACE:** Exercise 25 (accessibility)

These accessibility labsheets provide additional scaffolding for these Exercises.

PROBLEM
4.2
Area and Profit—What's the Connection?
Using Equations

▼ Problem Overview

> *Focus Question* How can two different contexts be represented by the same equation?

Problem Description

Students substitute equivalent expressions for quantities into a given equation and write equations for area and for profit. In the area situation, students find an expression for width in terms of length and substitute this into the area formula. To find the profit equation, students substitute one equivalent linear expression for a variable into a quadratic expression. In these two contexts, the resulting equations for profit and area have the same quadratic relationship. This shows that one equation can be used to model two different situations.

Problem Implementation

Students can work in groups of 2–4.

Note: You may want the students to work on Question A and summarize it before you go to Question B.

Materials

poster paper (optional)

Using Technology

You may want to allow students to use graphing calculators to make tables and graphs of the expressions and equations in this Problem.

Vocabulary

There are no new glossary terms introduced in this Problem.

Mathematics Background

- Combining Expressions
- Equivalent Expressions

At a Glance and Lesson Plan

- At a Glance: Problem 4.2 Say It With Symbols
- Lesson Plan: Problem 4.2 Say It With Symbols

▼ Launch

Connecting to Prior Knowledge

In the last Problem, you were given an equation that represented the amount of water remaining in a pool at a given number of hours after draining started. In the next Problem, two different situations are described, area and profit. You used an equivalent form of the equation to make sense of the pool situation. You might rewrite equations for area and profit to make them more helpful.

Presenting the Challenge

Tell students the story of Tony and Paco and how the boys plan to run a concession stand and rent water tubes to the visitors at Water Town. Tony is trying to find the maximum area of the concession stand given a fixed perimeter and Paco is trying to find the maximum profit from renting water tubes.

Suggested Questions

- Compare these contexts to others you have studied. (The situation in Question A is very similar to those studied in *Frogs, Fleas, and Painted Cubes*. The second situation is similar to the situation in Problem 2.2.)

- How might these two situations be related? (Students are not expected to have a complete answer for this at this point. Just listen to their suggestions without commenting. Students might say that in both cases the focus is on finding a maximum value. This might suggest that the relationships are both quadratic. Note their suggestions and return to them in the Summary.)

▼ Explore

Providing for Individual Needs

As students work on the Problem, check to see if they can write an equation for area in terms of length ℓ for Question A, part (1). If they are having difficulty with this, you may want to ask them the following questions.

Suggested Questions

- What is area in terms of length and width? ($A = \ell w$)

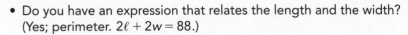

- Do you have an expression that relates the length and the width?
  (Yes; perimeter. $2\ell + 2w = 88$.)

- Can you use this equation to find an equivalent expression for w in terms
  of ℓ? (Yes; solve the equation for w. $w = 44 - \ell$.)

- How can you use this equation to write an equation for area in terms of
  length ℓ? (Use the expression $44 - \ell$ for w and make a substitution by
  replacing w with $44 - \ell$ in the area formula. The new equation for area is
  $A = \ell(44 - \ell)$.)

- How do you know that the area you got in Question A, part (2) is the
  maximum area? (Some students may remember that a square is the
  rectangle with the most area. Some will use the fact that the maximum
  point lies on a line of symmetry perpendicular to the horizontal axis
  and halfway between the two x-intercepts. In this case, $\ell = 22$ and
  area = 484.)

For Question B, make sure that students read the conditions carefully.

- Do Equations 1 and 2 in Question B match what you know about the
  conditions? (Yes; because Equation 1 reflects the fact that when tubes
  are free to rent (or use), 54 tubes will be used by visitors and also the
  second fact, that if the price is raised to $1, only 53 tubes are rented, and
  if the price is $2, only 52 tubes are rented, and so on. Equation 2 uses
  the information about the number of tubes rented (or used) multiplied by
  price to find the income from the rentals.)

- Does $n = 54 - (1)p$ make sense? (Yes; because 54 is the starting point
  (when $p = 0$) or y-intercept and the number of rentals is decreasing by
  one for every $1 increase in the rental price. Slope is -1.)

If students are confused about profit, ask them to explain how to calculate it.

- How can you calculate profit? (Income − Expenses)

- What is the income ℓ? What will you have to do to rewrite this in terms
  of n? ($\ell = np$. Replace p with an equivalent expression involving n.)

- How can you rewrite $n = 54 - p$ to find an expression for p in terms of n?
  How does this help you rewrite the equation for l? (Solve the equation for
  p to get $p = 54 - n$. Then $\ell = n(54 - n)$.)

- What are the expenses? (Expenses are $10 a day for each rented tube.
  $E = 10n$.)

- What is the daily profit? ($D = n(54 - n) - 10n$)

Planning for the Summary

What evidence will you use in the summary to clarify and deepen understanding of
the Focus Question?

What will you do if you do not have evidence?

▼ Summarize

Orchestrating the Discussion

To focus your discussion on the similarity of the two equations, ask your students:

Suggested Questions

- Compare the equations for profit and area. (They represent the same relationship between the variables. That is $D = n(54 - n) - 10n$ or $D = 44n - n^2$ and $A = (44 - \ell)\ell$ or $A = 44\ell - \ell^2$.)

- In the area and profit equations, different variables are used, but the relationships are the same. What does this mean in terms of particular solutions such as (44, 0) or (22, 484)? (The equations have the same solution pairs, same intercepts, same max, but the meanings of the solutions are different.)

- How can you use the information about maximum area in Question A to find the maximum profit in Question B? (The two equations are the same. Since the maximum area, 484 square meters, occurs when the length is 22 meters, then the maximum profit occurs when 22 water tubes are rented for a maximum profit of $484.)

- Compare the methods for combining equations or expressions to write one equation in this Unit. (In Problem 2.1, we added several expressions representing the amount of money each individual received in the walkathon to find one expression that would calculate the total amount of money collected by the group. In Problems 2.2 and 4.2, we substituted an equivalent expression for a quantity (variable) in an equation containing the quantity (variable) to create one equation. In these situations, the two equations contained three variables. For example in Problem 2.2, profit depends on the number of visitors and the number of visitors depends on the probability of rain. We can write one equation for profit in terms of the number of visitors or in terms of the probability of rain. In all three problems, we can calculate the final answer about the total amount of money, total profit, or area using one equation, or in stages, using two or more equations.)

Check for Understanding

- Write an equation for profit in terms of n and p. ($D = p(54 - p) - 10n$)

- How is this different from the equation you found in Question B, part (2)? (To calculate D, you must have two numbers n and p. However, you can use Equation 1 to find p if you know n and vice versa. Finding D this way is not as direct as calculating D using one equation after making the substitution.)

You may want to call students' attention to the NFL quarterback ratings discussed in the *Did You Know?* after Problem 2.2 in the Student Edition. This quarterback rating is based on a series of calculations. You might challenge the students to write a single equation for determining the quarterback ratings. ACE Exercise 57 asks students to compute the ratings for a specific quarterback.

Reflecting on Student Learning

Use the following questions to assess student understanding at the end of the lesson.

- What evidence do I have that students understand the Focus Question?
  - Where did my students get stuck?
  - What strategies did they use?
  - What breakthroughs did my students have today?
- How will I use this to plan for tomorrow? For the next time I teach this lesson?
- Where will I have the opportunity to reinforce these ideas as I continue through this Unit? The next Unit?

ACE Assignment Guide

- **Applications:** 5–7
- **Connections:** 29–39
- **Extensions:** 57

Generating Patterns
Linear, Exponential, Quadratic

▼ Problem Overview

> *Focus Question* How can you determine the patterns of change of a function from a table of data for the function?

Problem Description

Students write equations representing a linear, an exponential, and a quadratic function given two points on the graph of each function. First, they must determine the pattern of change from the two points. For linear and exponential functions, two points are sufficient to determine a unique function. For a quadratic, two points are not enough to determine a unique function; you need three points. So, for the quadratic pattern, there is more than one function that fits the two points. This Problem provides students with the opportunity to revisit situations from previous Units. What is more important for students is to investigate how symbolic statements capture the patterns of change in these three functions.

Problem Implementation

Students can work in groups of 2–4.

Note: For each function, linear, exponential, or quadratic, you can have students post their patterns in the classroom using poster paper.

Materials

poster paper (optional)
• **Teaching Aid 4.3:** Check for Understanding

Using Technology

You may want to allow students to use graphing calculators to make tables and graphs of the expressions and equations in this Problem.

Vocabulary

There are no new glossary terms introduced in this Problem.

Mathematics Background

• Predicting the Underlying Patterns of Change
• Equivalent Expressions

At a Glance and Lesson Plan

• At a Glance: Problem 4.3 Say It With Symbols
• Lesson Plan: Problem 4.3 Say It With Symbols

▼ Launch

Connecting to Prior Knowledge

Tell students that, in this Unit, they have revisited and extended their understanding of functions. Remind them that their understanding of functions now includes writing equivalent expressions to represent a situation and solving equations to find information to answer a question.

Presenting the Challenge

Explain to your students that they will make their own linear, exponential, and quadratic patterns. Then they will write equations to represent their patterns.

Give your students the coordinates of two points for a linear, an exponential, and a quadratic function. Their task is to generate four more points, or coordinate pairs, that fit each pattern of change. Then they will write an equation to represent each pattern of change. You might ask the students the question from the Student Edition in the Problem introduction and set them loose or you can ask the question and collect some responses to return to in the Summarize.

▼ Explore

Providing for Individual Needs

As students make their patterned data, you may want to ask them how they chose their patterns.

Suggested Questions

• How did you check whether your pattern was linear? Exponential? Quadratic? (For the linear pattern, students may take successive differences of y-values to check for a constant difference. For the exponential pattern, students may take successive ratios of y-values to check for a constant growth factor. For the quadratic pattern, some students may try to check the second differences to see if there is a constant second difference, or they may check their values using the equation $y = x^2$ to generate values. Also, they might use the symmetry of a parabola to find other coordinate pairs for the quadratic relationship.)

When students are working on finding equations for their patterns, they should be able to find the equation of a line, given two points.

For the exponential pattern, some students may need prompting.

- What is an example of an exponential equation? What do exponential equations look like? (You may want to remind students about the King of Montarek and the chessboard, or about rubas from *Growing, Growing, Growing* to help them remember what exponentials look like. Formally, exponential equations are of the form $y = a(b)^x$.)

- Can you figure out either of the values of *a* or *b* from the points given? Does this help you find additional points or find an equation? (Students might substitute the given points into the equation to get $1 = ab^2$ and $4 = ab^2$. They may say *b* is the growth factor, which is 4 for this function, or they may say they know that *a* is the *y*-intercept for the exponential function. Then they will have to work back to (0, *a*) in the table. With *a* and *b*, they will be able to generate more points, which can be used to check the equation they produce.)

For students that are working on the quadratic equation, you may need to remind them of the general form of a quadratic: $y = ax^2 + bx + c$. Students do not need to be experts at writing quadratic equations at this point. With some help, most students will be able to find additional points and write an equation. Some students will use the patterns they have noted in *Frogs, Fleas, and Painted Cubes* and say that if 3 is a first difference, then the next first difference should be 5, then 7, or some other pattern that generates constant second differences. They can use this pattern to work back in the table to the *y*-intercept. They must also decide where they want the minimum or maximum to be. Encourage them to sketch a graph and add additional points to the graph, paying attention to symmetry and to constant second differences. If students notice right away that $y = x^2$ works, then ask them if they can find another equation that will work. Some may know the relationship between the second difference and the coefficient from *Frogs, Fleas, and Painted Cubes*, i.e., the second difference is 2*a*. Others may use guess and check. They may guess values for *a* and *b* and check *y* until they find a pattern that is quadratic.

Planning for the Summary

What evidence will you use in the summary to clarify and deepen understanding of the Focus Question?

What will you do if you do not have evidence?

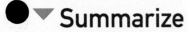

Summarize

Orchestrating the Discussion

Display the posters of student work around the classroom.

Give the class a few minutes to examine the posters and to leave a sticky note with a comment or question on each poster. Then have students explain their work on their posters and why the patterns they found are linear, exponential, or quadratic.

The following table shows the unique linear and exponential patterns and five other patterns that are possibly quadratic.

Be sure to have your students check whether the class patterns are correct. If the following quadratic functions are not displayed on the posters, you can suggest that the patterns are quadratic and have your students check them. This way you can see if your students understand quadratic functions.

x	Linear, y	Exponential, y	Quadratic, y				
			Example 1	Example 2	Example 3	Example 4	Example 5
1	1	1	1	1	1	1	1
2	4	4	4	4	4	4	4
3	7	16	9	8	6	16	8
4	10	64	16	13	7	64	13
5	13	256	25	18	7	16	19
6	16	1,024	36	23	6	4	26

Quad. Ex. 1 is $y = x^2$.

Quad. Ex. 2 is not quadratic; the second difference is not a constant.

Quad. Ex. 3 is $y = -0.5x^2 + 4.5x - 3$

Quad. Ex. 4 is not quadratic; the pattern was generated by using symmetry but not by using the pattern of second differences.

Quad. Ex. 5 is $y = -0.5x^2 + 1.5x - 1$.

Have students explain how they got their equations. The following responses come from CMP classes.

Linear Functions For the linear relationship, most students find the y-intercept for the linear pattern by working backward in the table. Then they use the y-intercept, -2, and the slope, 3, to write $y = -2 + 3x$.

One student begins with the first *x*-value in the table, 1, and notices that the
y-value "goes up by three each time." She uses this information to write $1 + 3x$.
When she checks her work, she notices that the values in the *x*-column are shifted
"one too high." So, she adjusts the equation to $1 + 3(x - 1)$. This makes "it work."
The equation $1 + 3(x - 1)$ is equivalent to $y = -2 + 3x$.

Exponential Functions There are several equivalent equations for the exponential
relationship.

Some students write correct equations $y = 4^{x-1}$ or $y = 4^x(0.25)$. In the second
equation, they find the *y*-intercept of 0.25 by dividing 1 by 4, working backward
in the table (using the growth rate of 4).

Some students write incorrect equations. The most popular incorrect equation
is $y = 1(4)^x$. We assume this is the result of those students thinking that 1 is the
y-intercept, since it is the first entry in the table. **Note:** $\frac{1}{4}(4^x) = 4^{-1}(4^x) = 4^{x-1}$.

Quadratic Functions Many students will write the simple function $y = x^2$. But
there are an infinite number of correct equations, since it takes at least three
points to determine a unique quadratic function.

Some students may just write down a symmetric sequence of numbers, such as 1, 4,
7, 9, 10, 9, 7, 4, 1. For these students, you may want to have them graph their points,
or ask whether the pattern 1, 4, 10, 20, 30, 20, 10, 4, 1 is quadratic. This way you can
see if they are using other criteria besides symmetry to generate the pattern.

Suggested Questions

- Is there a way to check whether your pattern is quadratic like the checking
  you did for your linear and exponential patterns? (Checking for constant
  second differences is a way to check whether a pattern is quadratic. Some
  may make a graph.)

- I notice that there is only one example for the linear equation. Is there
  one that we didn't think of that is not equivalent to the one we got? Why
  or why not? (No. Only one linear pattern can be produced given two
  points, since the two points determine the constant difference or rate of
  change and two points determine a straight line.)

- Do you think there is another possible exponential pattern if you have to
  go through (1, 1) and (2, 4)? Why or why not? (No. Only one exponential
  pattern can be drawn through two given points. **Note:** There are exactly
  two parameters, *a* and *b*, in the exponential equations $y = ab^x$. Also,
  it takes only two points to uniquely determine the growth factor for
  exponential functions. In this case, the growth factor is 4.

- How many points do you need to determine a line? (Two)

- How many points do you need to determine an exponential function? (Two)

- Can you think of another quadratic pattern that is not on the board?
  (Yes. There are infinitely many quadratic patterns that you can find that
  will pass through two points. See the answers to the problem below
  for an explanation. There are three parameters in the general quadratic
  equation, $ax^2 + bx + c$, so it takes three points to uniquely define a
  quadratic function.)

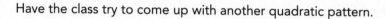
Have the class try to come up with another quadratic pattern.

- What if the point (3, 9) had to be included in your table? How many different quadratic patterns could you find? (If (3, 9) had to be used, then there would only be one pattern, since three points determine the second difference of 2 and the starting point of (0, 1). This is enough to determine the quadratic pattern. Students have talked about this in Investigation 1 when they were trying to find equivalent quadratic expressions. Two quadratic expressions are equivalent if they contain the same three points.)

The quadratic equation is the hardest to come up with unless it is the simplest quadratic, $y = x^2$. There is an explanation in the answer to this Problem about how to determine the quadratic equation. This is an advanced idea, and you may want to go through it with your students if they are interested or if they have already worked on it in Question C, part (1).

Check for Understanding

Now that you have revisited writing equations for linear, exponential, and quadratic functions, you can check students' ability to recognize the functions in symbolic form. Present a group of equations and ask students to identify which are linear, exponential, quadratic, inverse variations, cubic, or other functions. You can use **Teaching Aid 4.3: Check for Understanding** and ACE question #23 and #24 can guide this conversation.

Reflecting on Student Learning

Use the following questions to assess student understanding at the end of the lesson.

- What evidence do I have that students understand the Focus Question?
  - Where did my students get stuck?
  - What strategies did they use?
  - What breakthroughs did my students have today?
- How will I use this to plan for tomorrow? For the next time I teach this lesson?
- Where will I have the opportunity to reinforce these ideas as I continue through this Unit? The next Unit?

ACE Assignment Guide

- **Applications:** 8–10
- **Connections:** 40–51
- **Extensions:** 58

What's the Function?
Modeling With Functions

▼ Problem Overview

> *Focus Question* How can you determine which function to use to solve or represent a problem?

Problem Description

In this Problem, students are given several situations and asked to determine which function best represents the situation. They choose a function to represent the situation, they write an equation and a question that can be answered with the equation, and then they write the answer. They also describe the shape of the graph with as much detail as possible for each equation.

Problem Implementation

Students can work in groups of 2–4.

Note: You might assign different parts of Question A to different groups of students. Have students put their work on poster paper. This Problem can be posed as a card sort. Use **Labsheet 4.4: Function Matching** for the card sort activity, or as a follow-up to the Problem as a way to Summarize Part B.

Materials

• **Labsheet 4.4:** Function Matching (one per group)

poster paper (optional)

Using Technology

You may want to allow students to use graphing calculators to make tables and graphs of the expressions and equations in this Problem.

Vocabulary

There are no new glossary terms introduced in this Problem.

Mathematics Background

- Predicting the Underlying Patterns of Change
- Equivalent Expressions

At a Glance and Lesson Plan

- At a Glance: Problem 4.4 Say It With Symbols
- Lesson Plan: Problem 4.4 Say It With Symbols

▼ Launch

Connecting to Prior Knowledge

In this Problem, students will continue to apply their knowledge about functions and equations to decide which function best models a given situation. Remind students of the functions they will be using: linear, exponential, quadratic, and inverse variation.

Presenting the Challenge

Describe the challenge. Students are going to be given eight situations. Each situation involves some kind of relationship between variables. The task is to figure out which function relationship fits the situation. Then students have to write an equation and ask a question that can be answered by using their equation.

Suggested Questions

- When you are given a relationship in words, how do you decide what kind of function represents the relationship? (Look for a mention of the rate of change, make a table with the given data and look for a pattern, or make a diagram.)

▼ Explore

Providing for Individual Needs

If students need prompting to get started, you can help them look for clues.

Suggested Questions

- What clues suggest that a situation is a linear, exponential, or quadratic function, an inverse variation, or none of these? (Students might respond by saying that they looked for clues that show how the variables are related in each situation, that they created a table and looked for patterns of change, that they made a graph, or that they recognized that the problem was similar to one they had studied previously.)

Look for various strategies that students use and discuss these in the Summarize.

Planning for the Summary

What evidence will you use in the summary to clarify and deepen understanding of the Focus Question?

What will you do if you do not have evidence?

▼ Summarize

Orchestrating the Discussion

Use the student posters to discuss the Problem or make a table on the board with five columns: Linear, Exponential, Quadratic, Inverse Variation, and Other. Have students share their ideas about which situations belong with a function type.

Discuss the various strategies that students used to decide which function matches each situation. Ask them to think of other situations that are linear, exponential, quadratic, or inverse variation. Ask them about the similarities and differences of the situations grouped within a column.

Be sure to have students share by describing the features of a graph and examining the equation without graphing it.

Ask students to share the questions that they made that could be answered by the equation. Try to get examples of linear, exponential, and quadratic functions. Ask the class if the equations and questions fit the situations. You could have groups exchange their questions and answer them using the equations.

Reflecting on Student Learning

Use the following questions to assess student understanding at the end of the lesson.

- What evidence do I have that students understand the Focus Question?
  - Where did my students get stuck?
  - What strategies did they use?
  - What breakthroughs did my students have today?
- How will I use this to plan for tomorrow? For the next time I teach this lesson?
- Where will I have the opportunity to reinforce these ideas as I continue through this Unit? The next Unit?

ACE Assignment Guide

- **Applications:** 11–24
- **Connections:** 52–55
- **Connections:** 59, 60

▼ Mathematical Reflections

Possible Answers to Mathematical Reflections

1. If an equation can be put in the form $y = mx + b$, then it is linear. You may have to apply the Distributive or Commutative Properties in order to get the equation in this form. The highest exponent of the independent and dependent variable is 1. If an equation is of the form, $y = a(b)^x$ or is equivalent to an equation of this form, then it is exponential. If an equation can be written in the form $y = ax^2 + bx + c$ for real numbers a, b, and c; then the highest exponent of the independent variable is 2; and if the exponent of the dependent variable is 1, then it is quadratic. In factored form, a quadratic will have exactly two linear factors, and both factors must contain x^1. For example, the quadratic expression $3(x + 3)(2x - 1)$ has exactly two linear factors, $x + 3$ and $2x - 1$, each containing x^1.

2. **Linear Equations**, $y = mx + b$; the value of b gives the y-intercept, the value of m gives the slope and tells you whether the line is rising from left to right (when m is positive) or falling (when m is negative). m also tells you how steep the slope is.

   Exponential Equations, $y = a(b)^x$; the value of a gives the y-intercept and b tells you how fast the exponential is growing or decaying. b is the growth (or decay) factor for the function.

   Quadratic Equations, $y = ax^2 + bx + c$; the value of c gives the y-intercept and a tells you whether the parabola opens up (a is positive) or down (a is negative). With a, you can also find the constant second difference $2a$. The factored form of a quadratic expression makes seeing the x-intercepts easier. For example, if the quadratic equation is $y = (x + 3)(x - 1)$, then the x-intercepts are the values for x that make each factor equal to 0. The x-intercepts are -3 and 1. The value for x halfway between these two x-intercepts is the x-value of the maximum or minimum of the parabola. In the case of $y = (x + 3)(x - 1)$, the point $(-1, -4)$ is a minimum since the parabola opens up (positive a).

3. Answers will vary. Students may say something about looking for clues from the pattern of change—for example, additive patterns for linear functions and multiplicative patterns for exponential functions. Some students may generate tables to look for patterns of change. Some may say that a problem is similar to another problem they have solved. The last two strategies are commonly used for quadratic functions.

Possible Answers to Mathematical Practices Reflections

Students may have demonstrated all of the eight Common Core Standards for Mathematical Practice during this Investigation. During the class discussion, have students provide additional Practices that the Problem cited involved and identify the use of other Mathematical Practices in the Investigation.

One student observation is provided in the Student Edition. Here is another sample student response.

> When we were trying to decide which function we could use to represent the relationships in the situations in Problem 4.4, we were able to write an equation for almost all of the situations. At first, we had difficulty deciding which function was represented by the sequence of squares in A7. We thought it was linear since one more unit square was added to each figure, but then we created a table for the first five figures and found that the pattern of change was for a quadratic function. Then we were able to use the information to write an equation.
>
> **MP1: Make sense of problems and persevere in solving them.**

Investigation 4

Looking Back at Functions

Throughout your work in algebra, you have identified patterns of change between variables as linear, exponential, and quadratic functions. You have used tables, graphs, and equations to represent and reason about these functions. In this Unit, you have found that writing equivalent expressions for a quantity or variable can reveal new information about a situation. This Investigation will help pull these ideas together.

4.1 Pumping Water
Looking at Patterns of Change

 Magnolia Middle School needs to empty their pool for resealing. Ms. Theodora's math class decides to collect data on the amount of water in the pool and the time it takes to empty it.

Common Core State Standards

8.F.A.3 Interpret the equation $y = mx + b$ as defining a linear function, whose graph is a straight line; give examples of functions that are not linear.

8.F.B.5 Describe qualitatively the functional relationship between two quantities by analyzing a graph (e.g., where the function is increasing or decreasing, linear or nonlinear). Sketch a graph that exhibits the qualitative features of a function that has been described verbally.

Also **8.EE.C.7, 8.EE.C.7b, 8.F.A.1, 8.F.B.4, N-Q.A.1, N-Q.A.2, A-SSE.A.1, A-SSE.A.1a, A-SSE.A.1b, A-SSE.A.2, A-SSE.B.3, A-SSE.B.3a, A-CED.A.1, A-CED.A.2, A-REI.B.3, A-REI.B.4b, F-IF.C.9, F-BF.A.1, F-BF.A.1a, F-LE.A.1, F-LE.A.2, F-LE.B.5**

Notes _____

_____

_____

The class writes the following equation to represent the amount of water w (in gallons) in the pool after t hours.

$$w = -250(t - 5)$$

- What information does the -250 represent?
- What units should you use for -250?
- What information does $(t - 5)$ represent? What units should you use for $(t - 5)$?
- What units should you use for $-250(t - 5)$? Explain.

Problem 4.1

A Answer the following questions. Explain your reasoning.

   1. How many gallons of water are pumped out each hour?

   2. How long will it take to empty the pool?

   3. How many gallons of water are in the pool at the start?

B 1. Write an expression for the amount of water in the tank after t hours that is equivalent to the original expression.

   2. What information does this new expression tell you about the amount of water in the tank?

   3. Which expression is more useful in this situation? Explain.

C 1. Describe the pattern of change in the relationship between the two variables w and t.

   2. Without graphing the equation, describe the shape of the graph. Include as much information as you can.

D Suppose the equation for the amount of water w (in gallons) in the pool after t hours is $w = -450(2t - 7)$.

   1. How many gallons of water are pumped out each hour?

   2. How long will it take to empty the pool?

   3. How many gallons of water are in the pool at the start?

   4. Write an expression that is equivalent to $-450(2t - 7)$. Which expression is more useful? Explain.

A C E Homework starts on page 72.

Investigation 4 **Looking Back at Functions** 67

Notes _____

_____

_____

4.2
Area and Profit—What's the Connection?
Using Equations

In the next Problem, you will explore two familiar situations that have an interesting connection. Tony and Paco will operate the water tube concession stand at Water Town. Tony is responsible for designing the building that will store the tubes. Paco is responsible for deciding the rental fee for the tubes.

Problem 4.2

A Every concession stand must have a rectangular floor space and a perimeter of 88 meters. Tony wants the greatest area possible.

1. Write an equation for the area in terms of the length.

2. What is the maximum area for the rectangular floor space?

B Paco knows that on a typical day, the number of tube rentals n is related to the rental price for each tube p. Records from other water parks suggest:

- If the tubes are free (rental price = $0), there will be 54 rentals.

- Each increase of $1 in rental price will result in one fewer tube rented.

Paco uses this information to write the following equations:

Equation 1 $n = 54 - (1)p$

Equation 2 $I = np$, where I is the daily income

1. Do these equations make sense? Explain.

2. Write an equation for income in terms of the number of rentals n.

3. The expense for storage and maintenance of each rented tube is $10 per day. Write an equation for daily profit D in terms of the number of rentals n.

4. What number of rentals produces the maximum daily profit? What is the maximum profit? What price produces the maximum daily profit?

5. Compare the equation in part (3) to the equation in Question A, part (1).

A C E Homework starts on page 72.

Notes

4.3 Generating Patterns
Linear, Exponential, Quadratic

In this Problem, you are given two data points for a linear, exponential, and quadratic relationship. You will use these points to find more data points. Then you will write an equation for each relationship.

 Is it always possible to find a linear, exponential, or quadratic equation from two given points? Can you find more than one equation?

Problem 4.3

A The first two rows in a table of numbers are given below. Write four more numbers in each column to make a linear relationship, an exponential relationship, and a quadratic relationship.

Data Points

x	Linear y	Exponential y	Quadratic y
1	1	1	1
2	4	4	4
3	■	■	■
4	■	■	■
5	■	■	■
6	■	■	■

B Explain why the pattern in each column is correct.

C 1. Write an equation for each relationship. Explain what information the variables and numbers represent.

2. Compare your equations with those of your classmates. Do you all have the same equations? What properties of each kind of function helped you construct the table and equation for each?

ACE Homework starts on page 72.

Notes

4.4 What's the Function?
Modeling With Functions

In the following Problem, you are given descriptions of situations. You will decide if each situation can represent a linear, quadratic, exponential, or inverse variation relationship.

Problem 4.4

A For each of the following situations:

- Determine whether the situation can represent a linear function, a quadratic function, an exponential function, an inverse variation, or none of these.

- Write an equation that represents the function.

- Write a problem that you can solve using the equation. Then, solve the problem.

(1) A cylinder has a height of 16 inches. Consider the relationship between the volume and the radius of the cylinder.

(2) A rectangle has an area of 24 square inches. Consider the relationship between the width and the length of the rectangle.

(3) A laptop costs $800 and loses 50% of its value each year. Consider the relationship between the value of the laptop and time.

(4) Tim sells magazines for a fundraiser. His first customer buys 2 magazines. With his second customer, his sales total 4 magazines. With his fourth customer, his sales total 8 magazines. With his eighth customer, his sales total 16 magazines. Consider the relationship between the number of magazines sold and the number of customers.

(5) A cylinder has a radius of 4 inches. Consider the relationship between the volume and the height of the cylinder.

Notes

Problem 4.4 *continued*

(6) Jorge keeps track of the number of people who visit his new Web site each day. On the first day, he has 3 visitors. On the second day, he has 9 visitors. On the third day, he has 27 visitors. On the fourth day, he has 81 visitors. Suppose this pattern continues. Consider the relationship between the day number and the number of visitors.

(7) Unit squares are arranged as shown below. Figure 1 has one rectangle. Figure 2 has 3 rectangles. Figure 3 has 6 rectangles, and so on. Consider the relationship between the number of rectangles and the figure number.

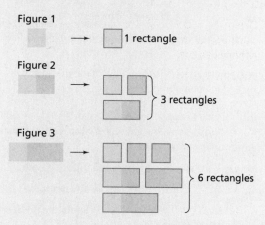

Figure 1 → 1 rectangle

Figure 2 → 3 rectangles

Figure 3 → 6 rectangles

(8) A basketball manufacturer needs to know the relationship between the volume of the ball and its radius. Consider the relationship between the volume of a sphere and its radius.

B Without graphing the relationship, describe the shapes of the graphs for the relationships in Question A. Give as much detail as possible, including patterns of change, intercepts, and maximum and minimum points.

A C E Homework starts on page 72.

STUDENT PAGE

Notes _____

_____

Applications

1. A pump is used to empty a swimming pool. The equation $w = -275t + 1,925$ represents the gallons of water w that remain in the pool t hours after pumping starts.

   a. How many gallons of water are pumped out each hour?

   b. How much water is in the pool at the start of pumping?

   c. Suppose there are 1,100 gallons of water left in the pool. How long has the pump been running?

   d. After how many hours will the pool be empty?

   e. Write an equation that is equivalent to $w = -275t + 1,925$. What information does it tell you about the situation?

   f. Without graphing, describe the shape of the graph of the relationship between w and t.

2. A new pump is used to empty the pool in Exercise 1. The equation $w = -275(2t - 7)$ represents the gallons of water w that remain in the pool t hours after pumping starts.

   a. How many gallons of water are pumped out each hour?

   b. How much water is in the pool at the start of pumping?

   c. Suppose there are 1,000 gallons of water left in the pool. How long has the pump been running?

   d. After how many hours will the pool be empty?

   e. Write an equation that is equivalent to $w = -275(2t - 7)$. What information does it tell you about the situation?

Notes _____

_____

_____

3. A truck has a broken fuel gauge. Luckily, the driver keeps a record of mileage and gas consumption. The driver uses the data to write an equation for the relationship between the number of gallons of gas in the tank g and the number of miles driven m since the last fill-up.

$$g = 25 - \frac{1}{15}m$$

a. How many gallons of gasoline are in a full tank? Explain.

b. Suppose the driver travels 50 miles after filling the tank. How much gas is left?

c. After filling the tank, how many miles can the driver travel before 5 gallons remain?

d. After filling the tank, how many miles can the driver travel before the tank is empty?

e. How many miles does the driver have to travel in order to use 1 gallon of gas? Explain.

f. In the equation, what do the numbers 25 and $\frac{1}{15}$ tell you about the situation?

4. A middle school orders some yearbooks. Their bill is shown below.

Yearbook Printer 123 Publishing Drive • Paperville, MA 02689

INVOICE # 090480

QUANTITY	DESCRIPTION	COST
400	Middle School Yearbook	$2,500
	TOTAL	$2,500

The school gives some free copies to the yearbook advisor and staff. They sell the rest to students. The equation below tells how close the school is to paying for the printing bill.

$$y = 2,500 - 15(N - 8)$$

Describe what information the numbers and variables represent in this situation.

Notes _____

_____

5. A farmer has 240 meters of fence. The farmer wants to build a rectangular fence that encloses the greatest possible land area.

   a. Write an equation for the fenced area A in terms of the length ℓ of the rectangular plot.

   b. What are the dimensions of the rectangle with the greatest area?

   c. Describe how you could find the information in part (b) from a graph of the equation.

   d. Does the equation for area represent a linear, quadratic, or exponential function, or none of these? Explain.

6. In Exercise 5, suppose the farmer uses the 240 meters of fence to enclose a rectangular plot on only three sides and uses a creek as the boundary of the fourth side.

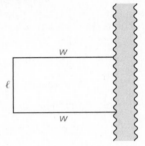

   a. Write an equation for the fenced area A in terms of the length ℓ of the rectangular plot.

   b. What are the dimensions of the rectangle with the greatest area?

   c. Does the equation represent a linear, quadratic, or exponential function, or none of these? Explain.

Notes _____

_____

_____

7. The math club is selling posters to advertise National Algebra Day. The following equation represents the profits P they expect for selling n posters at x dollars each.

$$P = xn - 6n$$

They also know that the number of posters n sold depends on the selling price x, which is represented by this equation:

$$n = 20 - x$$

   a. Write an equation for profit in terms of the number of posters sold. **Hint:** First solve the equation $n = 20 - x$ for x.

   b. What is the profit for selling 10 posters?

   c. What is the selling price of the posters in part (b)?

   d. What is the greatest possible profit?

8. The tables below represent the projected growth of certain species of deer. Use the three tables to answer parts (a)–(c).

Table 1

Year	Deer
2010	1,000
2011	1,030
2012	1,061
2013	1,093
2014	1,126

Table 2

Year	Deer
2010	1,000
2011	1,030
2012	1,060
2013	1,090
2014	1,120

Table 3

Year	Deer
2010	1,000
2011	3,000
2012	9,000
2013	27,000
2014	81,000

   a. Describe the growth represented in each table. Do any of these patterns represent linear, exponential, or quadratic functions?

   b. Write an equation for each pattern that represents a linear, exponential, or quadratic function.

   c. Does any table show a population of deer growing at a rate of 300% per year? Explain.

Notes _____

_____

_____

9. The Department of Natural Resources is collecting data on three different species of animals. They find that these species show different patterns of population growth. They write the equations below to represent the population P of each species after t years.

Species 1	Species 2	Species 3
$P_1 = 10{,}000 + 100t$	$P_2 = 10(3^t)$	$P_3 = 800 + 10t^2$

a. Describe what information the numbers and variables represent in each equation.

b. Describe the pattern of growth for each species. Explain how the patterns differ.

c. Pick any two species. After how many years will the populations of the two species be equal? Explain how you got your answer.

10. Suppose the figures shown are made with toothpicks.

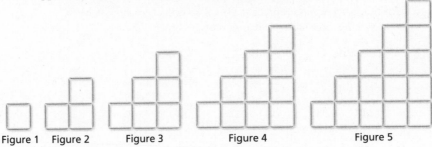

Figure 1   Figure 2   Figure 3   Figure 4   Figure 5

a. What patterns in the set of figures do you notice?

b. How many toothpicks do you need to make Figure 7?

c. Is the relationship between the perimeter and the figure number a linear, quadratic, or exponential function? Explain.

d. Is the relationship between the total number of toothpicks and the figure number a linear, quadratic, or exponential function?

e. Write an equation to represent the perimeter of Figure N. Explain your rule.

f. Write an equation to represent the total number of toothpicks needed to make Figure N. Explain your rule.

Notes

Use the four graphs to answer Exercises 11–13.

Graph 1

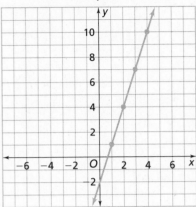

Graph 2

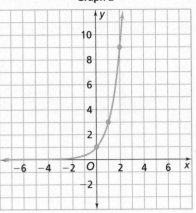

Graph 3

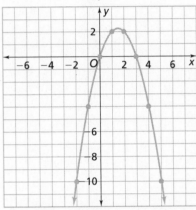

Graph 4

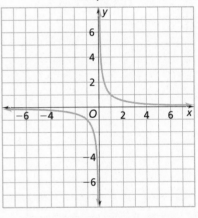

11. Which graph represents a linear function? A quadratic function? An exponential function?

12. Make a table of y-values for x = 1, 2, 3, . . . 6 for each function.

13. Write an equation for each function. Describe your strategy.

Notes _____

_____

Match each equation below with one of the graphs.

Graph A

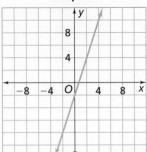

Graph B

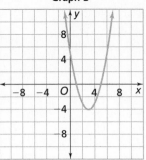

Graph C

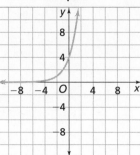

Graph D

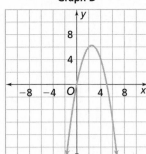

Graph E

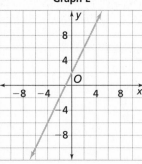

Graph F

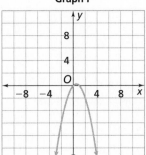

Graph G

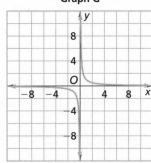

14. $y = \frac{1}{x}$

15. $y = x(5 - x)$

16. $y = (x - 1)(x - 5)$

17. $y = x(1 - x)$

18. $y = 2 + 2x$

19. $y = 5(2^x)$

20. $y = -2 + 3x$

Notes _____

21. For parts (a)–(c), use the set of equations below.

(1) $y = x^2 + 8x$ (4) $y = 2(x - 3) + 6$ (7) $y = 0.25^x$

(2) $y = 2x$ (5) $y = x(x + 8)$ (8) $y = 17 + x(x + 3)$

(3) $y = 4^{x-1}$ (6) $y = 0.25(4^x)$ (9) $y = (x + 1)(x + 17)$

a. Which equations represent linear, quadratic, or exponential functions?

b. Find any equations that represent the same function.

c. Without graphing the equation, describe the shape of the graph of each equation in part (b). Give as much detail as possible, including patterns of change, intercepts, and maximum and minimum points.

22. Pick a linear, quadratic, and exponential equation from Exercise 21. Describe a problem that can be represented by each equation.

23. Use the following equations for parts (a)–(c).

(1) $y = x^2 + 8x + 16$ (10) $y = (4x - 3)(x + 1)$

(2) $y = \frac{1}{3}(3^x)$ (11) $y = 20x - 4x^2$

(3) $y = 10 - 2x$ (12) $y = x^2$

(4) $y = 2x^3 + 5$ (13) $y = 3^{x-1}$

(5) $y = (x^2 + 1)(x^2 + 3)$ (14) $y = 16 - 2(x + 3)$

(6) $y = 0.5^x$ (15) $y = 4x^2 - x - 3$

(7) $y = 22 - 2x$ (16) $y = x + \frac{1}{x}$

(8) $y = \frac{3}{x}$ (17) $y = 4x(5 - x)$

(9) $y = (x + 4)(x + 4)$ (18) $y = 2(x - 3) + 6(1 - x)$

a. Which equations represent functions that are linear? Exponential? Quadratic?

b. For each function in part (a), find those equations that represent the same function.

c. Without graphing the equation, describe the shape of the graph of those equations in part (b). Give as much detail as possible, including patterns of change, intercepts, and maximum and minimum points.

24. Pick one linear, one quadratic, and one exponential equation from Exercise 23. Describe a problem that can be represented by each equation.

Connections

25. Betty's Bakery sells giant cookies for $1.00 each. This price is not high enough for the bakery to earn a profit anymore. Betty must raise the price, but she does not want to lose customers by raising the price too high or too quickly. She considers the following three plans.

> **Plan 1** Raise the price by $.05 each week until the price reaches $1.80.

> **Plan 2** Raise the price by 5% each week until the price reaches $1.80.

> **Plan 3** Raise the price by the same amount each week for 8 weeks. The price reaches $1.80 in the eighth week.

a. Make a table of prices for each plan. How many weeks will it take for the price to reach $1.80 under each plan?

b. Graph the data for each plan on the same coordinate grid. Compare the shapes of the graphs. What do the shapes mean in terms of changing the cookie price?

c. Are any of the graphs linear? Explain.

d. Which plan do you think Betty should implement? Give reasons for your choice.

26. Betty suspects that someone is stealing her chocolate chips.

a. There are one million chocolate chips in a new canister. Betty uses about 40,000 chips each day. How many days should the canister last?

b. Make a graph that shows the relationship between the number of days after Betty opens a new canister and the number of chips that should be in the canister at the end of each day.

c. Write an equation for the relationship from part (b).

Notes

d. After Betty opens a new canister, she begins keeping track of the chips at the end of each day. A gauge on the side of the chip canister allows Betty to estimate the remaining number of chips. Make a graph of the data below. Compare the graph with your graph from part (b). Are Betty's suspicions justified? Explain.

Chocolate Chip Daily Count

Day	1	2	3	4	5	6	7	8
Number of Chips Left (thousands)	800	640	512	410	330	260	210	170

27. Since Betty raised her prices, cookie sales have fallen. She calls in a business consultant who suggests conducting a customer survey. The survey asks, "Which price are you willing to pay for a cookie?" Here are the results:

Cookie Price Survey

Price	$1.75	$1.50	$1.25	$1.00
Number of Customers	100	117	140	175

a. Make a graph of the data. Draw a line or curve that models the trend.

b. Use your graph to predict the number of customers willing to pay $1.35 and the number willing to pay $2.00.

c. Do you think predictions based on your graph are accurate? Explain.

d. Consider your work in past Units. What situation from your previous work has a graph similar to this one?

Notes

28. Sabrina uses an area model to find the product $(x + 2)(x + 3)$.

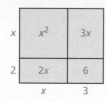

Tara uses the Distributive Property to multiply $(x + 2)(x + 3)$.

$$(x + 2)(x + 3) = (x + 2)x + (x + 2)3$$
$$= x^2 + 2x + 3x + 6$$
$$= x^2 + x(2 + 3) + 6$$
$$= x^2 + 5x + 6$$

a. Explain each step in Tara's method.

b. Explain how Tara's method relates to Sabrina's area model.

c. Use the Distributive Property to find each product.

    i. $(x + 5)(x + 3)$ **ii.** $(x + 4)(x + 1)$ **iii.** $(x - 2)(x + 4)$

29. a. A soccer team has 21 players. Suppose each player shakes hands with each of the other players. How many handshakes will take place?

b. Write an equation for the number of handshakes h among a team with n players.

c. Write an expression for the number of handshakes that is equivalent to the one in part (b).

30. a. Write an expression that is equivalent to $(x + 2)(x + 5)$.

b. Explain two methods for checking equivalence.

31. For the equation $y = (x + 2)(x + 5)$, find each of the following. Explain how you found each.

a. y-intercept   **b.** x-intercept(s)

c. maximum or minimum point   **d.** line of symmetry

Notes

For Exercises 32–37, find an equivalent expression.

32. $x^2 \cdot x^3$

33. $x \cdot x^0 \cdot x^5$

34. $\dfrac{x^2 \cdot x^3}{x}$

35. $\dfrac{x^8}{x^5}$

36. $\dfrac{x^5}{x^8}$

37. $\dfrac{4x^8}{2x^5}$

38. Mary's salary is $30,000 per year. What would be her new salary given each condition?

   a. She gets a 15% raise.

   b. Her salary grows by a factor of 1.12.

   c. Her salary increases by 110%.

39. Examine the three different cylinders.

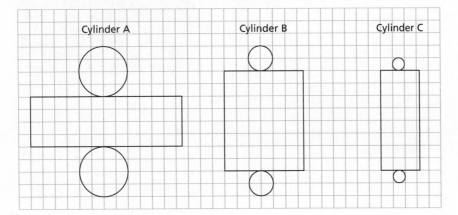

   a. Compare the three cylinders.

   b. Estimate the surface area of each cylinder. Which cylinder has the greatest surface area? Explain.

   c. Which cylinder has the greatest volume? Explain.

Notes _____

40. The equation $d = -16t^2 + 16t + 6.5$ represents the distance d, in feet, from the ground to the top of a basketball player's head t seconds after the player jumps. Find the distance to the top of the player's head after

    a. 0.1 second.　　　　**b.** 0.3 second.　　　　**c.** 1 second.

    d. What operations did you perform to calculate your answers in parts (a)–(c)? In what order did you perform the operations?

41. A bacteria colony begins with 5,000 bacteria. The population doubles every hour. This pattern of exponential growth can be modeled by the equation $b = 5,000(2^t)$, where b is the number of bacteria and t is the number of hours.

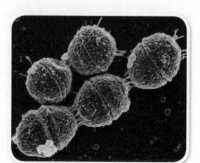

    a. What is the population of the colony after 3 hours? After 5 hours?

    b. What mathematical operations did you perform to calculate your answers in part (a)? In what order did you perform these operations?

For Exercises 42–47, write an expression equivalent to the given expression.

42. $5 - 6(x + 10) - 4$ 　　　　　　**43.** $-3(x - 4) - (x + 3)$

44. $x(x + 2) - 5x + 6$ 　　　　　　**45.** $6x^2 + 5x(x - 10) + 10$

46. $\frac{1}{2}x^2 + \frac{1}{4}x^2 + x^2 + 3x$ 　　　　**47.** $7x^2 - 3.5x + 0.75x - 8$

48. Write an equation for

    a. y in terms of z given $y = 6x + 10$ and $x = 2z - 7$.

    b. P in terms of n given $P = xn - 6n$ and $x = 12 - n$.

    c. A in terms of w given $A = \ell w$ and $\ell = 15 - w$.

Give an equation for each function.

49. a parabola with x-intercepts $(-3, 0)$ and $(2, 0)$

50. a line with a slope of -4 and an x-intercept of $(2, 0)$

51. an exponential function with a scale factor of 1.25

Notes _____

52. a. Sketch each equation below on the same coordinate grid.

$$y = 4x^2 \qquad y = -4x^2 \qquad y = \frac{1}{4}x^2 \qquad y = -\frac{1}{4}x^2$$

b. What is the effect of a change in the value of a on the graph of the equation $y = ax^2$?

53. a. Sketch each equation below on the same coordinate grid.

$$y = 4x^2 + 5 \qquad y = 4x^2 - 5 \qquad y = 4x^2 + 3 \qquad y = 4x^2 - 3$$

b. What is the effect of a change in the value of c on the graph of the equation $y = 4x^2 + c$?

54. You want to attach an anchor wire for a flagpole to the top of the pole and anchor it to the ground at a distance that is half the height of the pole. What is the height of the tallest flagpole you can support with a 60-foot anchor wire?

55. The figures show cones inside cylinders. Each cone shares the same radius and height as the cylinder containing it. Which cone has a volume of $3\pi x^2$ cubic units? Explain.

Cone 1

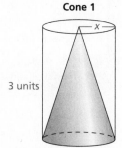

3 units

Cone 2

1 unit

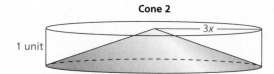

3x

Notes

Extensions

56. Caley's cell phone company offers two different monthly billing options for local phone service.

> **Plan 1** $25 for up to 100 minutes, plus $.50 for each extra minute

> **Plan 2** $50 for an unlimited number of minutes

a. Suppose Caley uses 200 minutes each month. What is the best option for him? Explain.

b. For what number of minutes are the costs of the two plans equal? Explain.

c. Write an equation for each plan. Describe how the variables and numbers represent the growth patterns of the plans.

d. Graph each equation on the same coordinate grid. Describe how the graphs describe the growth patterns of the phone plans.

57. A quarterback's statistics for one season are shown below. Use the equations and the statistics to find his overall rating that season.

Completion Rating: $CR = 5\left(\dfrac{completions}{attempts}\right) - 1.5$

Yards Rating: $YR = \dfrac{\dfrac{yards}{attempts} - 3}{4}$

Touchdown Rating: $TR = 20\left(\dfrac{touchdowns}{attempts}\right)$

Interception Rating: $IR = \dfrac{19 - 2\left(\dfrac{interceptions}{attempts}\right)}{8}$

OVERALL RATING $= 100\left(\dfrac{CR + YR + TR + IR}{6}\right)$

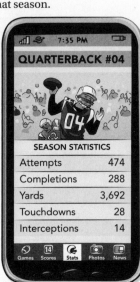

SEASON STATISTICS	
Attempts	474
Completions	288
Yards	3,692
Touchdowns	28
Interceptions	14

86   Say It With Symbols

Notes

58. The equation below represents the space s in feet between cars that is considered safe given the average velocity v in feet per second on a busy street.

$$s = \frac{v^2}{32} + v + 18$$

   a. Suppose a car travels at a rate of 44 feet per second. How far should it be from the car ahead of it in order to be safe?

   b. What is 44 feet per second in miles per hour?

   c. Suppose a taxi is 100 feet behind a car. At what velocity is it safe for the taxi to be traveling in feet per second? In miles per hour?

59. Below is the graph of $y = (x + 2)(x - 1)(x - 5)$.

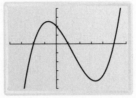

```
WINDOW
XMIN=0
XMAX=10
XSCL=1
YMIN=0
YMAX=10
YSCL=1
```

   a. What are the solutions to $(x + 2)(x - 1)(x - 5) = 0$? How are the solutions shown on the graph?

   b. What values of x satisfy the inequality $(x + 2)(x - 1)(x - 5) < 0$? How is your answer shown on the graph?

   c. How can you find the answer to part (b) without using the graph? **Hint:** Use what you know about multiplying positive and negative numbers.

60. a. Graph $y = x^2 + 4$. Is it possible to find x when $y = 0$? Explain.

   b. Give two examples of a quadratic equation ($ax^2 + bx + c = 0$, where a, b, and c are real numbers) with no solution.

   c. Give two examples of quadratic equations with 1 solution.

   d. Give two examples of quadratic equations with 2 solutions.

STUDENT PAGE

Notes

Mathematical Reflections 4

In this Investigation, you studied equations that represent linear, exponential, or quadratic functions. You also used expanded or factored expressions for *y* to make predictions about the shapes of the graphs of these functions. The following questions will help you summarize what you have learned.

Think about these questions. Discuss your ideas with other students and your teacher. Then write a summary of your findings in your notebook.

1. Describe how you can tell whether an equation is a linear, an exponential, or a quadratic function.

2. Describe how you can determine specific features of the graph of a function from its equation. Include its shape, *x*- and *y*-intercepts, maximum and minimum points, and patterns of change.

3. Describe how you can recognize which function to use to solve an applied problem.

Notes _____

_____

_____

Common Core Mathematical Practices

As you worked on the Problems in this Investigation, you used prior knowledge to make sense of them. You also applied Mathematical Practices to solve the Problems. Think back over your work, the ways you thought about the Problems, and how you used Mathematical Practices.

Ken described his thoughts in the following way:

When Jim and I were working on Problem 4.2, we were wondering how maximum area related to finding maximum profit. We thought that "maximum" was the connection and that each relationship was a quadratic function. We were correct.

We found a quadratic equation to represent the relationship between the two variables in each situation. The equations were exactly the same except for the variables. The equations were $A = 44\ell - \ell^2$ and $D = 44n - n^2$.

Common Core Standards for Mathematical Practice
MP2 Reason abstractly and quantitatively.

• What other Mathematical Practices can you identify in Ken's reasoning?

• Describe a Mathematical Practice that you and your classmates used to solve a different Problem in this Investigation.

Notes

▼ Investigation Overview

Investigation Description

Another important aspect of understanding symbols and writing equivalent expressions is their role in confirming or proving a conjecture. Sometimes, as we have seen in writing equivalent expressions, the symbolic statements can reveal additional patterns in the context. In this Investigation, students use their algebraic knowledge to explore why number puzzles work. They also make conjectures about the relationships between the operations on even and odd numbers and use algebraic expressions to confirm their conjectures. They also explore patterns that emerge from squaring an odd number and then subtracting one and again use algebra to confirm their conjecture.

Investigation Vocabulary

There are no new glossary terms introduced in this Investigation.

Mathematics Background

• Reasoning With Symbols

Planning Chart

Content	ACE	Pacing	Materials	Resources
Problem 5.1	1–3, 13–15, 26–29, 42	1 day	**Labsheet 5ACE:** Exercises 1–3 (accessibility) graphing calculators (optional) poster paper (optional)	
Problem 5.2	4–9, 16–25, 30–32, 40, 41, 43, 44	1 day	calculators (optional) poster paper (optional)	**Teaching Aid 5.2** Bianca's Method
Problem 5.3	10–12, 33–39, 45–47	1 day	graphing calculators (optional) poster paper (optional)	**Teaching Aid 5.3** Student Examples
Mathematical Reflections		½ day		
Looking Back		½ day		
Unit Project		Optional		
Self-Assessment		Take Home		• Self-Assessment • Notebook Checklist
Assessment: Unit Test		1 day		• Unit Test

▼ Goals and Standards

Goals

Equivalence Develop understanding of equivalent expressions and equations

- Model situations with symbolic statements

- Recognize when two or more symbolic statements represent the same context

- Use the properties of real numbers, such as the Distributive Property, to write equivalent expressions

- Determine if different symbolic expressions are mathematically equivalent

- Interpret the information that equivalent expressions represent in a given context

- Determine the equivalent expression or equation that is most helpful in answering a particular question about a relationship

- Use algebraic equations to describe the relationship among the volumes of cylinders, cones, and spheres that have the same height and radius

- Solve linear equations involving parentheses

- Determine if a linear equation has a finite number of solutions, an infinite number of solutions, or no solution

- Develop understanding and some fluency with factoring quadratic expressions

- Solve quadratic equations by factoring

- Recognize how and when to use symbols, rather than tables or graphs, to display relationships, generalizations, and proofs

Functions Develop understanding of specific functions such as linear, exponential, and quadratic functions

- Develop proficiency in identifying and representing relationships, expressed in problem contexts, with appropriate functions, and use these relationships to solve problems

- Analyze equations to determine the patterns of change in the related tables and graphs

- Relate parts of a symbolic statement or expression to the underlying properties of the relationship they represent and to the context of the problem

- Determine characteristics of a graph (intercepts, maxima and minima, shape, etc.) of an equation by looking at its symbolic representation

Mathematical Reflections

Look for evidence of student understanding of the goals for this Investigation in their responses to the questions in *Mathematical Reflections*. The goals addressed by each question are indicated below.

1. Describe how and why you could use symbolic statements to represent relationships and conjectures.

Goals

- Recognize how and when to use symbols, rather than tables or graphs, to display relationships, generalizations, and proofs
- Model situations with symbolic statements
- Recognize when two or more symbolic statements represent the same context
- Use the properties of real numbers, such as the Distributive Property, to write equivalent expressions
- Interpret the information equivalent expressions represent in a given context
- Determine the equivalent expression or equation that is most helpful in answering a particular question about a relationship

2. Describe how you can show that your conjectures are correct.

Goals

- Recognize how and when to use symbols, rather than tables or graphs, to display relationships, generalizations, and proofs
- Model situations with symbolic statements
- Recognize when two or more symbolic statements represent the same context
- Use the properties of real numbers, such as the Distributive Property, to write equivalent expressions
- Develop proficiency in identifying and representing relationships, expressed in problem contexts, with appropriate functions, and use these relationships to solve problems
- Relate parts of a symbolic statement or expression to the underlying properties of the relationship they represent and to the context of the problem

Standards

Common Core Content Standards

8.EE.C.7b Solve linear equations with rational number coefficients, including equations whose solutions require expanding expressions using the Distributive Property and collecting like terms. *Problems 1 and 2*

8.F.A.1 Understand that a function is a rule that assigns to each input exactly one output. The graph of a function is the set of ordered pairs consisting of an input and the corresponding output. *Problem 1*

8.F.A.2 Compare properties of two functions each represented in a different way (algebraically, graphically, numerically in tables, or by verbal descriptions). *Problems 1 and 2*

8.F.B.4 Construct a function to model a linear relationship between two quantities. Determine the rate of change and initial value of the function from a description of a relationship or from two (x, y) values, including reading these from a table or from a graph. Interpret the rate of change and initial value of a linear function in terms of the situation it models, and in terms of its graph or a table of values. *Problems 1 and 2*

N-RN.B.3 Explain why the sum or product of two rational numbers is rational; that the sum of a rational number and an irrational number is irrational; and that the product of a nonzero rational number and an irrational number is irrational. *Problem 2*

A-SSE.A.1 Interpret expressions that represent a quantity in terms of its context. *Problems 1, 2, and 3*

A-SSE.A.1a Interpret parts of an expression, such as terms, factors, and coefficients. *Problems 2 and 3*

A-SSE.A.1b Interpret complicated expressions by viewing one or more of their parts as a single entity. *Problems 1, 2, and 3*

A-SSE.A.2 Use the structure of an expression to identify ways to rewrite it. *Problems 1, 2, and 3*

A-SSE.B.3 Choose and produce an equivalent form of an expression to reveal and explain properties of the quantity represented by the expression. *Problems 1 and 2*

A-CED.A.1 Create equations and inequalities in one variable and use them to solve problems. *Problem 3*

A-CED.A.2 Create equations in two or more variables to represent relationships between quantities; graph equations on coordinate axes with labels and scales. *Problem 2*

F-BF.A.1 Write a function that describes a relationship between two quantities. *Problems 1 and 3*

Facilitating the Mathematical Practices

Students in *Connected Mathematics* classrooms display evidence of multiple Common Core Standards for Mathematical Practice every day. Here are just a few examples of when you might observe students demonstrating the Standards for Mathematical Practice during this Investigation.

Practice 1: Make sense of problems and persevere in solving them.

Students are engaged every day in solving problems and, over time, learn to persevere in solving them. To be effective, the problems embody critical concepts and skills and have the potential to engage students in making sense of mathematics. Students build understanding by reflecting, connecting, and communicating. These student-centered problem situations engage students in articulating the "knowns" in a problem situation and determining a logical solution pathway. The student-student and student-teacher dialogues help students not only to make sense of the problems, but also to persevere in finding appropriate strategies to solve them. The suggested questions in the Teacher Guides provide the metacognitive scaffolding to help students monitor and refine their problem-solving strategies.

Practice 3: Construct viable arguments and critique the reasoning of others.

In Problem 5.1, students use algebra to solve a puzzle that reveals a person's age. From the analysis of the puzzle, students determine how they can change the puzzle to make it work in other years besides the current year. Problems 5.2 and 5.3 present students with informal proofs, or arguments, of number patterns. First they analyze two proofs for the sum of two even numbers. Then they write their own arguments for the sum of an odd and even number and for sums and products involving rational and irrational numbers. They also look for patterns from squaring an odd number and subtracting one. This Problem is rich with opportunities to construct viable algebraic and geometric arguments for the number patterns. In the Summarize for Problem 5.3, they present and discuss their approaches with their classmates.

Students identify and record their personal experiences with the Standards for Mathematical Practice during the Mathematical Reflections at the end of the Investigation.

▼ Problem Overview

Focus Question How can you use algebra to solve a number trick?

Problem Description

Students explore why a familiar number trick works. They use symbolic statements and properties of equality with numbers to show why the trick works.

Problem Implementation

Students can work in groups of 2–4.

Materials

• **Labsheet 5ACE:** Exercises 1–3 (accessibility)

poster paper (optional)

Using Technology

You may want to allow students to use graphing calculators to make tables and graphs of the expressions and equations in this Problem.

Vocabulary

There are no new glossary terms introduced in this Problem.

Mathematics Background

• Reasoning With Symbols

At a Glance and Lesson Plan

• At a Glance: Problem 5.1 Say It With Symbols
• Lesson Plan: Problem 5.1 Say It With Symbols

Launch

Launch Video

This animation shows Elizabeth performing the math trick from the introduction in the Student Edition. Showing this will help students see how the calculations are done in the trick and provide a context for them to figure out how the trick works. Visit Teacher Place at mathdashboard.com/cmp3 to see the complete video.

Rather than showing the animation to launch the Problem, you may wish to consider showing it after students have worked through Question A.

Connecting to Prior Knowledge

So far in this Unit, students have applied algebraic knowledge to solve equations and they have connected this information to graphs of the equations. They have also learned which function can be used to represent and solve a problem. In this Problem, students will use algebraic knowledge to prove conjectures.

Presenting the Challenge

Briefly tell the story about the e-mail message that Elizabeth (or you) received. Ask students to pick a number from 1 to 9 and to perform the steps as you read them aloud.

Suggested Questions

• You should have a three-digit number. What is your three-digit number? (Call on different students to give you their number. As they tell you the number, tell them what number they picked and what their age is. Repeat this for a few more students.)

Ask students to use their algebraic knowledge to figure out the puzzle for Questions B and C.

▼ Explore

Providing for Individual Needs

To help your students get started, you can ask:

Suggested Questions

- How can you indicate multiplication of the number *n* by 2? ($2n$)

- How can you indicate the addition of 5 to this expression? ($2n + 5$)

- How can you indicate multiplying this expression by 50? ($50(2n + 5)$ or $100n + 250$)

Continue this line of questioning as needed.

Going Further

Ask students to design a different number trick. If they need a hint, you might suggest a puzzle that always ends in the number they started with or always ends with 10.

Planning for the Summary

What evidence will you use in the summary to clarify and deepen understanding of the Focus Question?

What will you do if you do not have evidence?

▼ Summarize

Orchestrating the Discussion

Ask one or two students to show their work.

Suggested Questions

- How does the current year figure into the series of statements? (The ending expression is $100n + 25 + 1{,}756 - 1{,}990$ or $100n +$ age in 2013. The age is obtained by subtracting the birth date from the present year. If this is year 2013 and you were born in 2000, then you would subtract the two to get 13. To disguise this obvious calculation, $2013 - 2000$, the trick splits 2013 into $250 + 1{,}763$ and then further disguises it by combining 250 with $100n$ to get $50(2n + 5)$. So, if we adjust the trick to fit a new year, then we have to adjust 1,763 by adding the number of years' difference between the present year and the year 2013.)

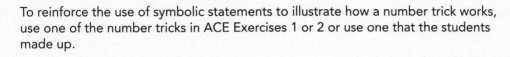

To reinforce the use of symbolic statements to illustrate how a number trick works, use one of the number tricks in ACE Exercises 1 or 2 or use one that the students made up.

Check for Understanding

The following is an amusing number trick. You can adjust the titles of the movies to reflect your students' interest. Teachers at one school use the following adaptation: "We put 1–12 as the most influential person in the student's life. We include people like Abe Lincoln, Einstein, Harriet Tubman, etc. On #9 we put our own name."

Amazing Math Quiz

Do not cheat and scroll down to the movies. Do *your* math, then compare the results to the list of movies at the bottom. You will be **amazed** at how accurate this test is.

Explain why this works.

- Pick a number from 1 to 9.
- Multiply that number by 3.
- Add 3.
- Multiply by 3 again.
- Your total will be a two-digit number. Add the first and second digits together to find your favorite show (of all time) in the list of 17 movies below:

Movie List:

1. *Gone With the Wind*
2. *E.T.*
3. *Blazing Saddles*
4. *Star Wars*
5. *Forrest Gump*
6. *The Good, the Bad, and the Ugly*
7. *Jaws*
8. *Grease*
9. Speech by the principal announcing longer school days (change to reflect your school)
10. *Casablanca*
11. *Jurassic Park*
12. *Shrek*

13. *Pirates of the Caribbean*

14. *Titanic*

15. *Raiders of the Lost Ark*

16. *Home Alone*

17. *Mrs. Doubtfire*

Reflecting on Student Learning

Use the following questions to assess student understanding at the end of the lesson.

- What evidence do I have that students understand the Focus Question?
  - Where did my students get stuck?
  - What strategies did they use?
  - What breakthroughs did my students have today?
- How will I use this to plan for tomorrow? For the next time I teach this lesson?
- Where will I have the opportunity to reinforce these ideas as I continue through this Unit? The next Unit?

ACE Assignment Guide

- **Applications:** 1–3
- **Connections:** 13–15, 26–29
- **Extensions:** 42
- **Labsheet 5ACE:** Exercises 1–3 (accessibility)

This labsheet provides more scaffolding for the Exercises.

PROBLEM

5.2   Odd and Even Revisited

▼ Problem Overview

> *Focus Question*   How can you use algebra to represent and prove a conjecture about numbers?

Problem Description

Students explore algebraic expressions that represent even and odd integers. They use these expressions to make conjectures about the sums and products of two evens, two odds, or an even and an odd. This conjecture was first explored in *Prime Time* using square tiles. In this Problem, students apply their algebraic skills to prove their conjectures.

Problem Implementation

Students can work in groups of 2–4.

Note: You might want some square tiles for your students. The tiles might suggest ways to design a proof first in words and then in symbols.

Questions A, B, and C are accessible by all students. Questions D and E are also accessible to all students, but they are strongly recommended for students who are taking this Unit as part of an algebra course.

Materials

• **Teaching Aid 5.2:** Bianca's Method

poster paper (optional)

Using Technology

You may want to allow students to use graphing calculators to make tables and graphs of the expressions and equations in this Problem.

Vocabulary

There are no new glossary terms introduced in this Problem.

Mathematics Background

• Reasoning With Symbols

At a Glance and Lesson Plan

• At a Glance: Problem 5.2 Say It With Symbols
• Lesson Plan: Problem 5.2 Say It With Symbols

▼ Launch

Connecting to Prior Knowledge

In an earlier Unit (*Prime Time*), you investigated patterns with even and odd numbers.

Suggested Questions

• What can you say about an even number? An odd number? (Even numbers are divisible by 2 and odd numbers will always have a remainder 1 when divided by 2.)

• If you add two even numbers, is the sum even or odd? (even)

• If you add two odd numbers, is the sum even or odd? (even)

• If you add an even and an odd number, is the sum even or odd? (odd)

• If you multiply two odd numbers, will the product be even or odd? What about two evens? What about an even and an odd? (The product of two evens is even; the product of two odds is odd; the product of an even and odd is even.)

• How can you show that these conjectures are true? (Students may suggest trying many examples. You can counter by saying, What happens if someone finds two numbers that contradict your conjecture, in other words, their example makes your conjecture false? Some students may suggest using square tiles or rectangles similar to those they used in *Prime Time* and earlier in this Unit when they used a rectangular model to multiply two binomials.)

• Is there another way to show that these conjectures are true? (Answers will vary. It is unlikely that students will suggest algebra.)

Presenting the Challenge

Pose the questions in the introduction.

Suggested Questions

- Daphne claims that you can represent an even number with the expression 2n, where n is any integer. Is this true? Why? (Yes; the number 2n has a factor of 2, so it must be even. If n = −2, −1, 0, 1, 2, 3, and so on, then we get −4, −2, 0, 2, 4, 6, . . .)

- Write an algebraic expression that will generate all odd numbers. Explain why it works. (2n + 1 represents an odd number. 2 is not a factor of 1, so it is not a factor of 2n + 1. If it were, you would be able to factor out a 2 and write 2n + 1 as 2(?).)

- What conjectures can you make about operations with rational and irrational numbers? (Answers will vary.)

If the following conjectures are not suggested, you can ask:

- Is a rational + a rational always a rational? What about a rational + an irrational? What about the product of a rational and an irrational? (Students may not have firm answers, but this is what they investigate in this Problem.)

Note: Students look briefly at adding real numbers in *Looking for Pythagoras*.

▼ Explore

Providing for Individual Needs

If students find Question B challenging, give them some square tiles or cut some out of grid paper to show them how to represent even and odd numbers. This was done in the Grade 6 Unit *Prime Time*.

For Question C, some students may want to write 2n and 2n + 1 for an even and an odd. You may have to use examples for n to show that these two will not randomly represent an even and an odd number, because once the n is picked, then both the even and the odd are determined. That is, they will be consecutive integers. The odd number should not depend on the even number.

You might suggest using area models to do Question C, part (2). Some students may be more comfortable with geometric arguments. Others may be content with verbal arguments. Encourage students to see the benefit of each method and the way the methods are related.

If students are challenged by the proof for an irrational + an irrational, you can show a couple of sample student proofs. Then ask students to analyze the proof. Most should be able to use number facts as a proof. See the answer for arguments.

Planning for the Summary

What evidence will you use in the summary to clarify and deepen understanding of the Focus Question?

What will you do if you do not have evidence?

▼ Summarize

Orchestrating the Discussion

Go over the steps students provided for Question A.

Compare the two methods for proving that the sum of two even numbers is even. You can ask students to associate the algebraic steps with the geometric model.

Some students may choose to use a geometric argument for Question C. Encourage the class to try both methods.

The product of an even and an odd number (or two odds) is a direct application of multiplying two binomials. $2n(2m + 1) = 4nm + 2n$. Since you can factor out 2 to write $2n(2mn + n)$, you now have an even number that is the product of 2 and the number $2mn + n$.

There are some interesting applications about divisibility rules that can be proven using algebraic reasoning. Some of these rules appear in the ACE.

Call on different groups to share their reasoning about rational and irrational numbers. Encourage the class to ask questions about the proofs.

Reflecting on Student Learning

Use the following questions to assess student understanding at the end of the lesson.

- What evidence do I have that students understand the Focus Question?
  - Where did my students get stuck?
  - What strategies did they use?
  - What breakthroughs did my students have today?
- How will I use this to plan for tomorrow? For the next time I teach this lesson?
- Where will I have the opportunity to reinforce these ideas as I continue through this Unit? The next Unit?

ACE Assignment Guide

- **Applications:** 4–9
- **Connections:** 16–25, 30–32, 40, 41
- **Extensions:** 43, 44

PROBLEM

5.3 Squaring Odd Numbers

▼ Problem Overview

> *Focus Question* What are some strategies for making and proving a conjecture?

Problem Description

Students explore the patterns that emerge from squaring an odd number s and then subtracting 1. They find an interesting connection to triangular numbers, or the number of handshakes, from *Frogs, Fleas, and Painted Cubes* in the pattern. That is, $s^2 - 1$ is equal to 8 multiplied by the $(n - 1)$th triangular number. Students translate verbal arguments into a series of equivalent expressions to show why a conjecture is true.

Problem Implementation

Students can work in groups of 2–4.

Materials

• **Teaching Aid 5.3:** Student Examples

poster paper (optional)

Using Technology

You may want to allow students to use graphing calculators to make tables and graphs of the expressions and equations in this Problem.

Vocabulary

There are no new glossary terms introduced in this Problem.

Mathematics Background

• Reasoning With Symbols

At a Glance and Lesson Plan

- At a Glance: Problem 5.3 Say It With Symbols
- Lesson Plan: Problem 5.3 Say It With Symbols

▼ Launch

Connecting to Prior Knowledge

In the last two Problems, you have you used your algebraic skills to prove conjectures. You expressed a conjecture about relationships with symbolic equations. You were then able to use the properties of real numbers and equality to write a series of equivalent equations to prove your conjecture. You also had a chance to use a proof that required you to assume that your conjecture was not true and then see if this led to a contradiction. This Problem provides another opportunity to hone your skills.

Presenting the Challenge

Pick an odd number, square it, and then subtract 1. Have the class do this for several odd numbers. Then they will look for patterns, explain why the patterns work, and make conjectures.

Your students will organize their work in a table for the first few odd numbers and observe patterns. They may even give verbal explanations for why their conjectures work. Some conjectures are that the numbers are even, 4 and 8 are factors, the pattern of change looks quadratic, and so forth.

▼ Explore

Providing for Individual Needs

Encourage your students to find interesting patterns and conjectures. When students are ready, encourage them to write a general expression of an odd number to carry out the procedure. They should be able to see that 4 is a factor of the final expression. To get the factor of 8, they will need to multiply the numerator and denominator by 2. This shows that 8 is a factor or multiple of the number, which is the expression for triangular numbers from *Frogs, Fleas, and Painted Cubes*.

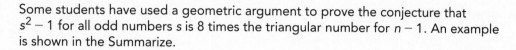
Some students have used a geometric argument to prove the conjecture that $s^2 - 1$ for all odd numbers s is 8 times the triangular number for $n - 1$. An example is shown in the Summarize.

If different strategies come up, have students put them on poster paper to use in the Summarize.

Planning for the Summary

What evidence will you use in the summary to clarify and deepen understanding of the Focus Question?

What will you do if you do not have evidence?

▼ Summarize

Orchestrating the Discussion

Let students share their work. You may have other conjectures other than the one that involves triangular numbers. The triangular numbers from *Frogs, Fleas, and Painted Cubes* are shown below.

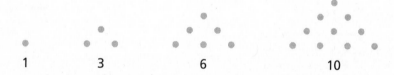

If students try this procedure for the first few odd numbers, they quickly see that the numbers are multiples of 8. If they rewrite each number as a product of 8, they also see that each of these numbers is 8 times a triangular number. The nth triangular number is represented by $\frac{n(n + 1)}{2}$.

Using a table, students show that $s^2 - 1$ can be rewritten as a product of 8 and the triangular numbers.

s	1	3	5	7
$s^2 - 1$	0	8	24	48
Pattern	8×0	8×1	8×3	8×6

Using algebraic reasoning, students might present the following argument.

Let $2n + 1$ represent an odd number.

$$(2n + 1)^2 - 1 = 4n^2 + 4n + 1 - 1$$
$$= 4n^2 + 4n$$
$$= 4n(n + 1), \text{ 4 twice a triangular number } \frac{n(n + 1)}{2}.$$
$$= \frac{4n(n + 1)}{1}\left(\frac{2}{2}\right), \text{ multiply the numerator and denominator by 2.}$$
$$= \frac{8n(n + 1)}{2} = 8 \times \frac{n(n + 1)}{2}, \text{ which shows 8 times a triangular number.}$$

In this situation, writing an equivalent expression for $4n(n + 1)$ as $\frac{8n(n + 1)}{2}$ reveals interesting new information.

Using a geometric argument, students might provide a diagram similar to the one shown below, which corresponds to the algebraic argument.

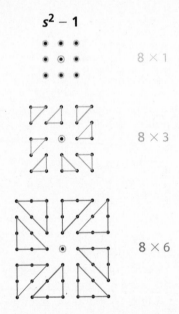

You might end the Problem by displaying the arguments for some of the conjectures as shown on **Teaching Aid 5.3: Student Examples**. One student conjectures that each number is a multiple of 4. Another student conjectures that each number is a multiple of 8. Two students conjecture that it is 8 times a multiple of a triangular number. Be sure to point out the geometric arrangements of dots in **Teaching Aid 5.3: Student Examples** to show the eight triangular numbers in an s-by-s array of dots. Pat and Brian have the same conjecture, but Pat proves it with symbolic statements, while Brian uses a geometric argument.

Reflecting on Student Learning

Use the following questions to assess student understanding at the end of the lesson.

- What evidence do I have that students understand the Focus Question?
  - Where did my students get stuck?
  - What strategies did they use?
  - What breakthroughs did my students have today?
- How will I use this to plan for tomorrow? For the next time I teach this lesson?
- Where will I have the opportunity to reinforce these ideas as I continue through this Unit? The next Unit?

ACE Assignment Guide

- **Applications:** 10–12
- **Connections:** 33–39
- **Extensions:** 45–47

▼ Mathematical Reflections

Possible Answers to Mathematical Reflections

1. Answers will vary. They should include things such as: symbolic statements are efficient ways to represent a conjecture or pattern.

2. The properties of numbers and equality can be applied to an equation to reveal information about the situation or to confirm a conjecture. Symbolic statements can also be used to analyze a given situation.

Possible Answers to Mathematical Practices Reflections

Students may have demonstrated all of the eight Common Core Standards for Mathematical Practice during this Investigation. During the class discussion, have students provide additional Practices that the Problem cited involved and identify the use of other Mathematical Practices in the Investigation.

One student observation is provided in the Student Edition. Here is another sample student response.

We thought it was interesting that the expression $N^2 - 1$ generated numbers that were 8 times the $(n - 1)$**th** triangular number for any odd whole number in Problem 5.3. We generated a table and could see that this was true for the first 10 odd numbers. We then used algebraic reasoning to prove it was true. To do this, we represented an odd whole number as $2n - 1$. We squared it and subtracted 1 and got $4n^2 - 4n$, which we wrote as $4n(n - 1)$. At first, we could not see multiples of 8 or the triangular numbers. Then Jeff suggested that we multiply the numerator and denominator by 2 to get $\dfrac{8n(n + 1)}{2}$.

MP1: Make sense of problems and persevere in solving them.

Notes

Investigation 5

Reasoning With Symbols

You have looked at patterns and made conjectures and predictions. You have given informal arguments to support your conjectures. In this Investigation, you will look at how algebra can help you justify some of your conjectures by providing evidence or proof.

5.1 Using Algebra to Solve a Puzzle

 People receive a lot of information by email. Some emails are useful, while others are for fun. A puzzle similar to the one below appeared in several emails in a recent year.

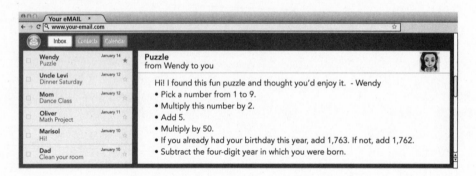

Puzzle
from Wendy to you

Hi! I found this fun puzzle and thought you'd enjoy it. - Wendy
• Pick a number from 1 to 9.
• Multiply this number by 2.
• Add 5.
• Multiply by 50.
• If you already had your birthday this year, add 1,763. If not, add 1,762.
• Subtract the four-digit year in which you were born.

Common Core State Standards

8.EE.C.7b Solve linear equations with rational number coefficients, including equations whose solutions require expanding expressions using the distributive property and collecting like terms.

Also **8.F.A.1, 8.F.A.2, 8.F.B.4, N-RN.B.3, A-SSE.A.1, A-SSE.A.1a, A-SSE.A.1b, A-SSE.A.2, A-SSE.B.3, A-CED.A.1, A-CED.A.2, F-BF.A.1**

90   Say It With Symbols

Problem 5.1

On February 1, 2013, Elizabeth shared the puzzle shown on the previous page with her classmates. She told them, "If you tell me your answer, I will tell you how old you are."

A 1. Work through the steps using the date above.

   2. You should have a three-digit number. Look at the first digit and the last two digits. What information do these numbers represent?

B Let *n* represent the number you chose in the first step. Repeat the steps with *n*. Use mathematical statements to explain why the puzzle works.

C Will the puzzle work for the current year? If not, how can you change the steps to make it work?

A C E Homework starts on page 95.

5.2 Odd and Even Revisited

In *Prime Time*, you looked at factors and multiples. You explored several conjectures about even and odd whole numbers, including:

> The sum of two even whole numbers is even.

> The sum of an even whole number and odd whole number is odd.

• Are these conjectures true for odd and even integers?

• How might you convince a friend that these conjectures are true?

Daphne claims that the algebraic expression $2n$, where n is any integer, will produce all even integers.

• Is Daphne correct? Explain.

• What symbolic expression will produce all odd integers? Explain why it works.

Notes

Problem 5.2

Rachel offers the following argument for showing that the sum of two even integers is even.

> • Let *n* and *m* represent any two integers.
>
> • Then 2*n* and 2*m* are two even integers.
>
> • 2*n* + 2*m* is the sum of two even integers.
>
> • And 2*n* + 2*m* = 2(*n* + *m*).
>
> • 2(*n* + *m*) is an even integer.
>
> • So, the sum of two even integers is even.

A Study Rachel's argument. Provide reasons for each step. Does her argument prove the conjecture that the sum of any two even integers is an even integer? Explain.

B Bianca offers the following argument:

> • Show two even numbers as rectangular arrays with one dimension equal to 2. Let *n* and *m* represent any two integers.
>
>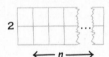
>
> • Then you can represent the sum of the two numbers as a single array with a dimension equal to 2.
>
>

Does Bianca's argument prove the conjecture about the sum of two even numbers? Explain.

Notes _____

_____

Problem 5.2 continued

C Show that the following conjectures are true.

1. The sum of an odd integer and an even integer is odd.

2. The product of an even integer and an odd integer is even.

D Rachel thinks that she may be able to use reasoning similar to Question A to convince Bianca that the product of two rational numbers is rational.

Let $\frac{a}{b}$ and $\frac{c}{d}$ be rational numbers, where a, b, c, and d are integers, $b \neq 0$, and $d \neq 0$.

1. How could Rachel convince Bianca that the product of two rational numbers is rational?

2. How could Rachel convince Bianca that the sum or difference of two rational numbers is rational?

E Rachel wonders about sums and products of rational and irrational numbers. Help her justify her claims.

1. Rachel thinks that the sum of a rational number p and an irrational number q is irrational. Is it possible that $p + q = s$, where s is a rational number? Does thinking about the same relationship as $q = s - p$ help? Explain.

2. Rachel thinks that the product of a rational number p and an irrational number q is irrational. Is it possible that $pq = y$, where y is a rational number? Explain.

A C E Homework starts on page 95.

5.3 Squaring Odd Numbers

In this Problem, you will operate on odd numbers and look for patterns.

Problem 5.3

A Perform the following operations on the first eight odd numbers. Record your information in a table.

- Pick an odd number.
- Square it.
- Subtract 1.

B What patterns do you see in the resulting numbers?

C Make conjectures about these numbers. Explain why your conjectures are true for any odd number.

ACE Homework starts on page 95.

Notes _____

_____

_____

Applications

Maria presents several number puzzles to her friends. She asks them to pick a number and to perform various operations on it. She then predicts the result. For Exercises 1 and 2, show why the puzzles work.

1.

Puzzle 1

- Pick a number.
- Double it.
- Add 6.
- Divide by 2.
- Subtract the number you picked.

Maria claims the result is 3.

2.

Puzzle 2

- Pick a number.
- Add 4.
- Multiply by 2.
- Subtract 6.
- Divide by 2.
- Subtract the number you picked.

Maria claims the result is 1.

3. a. Design a puzzle similar to Maria's puzzles. Try it on a friend.

 b. Explain why your puzzle works.

Show that the following conjectures are true.

4. The sum of two odd integers is even.

5. The product of two even integers is even.

6. The product of two odd integers is odd.

Notes _____

_____

7. Look at the product of three consecutive whole numbers.
For example:

$$1 \times 2 \times 3 \qquad 2 \times 3 \times 4 \qquad 3 \times 4 \times 5$$

a. What pattern do you see?

b. Make a conjecture about the product of three consecutive whole numbers. Show that your conjecture is true.

8. Look at the product of four consecutive whole numbers.

a. What patterns do you see?

b. Make a conjecture about the product of four consecutive whole numbers. Show that your conjecture is true.

9. Determine whether each sum or product is rational or irrational.

a. $0.\overline{3} + 0.\overline{234}$ **b.** $\sqrt{2} + 3$ **c.** $5 \cdot \sqrt{7}$

d. $6\sqrt{36}$ **e.** $\frac{987}{123} + \frac{123}{987}$ **f.** $\frac{26}{78} \cdot \frac{68}{17}$

10. **a.** Are the following numbers divisible by 2? Explain.

$$10,034 \qquad\qquad 69,883$$

b. How can you determine whether a number is divisible by 2? Explain.

11. Look at several numbers that are divisible by 4. What patterns do you notice among these numbers that can help you determine whether a number is divisible by 4? Explain.

12. Look at several numbers that are divisible by 5. What patterns do you notice among these numbers that can help you determine whether a number is divisible by 5? Explain.

Notes _____

_____

_____

Connections

13. Study the sequence of cube buildings below.

- What pattern do you notice?
- Use the pattern to construct the next building in the sequence.
- Think about your steps as you construct your building. The labels below show one way you might think about the pattern.

  1 cube

  1 cube in the center and 5 arms with 1 cube each

 1 cube in the center and 5 arms with 2 cubes each

a. Describe a pattern you see in the cube buildings.

b. Use your pattern to write an expression for the number of cubes in the *n*th building, where *n* is an integer.

c. Use your expression to find the number of cubes in the fifth building.

d. Use the Distributive and Commutative properties to write an expression equivalent to the one in part (b). Does this expression suggest another pattern in the cube buildings? Explain.

e. Look for a different pattern in the buildings. Describe the pattern and use it to write a different expression for the number of cubes in the *n*th building.

STUDENT PAGE

Notes

Suppose a chess tournament has n participants. Each participant plays each of the other participants twice.

14. a. Find the total number of games played for tournaments with 2, 3, 4, 5, and 6 participants.

   b. Look for a pattern in your data. Use the pattern to write an expression for the number of games played in a tournament with n participants.

15. Gina used a table to answer Exercise 14. Make a table like the one below to record wins (W) and losses (L) for a tournament with n participants.

Game 1

	P_1	P_2	P_3	...	P_n
P_1					
P_2					
P_3					
...					
P_n					

Game 2

   a. How many cells should your table have?

   b. How many cells in the table will not be used? Explain.

   c. Use your answers from parts (a) and (b) to write an expression for the total number of games played.

   d. Compare your expressions for the total number of games played in Exercises 14(b) and 15(c).

Solve each equation for x without using a table or a graph.

16. $(x - 4)(x + 3) = 0$

17. $x^2 + 4x = 0$

18. $x^2 + 9x + 20 = 0$

19. $x^2 + 7x - 8 = 0$

20. $x^2 - 11x + 10 = 0$

21. $x^2 - 6x - 27 = 0$

22. $x^2 - 25 = 0$

23. $x^2 - 100 = 0$

24. $2x^2 + 3x + 1 = 0$

25. $3x^2 + 10x + 8 = 0$

Notes _____

_____

_____

For Exercises 26–29, answer parts (a) and (b) below.

    a. Write two different but equivalent expressions for each situation. Show that the expressions are equivalent.

    b. Write a problem that can be solved by substituting a value into your expressions. Then solve your problem.

26. Suppose you go on an 8-hour car trip. For the first 6 hours, you travel at an average rate of r miles per hour on the highway. For the last 2 hours, you travel at an average rate of 30 mph slower in the city. Find the distance traveled.

27. A bag contains only dimes and quarters. The bag has 1,000 coins. Find the amount of money in the bag.

28. The length of a rectangular pool is 4 feet longer than twice the width. Find the area of the pool.

29. For a concert, there are x reserved and $(4,000 - x)$ general tickets. Find the amount of money collected for the concert given the prices below.

30. The height of a ball (in feet) t seconds after it is thrown is $h = -16t^2 + 48t$. Find parts (a)–(c) without using a table or graph.

    a. the height of the ball after 2 seconds

    b. the maximum height of the ball

    c. the total time the ball is in the air

    d. How could you use a table or graph to answer parts (a)–(c)? Explain.

Notes _____

_____

_____

For each expression, write an equation of the form *y = expression*.
Determine whether the two expressions are equivalent.

    a. with a table and graph

    b. without a table or graph

31. $9x - 5(x - 3) - 20$ and $5 - 4x$

32. $(10x - 5) - (4x + 2)$ and $10x - 5 - 4x + 2$

For Exercises 33–37, complete each table. Decide whether the
relationship is linear, quadratic, exponential, or none of these.

33.

x	−7	−5	−3	5
y = 4(x − 7) + 6	■	■	■	■

34.

x	−7	−5	−3	5
y = −3 − 7(x + 9)	■	■	■	■

35.

x	−7	−5	−3	5
y = 2(3)^x	■	■	■	■

36.

x	−7	−5	−3	5
y = 3x² − x − 1	■	■	■	■

37.

x	−7	−5	−3	5
y = 5(x − 2)(x + 3)	■	■	■	■

38. For Exercises 33 and 34, write an equivalent expression for *y* that
would make the calculations easier.

Notes

39. Study the pattern in each table. Write an equation for those that are linear, exponential, or quadratic. Otherwise, write *none of these*.

Table 1

x	y
−2	15
0	9
2	3
3	0
4	−3

Table 2

x	y
0	−16
1	−15
2	−12
3	−7
4	0

Table 3

x	y
−2	2
−1	1
0	0
1	1
2	2

Table 4

x	y
0	3
1	12
2	48
3	192
4	768

Table 5

x	y
1	4
2	2
3	$\frac{4}{3}$
4	1
5	$\frac{4}{5}$

40. Suppose triangle *ABC* is a right triangle and the lengths of its two legs are integers.

a. Can the perimeter be a rational number? If so, give an example. If not, justify why it cannot be a rational number.

b. Can the perimeter be an irrational number? If so, give an example. If not, justify why it cannot be an irrational number.

41. A 30-60-90 triangle has a hypotenuse that is an integer.

a. Can the perimeter be a rational number? If so, give an example. If not, justify why it cannot be a rational number.

b. Can the perimeter be an irrational number? If so, give an example. If not, justify why it cannot be an irrational number.

Extensions

42. a. Find the next statement for the following pattern.

$$1^2 + 2^2 = 3^2 - 2^2$$
$$2^2 + 3^2 = 7^2 - 6^2$$
$$3^2 + 4^2 = 13^2 - 12^2$$
$$4^2 + 5^2 = 21^2 - 20^2$$

b. Make a conjecture about these statements.

c. Show that your conjecture is correct.

Notes

43. For many years, mathematicians have been looking for a way to generate prime numbers. One of their proposed rules follows.

$$P = n^2 - n + 41$$

The rule suggests that if n is a whole number, then $n^2 - n + 41$ is a prime number.

George claims the rule is not true because he tested it for several values of n and found one that did not yield a prime number.

a. Test the rule for several values of n. Is each result prime?

b. Is George correct? Explain.

44. Find an example for each conjecture.

a. The sum of two irrational numbers is an integer.

b. The sum of two irrational numbers is rational, but not an integer.

c. The sum of two irrational numbers is irrational.

45. Look at several numbers that are divisible by 3. What patterns do you notice among these numbers that can help you determine whether a number is divisible by 3? Explain.

46. Look at several numbers that are divisible by 6. What patterns do you notice among these numbers that can help you determine whether a number is divisible by 6? Explain.

47. Judy thinks she knows a quick way to square any number whose last digit is 5. For example, 25 squared is 625.

> **Example: 25**
>
> • Look at the digit to the left of 5. Multiply it by the number that is one greater than it. (Example: 2 x 3 = 6)
>
> • Write the product followed by 25. This is equal to the square of the number. (Example: 625 = 25²)

a. Try this squaring method on two other numbers that end in 5.

b. Explain why this method works.

Notes _____

_____

_____

Mathematical Reflections 5

In this Investigation, you made conjectures about patterns that you observed and represented these conjectures in symbolic statements. You also found ways to show that your conjectures were valid. The following questions will help you summarize what you have learned.

Think about these questions. Discuss your ideas with other students and your teacher. Then write a summary of your findings in your notebook.

1. **Describe** how and why you could use symbolic statements to represent relationships and conjectures.

2. **Describe** how you can show that your conjectures are correct.

Notes _____

_____

Common Core Mathematical Practices

As you worked on the Problems in this Investigation, you used prior knowledge to make sense of them. You also applied Mathematical Practices to solve the Problems. Think back over your work, the ways you thought about the Problems, and how you used Mathematical Practices.

Shawna described her thoughts in the following way:

The number puzzle in Problem 5.1 was cool. We used algebraic statements for each step to show why the puzzle worked. We also had to use our knowledge of place value to interpret some of the steps, particularly the last one, which solved the mystery.

Common Core Standards for Mathematical Practices
MP2 Reason abstractly and quantitatively.

- What other Mathematical Practices can you identify in Shawna's reasoning?

- Describe a Mathematical Practice that you and your classmates used to solve a different Problem in this Investigation.

Notes

In this Unit, you learned and practiced the standard rules for writing and interpreting symbolic expressions in algebra. You used properties of numbers and operations to write algebraic expressions in equivalent forms and to solve linear and quadratic equations with algebraic reasoning. You also identified which function to use to solve a problem.

Use Your Understanding: Symbols

Test your understanding and skill in the use of algebraic notation and reasoning by solving these problems about managing a concert tour.

The promoter pays appearance fees to each group on the concert program. Some groups also get a portion of the ticket sales.

- The lead group earns $15,000, plus $5 for every ticket sold.
- The second group earns $1,500, plus $1.50 for every ticket sold.
- The third group earns $1,250 flat.

1. For parts (a)–(c), use E for the promoter's expenses and t for the number of tickets sold.

   a. Write an equation to show payments to each group.

   b. Write an equation to show payment to the lead group and the combined payments to the other groups.

   c. Write an equivalent equation different from parts (a) and (b) to show the simplest calculation of the total amount paid to the performers.

2. Tickets cost $25, $30, and $40.

   a. Write an equation that shows how the promoter's income from ticket sales I depends on the number of each type of ticket sold x, y, and z.

   b. The promoter sells 5,000 tickets at $25, 3,000 tickets at $30, and 950 tickets at $40. Find the average income for each ticket.

   c. Write an equation that shows how the average income for each ticket sold V depends on the variables x, y, z, and t.

Notes _____

3. Square tiles were used to make the pattern below.

a. Write an equation for the number of tiles T needed to make the nth figure. Explain.

b. Find an equivalent expression for the number of tiles in part (a). Explain why they are equivalent.

c. Write an equation for the perimeter P of the nth figure.

d. Identify and describe the figure in the pattern that can be made with exactly 420 tiles.

e. Describe the relationship represented by the equations in parts (a) and (c). Do any of these represent linear, exponential, or quadratic functions? Explain.

4. A company packages its three beverages in containers of different shapes: a cylinder, a cone, and a sphere. Mary compares the costs of the drinks. She arranges the data in a table. Which drink is the best buy? Explain.

Beverage Containers

Shape	Cylinder	Cone	Sphere
Height	6 in.	10 in.	6 in.
Diameter	4 in.	6 in.	6 in.
Cost	$1.25	$1.40	$1.30

Explain Your Reasoning

When you solve problems by writing and operating on symbolic expressions, you should be able to explain your reasoning.

5. How can writing two different equivalent expressions for a situation be helpful?

6. How can solving a linear or quadratic equation be helpful?

7. How can a symbolic statement be helpful in expressing a general relationship or conjecture?

Notes

English / Spanish Glossary

C **Commutative Property of Addition** A mathematical property that states that the order in which quantities are added does not matter. It states that $a + b = b + a$ for any two real numbers a and b. For example, $5 + 7 = 7 + 5$ and $2x + 4 = 4 + 2x$.

propiedad conmutativa de la suma Una propiedad matemática que establece que el orden en que se suman las cantidades no tiene importancia. Esta propiedad establece que para dos números reales cualesquiera a y b, $a + b = b + a$. Por ejemplo, $5 + 7 = 7 + 5$ y $2x + 4 = 4 + 2x$.

Commutative Property of Multiplication A mathematical property that states that the order in which quantities are multiplied does not matter. It states that $ab = ba$ for any two real numbers a and b. For example, $5 \times 7 = 7 \times 5$ and $2x(4) = (4)2x$.

propiedad conmutativa de la multiplicación Una propiedad matemática que establece que el orden en que se multiplican los factores no tiene importancia. Esta propiedad establece que para dos números reales cualesquiera a y b, $ab = ba$. Por ejemplo, $5 \times 7 = 7 \times 5$ y $2x(4) = (4)2x$.

D **describe** Academic Vocabulary To explain or tell in detail. A written description can contain facts and other information needed to communicate your answer. A diagram or a graph may also be included.

related terms *express, explain, illustrate*

sample Without graphing, describe the shape of the graph of the equation $y = 2x^2 + 1$.

describir Vocabulario académico Explicar o decir con detalle. Una descripción escrita puede contener datos y otra información necesaria para comunicar tu respuesta. También se puede incluir un diagrama o una gráfica.

términos relacionados *expresar, explicar, ilustrar*

ejemplo Sin hacer una gráfica, describe la forma de la gráfica de la ecuación $y = 2x^2 + 1$.

The equation is quadratic, so the graph is a parabola. The graph opens upward because 2 is positive. It is narrower than the graph of $y = x^2$ because the absolute value of 2 is greater than 1.

La ecuación es cuadrática, por tanto la gráfica es una parábola. La gráfica se abre hacia arriba porque 2 es positivo. Es más estrecha que la gráfica de $y = x^2$ porque el valor absoluto de 2 es mayor que 1.

Notes _____

Distributive Property A mathematical property used to rewrite expressions involving addition and multiplication. The Distributive Property states that for any three real numbers a, b, and c, $a(b + c) = ab + ac$. If an expression is written as a factor multiplied by a sum, you can use the Distributive Property to *multiply* the factor by each term in the sum.

$$4(5 + x) = 4(5) + 4(x) = 20 + 4x$$

If an expression is written as a sum of terms and the terms have a common factor, you can use the Distributive Property to rewrite the expression as the common factor multiplied by a sum. This process is called *factoring*.

$$20 + 4x = 4(5) + 4(x) = 4(5 + x)$$

propiedad distributiva Una propiedad matemática que se usa para volver a escribir expresiones que incluyen la suma y la multiplicación. La propiedad distributiva establece que para tres números reales cualesquiera a, b y c, $a(b + c) = ab + ac$. Si una expresión está escrita como un factor multiplicado por una suma, se puede usar la propiedad distributiva para *multiplicar* el factor por cada término de la suma.

$$4(5 + x) = 4(5) + 4(x) = 20 + 4x$$

Si una expresión se escribe como una suma de términos y los términos tienen un factor común, se puede usar la propiedad distributiva para volver a escribir la expresión como el factor común multiplicado por una suma. Este proceso se llama *descomponer en factores*.

$$20 + 4x = 4(5) + 4(x) = 4(5 + x)$$

E **equivalent expressions** Expressions that represent the same quantity. For example, $2 + 5$, $3 + 4$, and 7 are equivalent expressions. You can apply the Distributive Property to $2(x + 3)$ to write the equivalent expression $2x + 6$. You can apply the Commutative Property to $2x + 6$ to write the equivalent expression $6 + 2x$.

expresiones equivalentes Expresiones que representan la misma cantidad. Por ejemplo, $2 + 5$, $3 + 4$ y 7 son expresiones equivalentes. Puedes aplicar la propiedad distributiva a $2(x + 3)$ para escribir la expresión equivalente $2x + 6$. Puedes aplicar la propiedad conmutativa a $2x + 6$ para escribir la expresión equivalente $6 + 2x$.

Notes _____

estimate Academic Vocabulary
To find an approximate answer.

related terms *guess, predict*

sample A partial net of a cone is shown below. Estimate the lateral surface area of the cone.

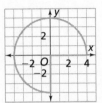

I can count the number of unit squares. The net has three equal sections. I estimate one of the sections to be about 13 square units, so the total is about 39 square units.

Hacer una estimación Vocabulario académico Hallar una respuesta aproximada.

términos relacionados *suponer, predecir*

ejemplo A continuación se muestra el modelo plano parcial de un cono. Estima el área total lateral del cono.

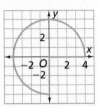

Puedo contar el número de unidades cuadradas. El modelo plano tiene tres secciones iguales. Estimo que una de las secciones tiene aproximadamente 13 unidades cuadradas, por tanto, el total es aproximadamente 39 unidades cuadradas.

expanded form The form of an expression made up of sums or differences of terms rather than products of factors. The expressions $x^2 + 7x + 12$ and $x^2 + 2x$ are in expanded form.

forma desarrollada La forma de una expresión compuesta de sumas o diferencias de términos en vez de productos de factores. Las expresiones $x^2 + 7x + 12$ y $x^2 + 2x$ están representadas en forma desarrollada.

Notes _____

_____

explain Academic Vocabulary
To give facts and details that make an idea easier to understand. Explaining can involve a written summary supported by a diagram, chart, table, or a combination of these.

related terms *analyze, clarify, describe, justify, tell*

sample The equation shows the relationship between the number of gallons g of water in a tank and the number of minutes m a shower is on.

$$g = 50 - 2.5m$$

How many gallons of water are in a full tank before the shower begins? Explain.

I can substitute 0 into the equation for the number of minutes m and solve for g.
$g = 50 - 2.5m$
$g = 50 - 2.5(0)$
$g = 50$
There are 50 gallons in a full tank.

explicar Vocabulario académico
Dar hechos y detalles que hacen que una idea sea más fácil de comprender. Explicar puede incluir un resumen escrito apoyado por un diagrama, una gráfica, una tabla o una combinación de estos.

términos relacionados *analizar, aclarar, describir, justificar, decir*

ejemplo La ecuación muestra la relación entre el número de galones g de agua en un tanque y el número de minutos m que una ducha ha estado funcionando.

$$g = 50 - 2.5m$$

¿Cuántos galones de agua hay en un tanque lleno antes de que comience la ducha? Explícalo.

Puedo sustituir 0 en la ecuación para el número de minutos m y resolver para g.
$g = 50 - 2.5m$
$g = 50 - 2.5(0)$
$g = 50$
Hay 50 galones en un tanque lleno.

F **factored form** The form of an expression made up of products of factors rather than sums or differences of terms. The expressions $(x + 3)(x + 4)$ and $x(x + 2)$ are in factored form.

forma factorizada Una expresión compuesta de productos de factores, en vez de sumas o diferencias de términos. Las expresiones $(x + 3)(x + 4)$ y $x(x + 2)$ están representadas en forma factorizada.

P **properties of equality** The properties of equality state that if you add or subtract the same quantity from each side of an equation, the two sides of the equation remain equal. If you multiply or divide each side of an equation by the same nonzero quantity, the two sides of the equation remain equal.

propiedades de la igualdad Las propiedades de la igualdad establecen que si se suma o resta la misma cantidad a ambos lados de una ecuación, los dos lados de la ecuación se mantienen iguales. Si se multiplica o divide ambos lados de una ecuación por el mismo número distinto de cero, los dos lados de la ecuación se mantienen iguales.

Notes

R **roots** The roots of a two-variable equation are the values of x that make y equal 0. For example, the roots of $y = x^2 + 5x$ are -5 and 0 because $(-5)^2 + 5(-5) = 0$ and $0^2 + 5(0) = 0$. The roots of $y = x^2 + 5x$ are the solutions to the equation $0 = x^2 + 5x$. The roots of a two-variable equation are the x-intercepts of its graph.

raíces Las raíces de una ecuación de dos variables son los valores de x que hacen que y sea igual a 0. Por ejemplo, las raíces de $y = x^2 + 5x$ son -5 y 0 porque $(-5)^2 + 5(-5) = 0$ y $0^2 + 5(0) = 0$. Las raíces de $y = x^2 + 5x$ son las soluciones de la ecuación $0 = x^2 + 5x$. Las raíces de una ecuación de dos variables son los interceptos en x de su gráfica.

S **solve** Academic Vocabulary
To determine the value or values that make a given statement true. Several methods and strategies can be used to solve a problem including estimating, isolating the variable, drawing a graph, or using a table of values.

related terms *find, graph*

sample Solve the equation $0 = x^2 + 6x - 7$ for x.

resolver Vocabulario académico
Determinar el valor o valores que hacen verdadero un enunciado. Se pueden usar varios métodos o estrategias para resolver un problema, entre ellos la estimación, aislar la variable, hacer una gráfica o usar una tabla de valores.

términos relacionados *hallar, hacer una gráfica*

ejemplo Resuelve la ecuación $0 = x^2 + 6x - 7$ para x.

The equation is quadratic. I can solve the equation by factoring the right side of the equation into two factors and setting each factor equal to zero.
$0 = x^2 + 6x - 7$
$0 = (x + 7)(x - 1)$
$(-7, 0)$ $(1, 0)$
$x + 7 = 0$ or $x - 1 = 0$
   $x = -7$ or $x = 1$
I can also solve the quadratic by graphing and identifying the x-intercepts at $(-7, 0)$ and $(1, 0)$.

La ecuación es cuadrática. Puedo resolver la ecuación descomponiendo en factores el lado derecho de la ecuación en dos factores y estableciendo cada factor igual a cero.
$0 = x^2 + 6x - 7$
$(-7, 0)$
$0 = (x + 7)(x - 1)$
$(1, 0)$
$x + 7 = 0$ or $x - 1 = 0$
   $x = -7$ or $x = 1$
También puedo resolver la ecuación cuadrática al hacer una gráfica e identificar los interceptos en x en $(-7, 0)$ y $(1, 0)$.

English / Spanish Glossary

END MATTER

STUDENT PAGE

Notes

Index

ACE
  combining expressions, 34–43
  equivalent expressions, 15–24
  functions, 72–87
  reasoning with symbols, 95–102
  solving equations, 55–63

addition and subtraction, 27–28, 44, 47

algebra, solving puzzles with, 90–91, 95, 104

algebraic expressions, 91, 107

algebraic reasoning, 4, 107

area and perimeter
  algebraic expressions and, 37
  determining equivalence, 10
  equations and, 24, 68, 108
  equivalent expressions and, 8–9, 13, 15–17, 19, 20, 21
  finding, 61
  functions and, 70, 76, 89
  interpreting symbolic expressions and, 10–11
  rational and irrational numbers and, 101
  reasoning with symbols and, 99
  rectangles, 74
  surface area, 83

area models, 50, 52, 59, 82

Ask Yourself, 4

circles, 61

Common Core Mathematical Practices, 5–6, 26, 45, 65, 89, 104

commutative properties
  Distributive Property and, 18

equivalent expressions and, 13, 14, 25
expressions and, 97
solving equations and, 47, 60

Commutative Property of Addition, 109

Commutative Property of Multiplication, 109

cones, 31–32, 33, 36, 43, 44, 108. *See also* cylinders, cones, and spheres

conjectures
  about patterns, 103
  odd and even numbers, 91, 92, 93, 95
  patterns and, 101
  products of whole numbers, 96
  rational and irrational numbers, 102
  squaring odd numbers, 94
  symbolic reasoning and, 4, 108

coordinate grids, 63, 80, 85, 86

cost data
  equations and, 86
  equivalent expressions and, 23
  modeling with functions, 70
  solving equations and, 48–49, 57, 60
  substituting expressions, 29–30

cube buildings, 97

cubic functions, 70

cylinders, cones, and spheres
  faces of, 43
  income and expense data, 108
  volume of, 31–32, 33, 36, 37–38, 44, 61, 70, 83, 85

data points, equations and, 69

differences, 21, 93

distance, finding, 84

Distributive Property
  defined, 110
  equivalent expressions, 12–14, 18, 25, 39, 47
  expressions and, 97
  multiplication and, 82
  solving equations and, 60

division, whole numbers, 96, 102

equations
  area and perimeter, 17, 24
  combining expressions, 44
  finding surface area and, 105–106
  functions and, 68, 70, 77, 78, 82
  income and expense data, 34, 35, 36, 40, 107
  patterns and, 72–73, 80–81, 108
  properties of equality, 41
  reasoning with symbols and, 98
  relationships among variables, 3
  speed and distance data, 87
  substituting expressions, 29–30
  tables and graphs and, 39, 87
  time, rate, and distance, 84
  writing equivalent expressions, 9, 10, 84

equations, solving
  ACE, 55–63
  factoring quadratic equations, 50–52
  linear equations, 46–49
  Mathematical Reflections, 64–65
  solving quadratic equations, 52–54

Notes

Notes

Notes

Notes _____

Notes

Acknowledgments

Cover Design

Three Communication Design, Chicago

Text

National Football League
030, 086 "*National Football League Passer Rating Formula*" from WWW.NFL.COM.
Used by permission.

Photographs

Photo locators denoted as follows: Top (T), Center (C), Bottom (B), Left (L),
Right (R), Background (Bkgd)

002 Dennis MacDonald/PhotoEdit; **003** Leonid Serebrennikov/Alamy;
053 Dennis MacDonald/PhotoEdit; **054** The Art Gallery Collection/Alamy;
084 Dr. Gary Gaugler/Science Source.

Notes _____

_____

_____

END MATTER

STUDENT PAGE

Notes

Say It With Symbols   **Acknowledgments**

1.1 Tiling Pools: Writing Equivalent Expressions

> **Focus Question** What expression(s) represents the number of border tiles needed to surround a square pool with side length *s*?

Launch

Pose the situation and questions concerning the two different expressions for the perimeter of a rectangle. Ask students to justify why both expressions for the rectangle's perimeter, $2(L + W)$ and $2L + 2W$, are correct and why Alberto used parentheses in his equation. Students may offer examples or talk generally about the dimensions and perimeter of any rectangle.

If necessary, direct the conversation to focus on the method each expression represents.

- *Describe the method each student is using to compute the perimeter.*
- *Could Alberto have written $2L + W$?*
- *Are $3(x + 5)$ and $3x + 5$ equivalent? Explain.*

Remind students that these expressions for the perimeter of a rectangle, $2(L + W)$ and $2L + 2W$, are equivalent expressions.

> **Key Vocabulary**
> - equivalent expressions
>
> **Materials**
>
> **Labsheet**
> - 1.1: Pool Problem
>
> **Teaching Aid**
> - 1.1: Tiling Pools
> - unit squares or tiles (optional)

Explore

Having students articulate how they visualize the situation will help them to make the transition to interpreting the reasoning represented by the symbols. Different ways of reasoning about the Problem lead to different strategies, which in turn result in different equations. Encourage students to find more than one way to reason about the situation. (Problem 1.2 presents several ways of thinking about this situation, some of which your students will discover.)

Look for interesting ways that students are thinking about the Problem. Also look for the interesting ways they show that two expressions for the number of border tiles are equivalent.

Summarize

Have the class examine the posters from each pair of students and then allow them time to ask questions about each piece of work.

For each equation, ask the class:

- *Can you explain the reasoning that was used to arrive at this equation?*
- *How do the parts of the equation relate to the elements of the Problem?*

Be sure to look at tables and graphs for the equations that are generated in class.

ACE

Assignment Guide for Problem 1.1

Applications: 1, 2 | Connections: 18–24

Answers to Problem 1.1

A. 1. One possible answer: You could add the number of tiles needed for each side to the four tiles in the corner. One possible expression: $s + s + s + s + 4$. See the Summarize for more examples.

2. One possible answer: You could double the number of tiles needed for a side plus two corner tiles, and add that answer to the number of tiles needed for the two remaining sides. One possible expression: $s + 2 + s + 2 + s + s$.

3. One possible answer: These expressions are equivalent because they both represent the same number of side and corner tiles.

B. 1. A table and graph for $N = s + s + s + s + 4$ and for $N = s + 2 + s + 2 + s + s$ is shown. The graphs and tables will be the same for all equations (except for graph scales and specific table entries).

2. Because the table and the graph are the same for each equation, it appears that the expressions are equivalent.

s	1	2	3	4	5	6	7	8	9
N	8	12	16	20	24	28	32	36	40

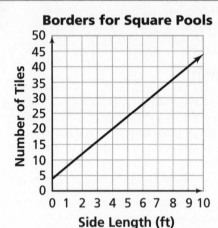

Borders for Square Pools

C. One possible answer: The relationship between the side length of the pool and the border tiles is linear because the graph is straight line, and in the table you can see that the side length of the pool and the number of tiles increase at a constant rate.

At a Glance   Problem 1.2   Pacing 1 Day

1.2 Thinking in Different Ways: Determining Equivalence

> *Focus Question* How can you determine if two or more expressions are equivalent?

Launch

Some of this Problem may have been discussed in the Summarize of Problem 1.1. If so, have students use the equations for the number of border tiles from ACE Exercise 4, or direct the students to Question B of this Problem.

- *If a pair of values for (s, N) such as (4, 20) satisfies two different expressions, are the expressions equivalent?*

If your students didn't discuss the equations in Question A, ask them about Takashi's picture of $N = 4s + 4$.

- *What equation do you think Takashi wrote to relate N and s?*

Explain to students that they will be drawing pictures to illustrate the thought process behind these equations.

Materials

Materials

Accessibility Labsheet
- 1ACE: Exercise 3

Explore

Encourage students to think about whether checking one value of s for two expressions is sufficient to show equivalence.

- *How many values do you need to try before you are convinced that the two expressions are equivalent?*

Some students may try to find other expressions. Keep these in mind and use them during the Summarize to test various conjectures that occur.

Summarize

Notice that Hank's expression is not equivalent to Takashi's.

- *Is one value enough to check in order to prove that two expressions are equivalent?*

If students say yes, then write $N = 2s + 1$ and $N = s + 2$ on the board.

- *Find N if s = 1. Find N if s = 3.*

Write two more expressions on the board: $N = 4(s + 2) - 4$ and $N = 4(s + 1)$.

- *Suppose you try two values of s, and the N-value is the same in both cases. Is this sufficient to show that two expressions are equivalent? Suppose you try s = 5 and s = 10.*

- *So if you know that two distinct points, (5, 24) and (10, 44), lie on the graphs of two linear equations, what can you say about the graphs?*

Answers to Problem 1.2

Note: Students' illustrations and ideas will vary. If all or most of these expressions arose in the discussion of Problem 1.1, you may want to encourage students to use their intuitive sense of the Distributive Property to show that the expressions are equivalent.

A. 1.

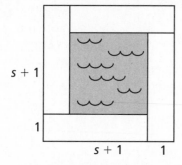

$$N = 4\left(1 \quad \boxed{} \atop s+1\right)$$

2.

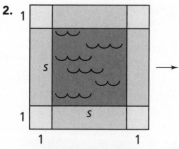

3. See Takashi's sketch. This equation is not correct since the corner tiles are all counted twice.

4.

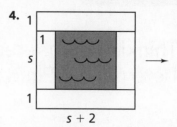

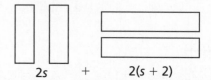

$$2s \quad + \quad 2(s+2)$$

B. Stella's, Jeri's, and Sal's expressions yield the same result of 44 for $s = 10$. It is possible that the expressions are all equivalent, but you cannot conclude this from checking one value. (See discussion above in the Summarize). Hank's expression is not equivalent to the other three because it yields a result of 48 for $s = 10$.

C. Students may use geometric reasoning and say that Stella's, Jeri's, and Sal's expressions are equivalent to the expression represented by Takashi's sketch because the expressions all represent the 4 sides of the pool and the 4 corner tiles. Hank's is not equivalent because he counted all of the corners twice. Students may also use tables, graphs, or symbol manipulation to explain their ideas about the equivalences. The graphs and tables of Stella's, Jeri's, and Sal's expressions are the same, which supports the idea that the expressions are all equivalent.

s	1	2	3	4	5	6	7	8	9	10
N	8	12	16	20	24	28	32	36	40	44

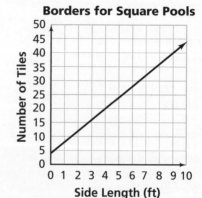

Borders for Square Pools

1.3 The Community Pool Problem: Interpreting Expressions

> *Focus Question* What information does an expression represent in a given context?

Launch

Display Teaching Aid 1.3 and distribute Labsheet 1.3. You might ask students to describe the shape of the indoor part of the pool. Be sure that they know that the outdoor part of the pool is not shown.

Explore

Students should be comfortable with the area of a circle. If not, ask another student for the formula and why this formula works.

- *What are the dimensions of the rectangle?*
- *What is the something else? How can you find it? Draw the missing dimension.*

For Question C, if students are struggling with the interpretation, ask:

- *How are $\frac{\pi x^2}{8}$ and $\frac{\pi x^2}{4}$ related?*

Challenge students to determine the type of relationship that the equation for the area represents.

- *Does the equation for the area of the pool represent a linear, exponential, or quadratic relationship, or none of these?*

Summarize

Go over Questions A and B. For the outdoor pool, some students might represent x^2 as a square, and others might represent it as a rectangle with dimensions $\frac{x}{2}$ and $2x$. Some will add a quarter of a circle to the square or rectangle. Others may split the quarter circle into two equal eighths of a circle.

- *Describe how each shape might be useful for different water activities.*

For Question C, allow students time to discuss why certain expressions are equivalent for the outside part of the pool. Introduce two ways of thinking about the outside pool design, which may or may not have been addressed already.

- *How might Stella and Jeri have drawn the outdoor part of the pool? How do you know that their expressions are equivalent to the original expression for the outside of the pool?*

> ### Materials
>
> **Labsheet**
> - 1.3: The Community Pool Problem
>
> **Teaching Aid**
> - 1.3: The Community Pool Problem

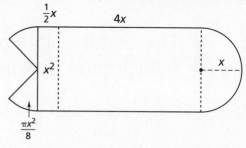

$$\frac{\pi x^2}{8}$$

Assignment Guide for Problem 1.3

Applications: 5, 6 | Connections: 35–52
Extensions: 59

Answers to Problem 1.3

A. 1. Area of indoor part: $\frac{\pi x^2}{2} + 8x^2$. The area of the indoor part is the area of a half circle with radius x plus a rectangle with length $4x$ and width $x + x = 2x$ (since the diameter of the circle is the width of the rectangle). So the area of the indoor part of the pool is $\frac{1}{2}(\pi x^2) + (4x)(2x) = \frac{\pi x^2}{2} + 8x^2$.

2. Area of outdoor part: $x^2 + \frac{\pi x^2}{4}$. The area of the outside part is what is left over when you subtract the indoor parts.

B. 1. Answers will vary. Here are some possible student drawings for the entire pool:

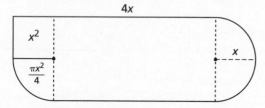

Another possibility: From the diagram above, evenly split the quarter of the circle and move the portions to the left and right of the square.

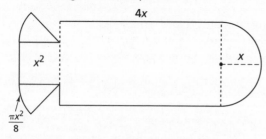

Another possibility: Draw a rectangle with dimensions $\frac{1}{2}$ by $2x$. Then, draw two eighths of a circle to match the $2x$ dimension of the rectangle.

2. Answers will vary. Some students may think that their drawing in part (1) is the only one. Some may think that there is another one but cannot draw it. For possible student pictures see part (1).

C. 1. Stella probably had a square piece with a side length of x and two eighth-of-a-circle pieces for the outside of the pool, since the outside of the pool is represented by $A = x^2 + \frac{\pi x^2}{4}$, which is the original equation. Stella may have pictured the second pool in Question B, part (1). Jeri may have been picturing a pool similar to the third pool in Question B, part (1). However, this expression combines the two eighths shown in the third pool into a quarter circle to account for the $\frac{\pi x^2}{4}$ part of the expression, and the $\left(\frac{1}{2}x\right)(2x)$ is represented by the rectangle with width and length $\left(\frac{1}{2}x\right)$ and $2x$.

2. The expressions are equivalent. Students may use a table or graphing calculator to show that they are equivalent. If students check points to show equivalence, they must check three points in each expression. This is because the expressions are quadratic and three points determine a unique quadratic equation. This is discussed more in the Teacher's Guide for Investigation 4. Students also may reason using the picture since the expressions both represent the same area, or symbolically by giving reasoning like $\frac{\pi x^2}{8}$ plus $\frac{\pi x^2}{8}$ is $\frac{2\pi x^2}{8}$, which is equal to $\frac{\pi x^2}{4}$.

D. Quadratic; the area of the pool represents a quadratic relationship because the equation for area has the highest power of x appearing as 2.

At a Glance   Problem 1.4   Pacing 1 Day

1.4 Diving In: Revisiting the Distributive Property

Focus Question How can you use the distributive and commutative properties to show that two expressions are equivalent?

Launch

Display Teaching Aid 1.4: Different Dimensions and review the Distributive Property. If your students have studied the Grade 8 Unit *Frogs, Fleas, and Painted Cubes*, this should be a brief discussion.

- *Find two equivalent expressions for the area of each rectangle.*
- *Explain how these illustrate the Distributive Property.*
- *Describe how you can use the Distributive Property to show that two expressions are equivalent.*

You may want to write the Distributive Property and the Commutative Property for Addition and Multiplication on the board. Ask the class to give examples of each.

Tell students that they will be using the distributive and commutative properties to rewrite expressions. They will also use the properties to determine whether two expressions are equivalent, including some of the expressions from Problem 1.2.

Explore

Look for students who need a further discussion on the distributive and commutative properties. This is an opportunity for you to assess their level of understanding.

After the groups complete Questions A and B, have a class discussion on strategies for using the properties. It is important that throughout this Unit you continue to make sure that students are using the Distributive Property correctly in the Explore. Have students work on the rest of the Problem.

For Question C, ask:

- *What is an equivalent expression for $(s + 2)^2$?*

While students are working on Question C, this is a good opportunity to remind students about the Order of Operations.

- *What is the order of steps that correctly simplifies Sal's expression $2s + 2(s + 2)$?*

Make sure that students understand the directions for Question E. Explain that you must place the parentheses before simplifying the expression to the left of the equal sign.

Key Vocabulary

- Commutative Property of Addition
- Commutative Property of Multiplication
- Distributive Property
- expanded form
- factored form

Materials

Teaching Aid
- 1.4: Different Dimensions

Assessment
- Check Up 1

Summarize

Go over Questions C–E. For Question C, you could include other equations that occurred in your class for Problem 1.1 to check students' understanding.

For Question D, if students do not use linearity in their answer, ask:

- *Suppose you set y equal to one of the expressions. What relationship does each equation (or expression) represent?*
- *What must be true about equivalent linear expressions?*
- *How could you use this information to show which linear expression is not equivalent?*

After students have shared their reasoning for Question E, challenge them to find another way to write the expression $6p + 2 - 2p$ using parentheses and to give a different resulting expression. Ask students to share their final expression and have the rest of the class guess how they placed the parentheses. For example, a student may give $12 - 6p$. For this result, the parentheses would have to occur as follows: $6(p + 2 - 2p)$.

(A)(C)(E)
Assignment Guide for Problem 1.4

Applications: 7–17 | Connections: 53–57
Extensions: 60

Answers to Problem 1.4

A. 1. $3x + 15$

   2. $6x - 20$

   3. $2x^2 + 10x$

   4. $x^2 + 2x + 5x + 10$, or $x^2 + 7x + 10$

B. 1. $12(1 + 2x)$

   2. $3(x + 2)$, because $x + x + x + 6 = x(1 + 1 + 1) + 6 = 3x + 6$, and the factored form is $3(x + 2)$.

   3. $x(x + 3)$

   4. $(x + 3)(x + 1)$

C. $4(s + 1) = 4s + 4$

$s + s + s + s + 4 = s(1 + 1 + 1 + 1) + 4 = s(4) + 4 = 4s + 4$

You may have to remind students that $s = 1s$. Students may also reason that $s + s + s + s$ is the same as taking s four times or $4 \times s$.

$2s + 2(s + 2) = 2s + 2s + 4 = (2 + 2)s + 4 = 4s + 4$

$4(s + 2) - 4 = 4s + 8 - 4 = 4s + 4$

$(s + 2)^2 - s^2 = s^2 + 4s + 4 - s^2 = s^2 - s^2 + 4s + 4 = 4s + 4$

$2(2(s + 2) - 2) = 4(s + 2) - 4 = 4s + 8 - 4 = 4s + 4$

There are different ways students could do this, such as

$2(2s + 4 - 2) = 2(2s + 2) = 4s + 4.$

D. Expression 2; $10 - x$ is not equivalent to the other three. For expressions 1, 3 and 4, using the commutative and distributive properties, you find that they all are equivalent to $10 - 10x$:

$2x - 12x + 10 = (2 - 12)x + 10 = -10x + 10 = 10 - 10x$

$10(1 - x) = 10 - 10x$

$\frac{20(-x + 1)}{2} = 10(-x + 1) = 10(1 - x) = 10 - 10x$

Explanations may vary. You could graph all the equations and see if they make the same graph. You could also make a table and see if the entries are different. Another method is to test two values in each expression because all the expressions are linear. If the values of the expressions are different for either of the two values, then the expressions are not equivalent.

E. 1. $6(p + 2) - 2p = 4p + 12$

   2. $6p + (2 - 2)p = 6p$

At a Glance   Problem 2.1   Pacing 1 Day

2.1 Walking Together: Adding Expressions

> **Focus Question** What are the advantages and disadvantages of using one equation rather than two or more equations to represent a situation?

Launch

Remind students about the walkathon from *Moving Straight Ahead*. Write the following information on the board:

Leanne: $10 from each of her sponsors

Gilberto: $2 from each sponsor for each kilometer that he walks

Alana: $5 plus $.50 from each sponsor for each kilometer that she walks

Each student will walk the same number of miles, *x*, but each student has a different number of sponsors: 16 for Leanne, 7 for Gilberto, and 11 for Alana.

- *How could you calculate the total amount of money the three students will collect?*

Using student suggestions, find total amounts for different numbers of kilometers. Have students guide the calculations and justify the steps.

Materials

Accessibility Labsheet
- 2ACE: Exercise 1

- graphing calculators (optional)

Explore

As students write an equation, ask them how they know it is correct. Suggest that they try to use their equation to compute the money for the number of kilometers you used in the Launch. If students have difficulty getting started with Question A, ask:

- *How much will Leanne (Gilberto, Alana) raise per kilometer from each of her (his) sponsors?*
- *How many sponsors does Leanne (Gilberto, Alana) have?*
- *So, how much will she (he) raise for walking x kilometers?*
- *Now, write an expression that shows the total amount for all three.*

For Question B, if students are having trouble, you can ask:

- *What would be an equivalent expression for Alana's total?*

Summarize

Have students share their equations for the total amount that the walkathon team will raise.

- *What ways do you know for checking whether two expressions are equivalent?*
- *Pick one of your expressions to find the total amount the team will raise. Use the expression to find the total amounts if the students walk 5 kilometers and if they walk 8 kilometers.*

At a Glance   **307**

- *What are the advantages and disadvantages of using one expression rather than two or more expressions to represent a situation?*
- *Does the equation for total money raised represent a linear function? How can you tell?*

Write a few expressions on the board. Several of these expressions should be equivalent.

- *Identify the expressions that are equivalent in the list.*

$2x + 3 + 7x$	$9x + 32x + 10x$	$2x(3 + 7x)$	$7x + 2x + 3$
$2x(3 + 7x)$	$2(x + 3) + 7x$	$3(3x + 1)$	

· ·

ⒶⒸⒺ

Assignment Guide for Problem 2.1

Applications: 1–5 | Connections: 17–21
Extensions: 40

Answers to Problem 2.1

A. **1.** $M_{Leanne} = 16(10)$ or 160;
$M_{Gilberto} = 7(2x)$ or $14x$;
$M_{Alana} = 11(5 + 0.50x)$ or $55 + 5.50x$

2. $M_{Total} = 16(10) + 7(2x) + 11(5 + 0.50x)$ or $160 + 14x + 55 + 5.50x$ or some other equivalent form.

Note: The x's in the above equations are the same in this context because all three students walk exactly x kilometers together. If the students had walked different distances, you could not use the same variable x to combine the expressions, since the x's would represent a different amount for each person.

B. **1.** Possible answer. $M_{Total} = 160 + 14x + 55 + 5.50x = 215 + 19.50x$. The new expression is equivalent because it combines the constants 160 and 55 into a single constant, 215, and combines the x terms $14x$ and $5.50x$ into a single term, $19.50x$. Using the Commutative Property of Addition, you can reorder and add the terms. For the x terms, the Distributive Property justifies combining $14x + 5.50x = x(14 + 5.50) = 19.50x$.

2. The 19.50 represents the combined amount of money that Leanne, Gilberto, and Alana make at a per-kilometer rate. Leanne makes $10 for each of 16 sponsors for a total of $160. Gilberto will raise $2 per kilometer from each of his 7 sponsors for a total of $14 per kilometer. Alana will raise $.50 per kilometer from each of her 11 sponsors for a total of $5.50 per kilometer. This results in a total rate of $14 + 5.50 = 19.50$ per kilometer. The 55 is the amount that Alana collected from her 11 sponsors in addition to her 50-cent rate per kilometer.

3. Possible answer: I used the expression from Question B, part (2), because it was the shortest.

C. The relationship between kilometers walked and money raised is linear. Students may reason about this by using a graph or a table, or by noticing that the expression $215 + 19.50x$ that relates kilometers x to money raised y is of the form $y = mx + b$, where $m = 19.50$ is the slope and $b = 215$ is the y-intercept.

2.2 Predicting Profit: Substituting Expressions

> *Focus Question* What are some ways that you can combine one or more expressions (or equations) to create a new expression (or equation)?

Launch

Tell the story about the amusement park. Write the two equations $P = 2.50V - 500$ and $V = 600 - 500R$ on the board.

Materials

• poster paper
• markers
• graphing calculators (optional)

- *What information do the numbers and variables represent in this situation?*

Challenge students to find one equation that will predict the profit based on the probability of rain.

Explore

Question A, part (1) is mostly a review. Check to see whether students are evaluating the expressions using the Distributive Property, the Commutative Property, and the Order of Operations. Make sure that students are using percents correctly. If students are having difficulty writing one equation for profit that is based on the probability of rain, ask:

- *What is the probability of rain?*
- *How can you use the probability to find the number of visitors?*
- *How can you use the number of visitors to find the profit?*

For Questions B and C, distribute poster paper to a few students to display how they found different expressions for profit. Ask them to show why the two expressions for profit are equivalent.

Summarize

Ask students to explain how the expressions for profit are equivalent.

- *Why does $2.50(600 - 500R) - 500 = 1,000 - 1,250R$?*

Talk about the slope and intercept of the equation $P = 1,000 - 1,250R$ and what each means in this context.

- *Describe the relationship that this equation represents.*

Have students share their strategies for Question C, part (2). If no one suggests it, use the new equation $P = 2.50(600 - 500R) - 500$ to demonstrate how to solve the equation for R given a specific value of P, say 600. Review other methods for solving an equation.

- *What is the range for the values of the probability?*
- *What is the range for the profits?*
- *Describe why and how you combined the two equations into one equation.*
- *Compare the work you did in this Problem of creating a new equation to the work in Problem 2.1 for creating new equations.*

Answers to Problem 2.2

A. 1. $687.50; substitute 0.25 for R in the equation $V = 600 - 500R$. Solve for V, and then substitute the value for V into the equation $P = 2.50V - 500$ to find the profit P.

$V = 600 - 500(0.25) = 600 - 125 = 475$;
$P = 2.50(475) - 500 = 1{,}187.50 - 500 = 687.50$

2. 30%; substitute 625 for P and solve for V in the equation $P = 2.50V - 500$. Then substitute the value for V into the equation $V = 600 - 500R$ to find the probability of rain R.

$$625 = 2.50V - 500$$
$$625 + 500 = 2.50V - 500 + 500$$
$$1{,}125 = 2.50V$$
$$V = 450$$
$$450 = 600 - 500R$$
$$450 - 600 = 600 - 500R - 600$$
$$-150 = -500R$$
$$R = \frac{-150}{-500}$$
$$R = 0.30 = 30\%$$

B. 1. $P = 2.50(600 - 500R) - 500$ or any equivalent form.

2. $687.50; for a 25% chance of rain,

$P = 2.50[600 - 500(0.25)] - 500$
$P = 2.50[600 - 125] - 500$
$P = 2.50[475] - 500$
$P = 687.50$

The answer is the same as the one in Question A, part (1).

C. 1. To find an equivalent expression for the profit, you can use the Distributive Property and multiply 2.50 times 600 and 2.50 times $-500R$. Then you combine like terms.

$P = 2.50(600 - 500R) - 500$
$P = 1{,}500 - 1{,}250R - 500$
$P = -1{,}250R + 1000$

The two expressions are equivalent because, to get from one to the other, you use the Distributive Property and the Commutative Property. Students may also compare tables and graph or test two points in both equations to justify equivalence.

2. 30%; using the equation $P = -1{,}250R + 1{,}000$, solve for R when $P = 625$.

$$625 = -1{,}250R + 1{,}000$$
$$625 - 1{,}000 = -1{,}250R + 1{,}000 - 1{,}000$$
$$-375 = -1{,}250R$$

So, $R = \frac{-375}{-1{,}250} = 0.30$, or 30%, which is the same as the answer for Question A, part (2).

3–4. Answers will vary. Students may use either the two equations or their equation from Question B, part (1) or Question C, part (1).

3. 1,000; this is the starting value or y-intercept in the equation $P = -1{,}250R + 1{,}000$. This answer makes sense because, when the probability of rain is 0%, more people should come to the park, which generates more profit than when the probability of rain is 100%.

4. $-$250 or a loss of 250 dollars; substitute 1 (i.e. 100%) for R in the equation $P = -1{,}250R + 1{,}000$. When the probability of rain is 100%, there will not be many visitors to the park, so the park will probably lose money. For this reason, the profit of -250 dollars makes sense.

D. The relationships in Questions B and C are both linear functions. They can both be put into the form of $y = mx + b$, which is the equation of a line. Also they both have constant rates of change between the two variables.

2.3 Making Candles: Volumes of Cylinders, Cones, and Spheres

> *Focus Question* What equations represent the relationships among the volumes of cylinders, cones, and spheres?

Launch

Tell the story about Rocky Middle School and the plans for the charity event. The school plans to make and sell candles that come in three shapes—cylinders, cones, and spheres—at the event. The candles have the same height and radius. The school needs to know how much wax to buy.

- *How can you find the volume of a cylinder?*

Remind students of the experiment that they did in *Filling and Wrapping*, where they created prisms with polygonal bases.

- *How can you find the volume of a prism? Will the same method work for a cylinder?*

Materials

- equal dimension plastic geometric cones, cylinders, and spheres (optional)
- graphing calculators (optional)
- Pouring and Filling

Explore

Encourage students to find several relationships among the three shapes for volume. Using the relationships, ask students to find equivalent expressions for the volumes of the shapes in terms of the dimensions *r* and *h*. Students may use the Distributive and Commutative properties.

Urge them to find an expression that represents the volume of a cone and sphere. For many students, the visual image of using three cones to fill a cylinder helps them to express the volume of a cone as $\frac{1}{3}\pi r^2 h$. You can ask them to write the formula for the volume of a sphere in terms of its radius, $V = \frac{4}{3}\pi r^3$, and justify their reasoning.

Question C provides an opportunity to review ratios since the ratio of the volume of a cone to a sphere to a cylinder is 1 : 2 : 3.

Summarize

Have the groups put up the relationships they found among the shapes. Pick one or two equations and ask the class to write a simpler equivalent equation.

- *The volume of a cylinder minus the volume of a sphere is equal to the volume of a cone. Write a symbolic equation for this statement.*
- *Write a simpler expression for the volume of the cone in this relationship.*
- *How can you use the formula for the volume of a prism to help you recall the formula for the volume of a cylinder?*
- *How can you use the formula for the volume of a cylinder to help you recall the formula for the volume of a cone? A sphere?*

Answers to Problem 2.3

A. **1.** Noah is correct. The volume of a prism is the area of the base × height. The area of the base tells you how many unit cubes fit on the bottom. The height tells you how many layers it takes to fill the prism.

2. Yes; the volume of a cylinder is the area of the base × height, $V = \pi r^2 h$; however, the expression for the base of the cylinder is πr^2, which is different from the expression for the base of the prism. The area of the base tells you how many unit cubes fit on the bottom. The height tells you how many layers it takes to fill the cylinder.

B. **1.** There are several relationships. Some examples are:

The volume of a cone is $\frac{1}{3}$ the volume of a cylinder. $V_{cone} = \frac{1}{3}(\pi r^2 h)$

The volume of a sphere is $\frac{2}{3}$ the volume of a cylinder. $V_{sphere} = \frac{2}{3}(\pi r^2 h)$, or $\frac{4}{3}\pi r^3$

The volume of a cone + the volume of a sphere equals the volume of a cylinder.

$$\tfrac{1}{3}\pi r^2 h + \tfrac{2}{3}\pi r^2 h = \pi r^2 h$$

The volume of a cone is $\frac{1}{2}$ the volume of a sphere.

$$\tfrac{1}{3}\pi r^2 h = \tfrac{1}{2}\left(\tfrac{2}{3}\pi r^2 h\right)$$

The volume of a sphere is 2 times the volume of a cone.

$$\tfrac{2}{3}\pi r^2 h = 2\left(\tfrac{1}{3}\pi r^2 h\right)$$

The volume of a cylinder is 3 times the volume of a cone.

$$\pi r^2 h = 3\left(\tfrac{1}{3}\pi r^2 h\right)$$

The volume of a cylinder is $1\frac{1}{2}$ times the volume of a sphere.

$$\pi r^2 h = \tfrac{3}{2}\left(\tfrac{2}{3}\pi r^2 h\right)$$

The volume of a cylinder − the volume of a cone equals the volume of a sphere.

$$\pi r^2 h - \tfrac{1}{3}\pi r^2 h = \tfrac{2}{3}\pi r^2 h$$

2. **a.** The volume of a cone $= \frac{1}{3}(\pi r^2 h)$

b. The volume of a sphere $= \frac{2}{3}(\pi r^2 h)$, or $\frac{4}{3}\pi r^3$

C. The ratio of the volumes of a cone, a sphere, and cylinder is 4 : 8 : 12. Thus, the price is $4 for the cone-shaped candle and $8 for the spherical candle.

D. **1.** The volume of liquid wax is approximately 424.115. Andy would probably round up, so that he would have enough, and order 424 in.^{3}.

2. Possible answer: Using 424 in.^{3} as the volume, area of the base is 28.3 in.^{2} and height is 15 in. The base could be broken down further as 9.4 × 3. The dimensions of the rectangular prism are 3 in. by 9.4 in. by 15 in. Another possible answer is height ≈ 44.1 in. and the area of the base is ≈ 9.4 in.^{2}.

Note: This is an opportunity to discuss what would be reasonable accuracy for the answer. In this case, measuring to the nearest inch makes sense.

2.4 Selling Ice Cream: Solving Volume Problems

Focus Question What formulas are useful in solving problems involving volumes of cylinders, cones, and spheres?

Launch

Continue the story about Rocky Middle School and the charity event. In addition to selling candles, the school is selling ice cream and needs to determine how many cartons of ice cream to order.

Explore

If your students are having difficulty applying the formulas, ask:

- *How many scoops of ice cream does the school need?*
- *How do you find how much ice cream is in 100 scoops?*
- *How will this information help you determine how many cartons of ice cream to buy?*
- *How do you find how much ice cream is needed for the souvenir cup?*

Summarize

Collect answers to the Questions. Ask students to explain how they found their answers.

You might end this Investigation by having groups of students write application problems involving the volumes of cylinders, cones, and spheres. These problems could be exchanged among groups and solved, or they could be posted around the room to show a variety of applications and solutions using the volume formulas.

Materials

Assessment
- Partner Quiz

- graphing calculators (optional)

Answers to Problem 2.4

A. The volume of a scoop is $\frac{4}{3} \times \pi \times 3^3 \approx$ 113.1 cm³; 100 scoops is 11,310 cm³.

The volume of one ice cream carton is area of the base times height;

$\pi \times 11^2 \times 30 \approx 11,404$ cm³. That is, one ice cream carton holds 11,404 cm³ of ice cream.

At least 1 carton since 11,404 ÷ 11,310 ≈ 1.008.

B. 1. The volume of one cup is the sum of the volume of a cone and the volume of half of a sphere.

$$V_{cone} = \frac{1}{3}\pi \times 3^2 \times 16 \approx 150.80 \text{ cm}^3$$

$$V_{half\ sphere} = \frac{1}{2} \times \frac{4}{3} \times \pi \times 3^3 = \frac{2}{3} \times \pi \times 3^3$$
$$\approx 56.55 \text{ cm}^3$$

$$V_{cone} + V_{half\ sphere} \approx 207.35 \text{ cm}^3$$

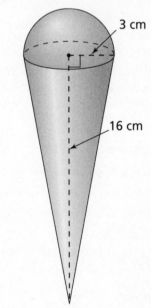

3 cm

16 cm

To make 50 cups, 50 × the volume of one cup = 50 × 207.35 = 10,367.26 cm³.

2. One more carton of ice cream is needed in addition to the carton from Question A. The volume of ice cream for 100 scoops and for 50 cups is 11,304 + 10,368 = 21,672 cm³ and 21,672 ÷ 11,404 ≈ 1.9, so 2 ice cream cartons are needed.

3.1 Selling Greeting Cards: Solving Linear Equations

> *Focus Question* What strategies can you use to solve equations that contain parentheses?

Launch

Use the questions in the Introduction to the Problem to review the strategies for solving linear equations. You may want to display Teaching Aid 3.1. Ask the class to provide a reason for each step.

For steps (1) and (2), the property of equality was used; it states that subtracting the same quantity from each side of the equation maintains equality. In (1), the quantity was $4x$; for (2) it was 25.

- *Could you begin with a different first step?*
- *How could you check that 25 is the correct solution?*
- *Describe another method for finding the solution to the equation.*

By the end of this discussion, students should be comfortable with using the principles of equality to solve equations. The principles state that equality is maintained by adding the same quantity to or subtracting the same quantity from each side of an equation and by multiplying or dividing each side of an equation by the same nonzero quantity.

> *Key Vocabulary*
> - properties of equality
>
> *Materials*
>
> **Teaching Aid**
> - 3.1: Solving Linear Equations

Explore

Point to various parts of the equation and ask what information each part represents. For Question A, part (3), some students may need to be reminded of what break-even means.

- *How do you find the break-even point?*

Look at the ways students are solving the equation. Suggest to students who are solving using a table or graph to try solving without a table or graph.

This Problem is another opportunity to see how students use the units associated with the context.

- *What information does 5s represent? What units should be attached to this expression?*

Summarize

Be sure students give a reason for each step, or have someone else give a reason for each step as a student presents his/her solution.

- *In Question A, part (2), is there another way to solve the equation $200 = 5s - (100 + 2s)$?*

Summarize strategies for solving equations with parentheses. Take note of how students use the Order of Operations. Then let the class solve the equations in Question C. Pick one or two of the equations and ask stduents to show the solution on a graph or table.

Answers to Problem 3.1

A. 1. The $5s$ represents the income, so the school choir makes $5 for each box of greeting cards it sells. The $100 + 2s$ represents the expenses, so the start-up cost is $100 and it costs $2 to produce each box of greeting cards.

2. 100 boxes; the equation that students must solve is $200 = 5s - (100 + 2s)$.

3. 34 boxes; the solution to the equation $P = 5s - (100 + 2s)$ when $P = 0$ is $s \approx 33.333$. So to break even, the school choir must sell 34 boxes.

4. $P = 3s - 100$; the 3 represents the income made per box sold and the 100 is the start-up cost. Students may find other equivalent expressions such as $P = 5s - 100 - 2s$, but these expressions do not provide as much new information.

5. Yes; $5s - 2(50 + s)$ is equivalent to $5s - (100 + 2s)$ by applying the Distributive Property to factor out a common factor of 2. Students can also check two different values for s and show that they produce the same value for P in each expression since the expressions are linear. Or students can use a graph or table to show that both expressions are equivalent.

B. One possible strategy: To solve an equation like $200 = 5s - (100 + 2s)$, first replace the right hand expression with the equivalent expression $5s - 100 - 2s$. This expression is equivalent since you can rewrite the equation as $200 = 5s + (-1)(100 + 2s)$ and then distribute the -1. Make sure students recognize that replacing an expression in an equation with an equivalent expression does not change the equality. This results in $200 = 5s - 100 - 2s$. You can replace $5s - 100 - 2s$ with the equivalent expression $3s - 100$, resulting in $200 = 3s - 100$.

Using the properties of equality on $200 = 3s - 100$ results in:

$200 + 100 = 3s - 100 + 100$ (Add 100 to each side.)

$\quad 300 = 3s$ (Combine like terms.)

$\quad 100 = s$ (Divide each side by 3.)

To solve an equation involving parentheses, distribute the number in front of the parentheses and then combine like terms. Next, continue to use the properties of equality to write simpler equations until it is easy to read the solution.

C. 1. $0 = 5 + 2(3 + 4x)$

$\quad 0 = 5 + 6 + 8x$

$\quad 0 = 11 + 8x$

$\quad 0 - 11 = 11 + 8x - 11$

$\quad -11 = 8x$

$\quad -\dfrac{11}{8} = x$

2. $0 = 5 - 2(3 + 4x)$

$\quad 0 = 5 - 6 - 8x$

$\quad 0 = -1 - 8x$

$\quad 0 + 1 = -1 - 8x + 1$

$\quad 1 = -8x$

$\quad -\dfrac{1}{8} = x$

3. $0 = 5 + 2(3 - 4x)$

$\quad 0 = 5 + 6 - 8x$

$\quad 0 = 11 - 8x$

$\quad 0 - 11 = 11 - 8x - 11$

$\quad -11 = -8x$

$\quad \dfrac{11}{8} = x$

4. $0 = 5 - 2(3 - 4x)$

$\quad 0 = 5 - 6 + 8x$

$\quad 0 = -1 + 8x$

$\quad 0 + 1 = -1 + 8x + 1$

$\quad 1 = 8x$

$\quad \dfrac{1}{8} = x$

3.2 Comparing Costs: Solving More Linear Equations

> *Focus Question* What are strategies for finding a solution that is common to two-variable linear equations?

Launch

In the last Problem, students discussed the profit for selling boxes of greetings cards. The profit was given as an equation in terms of the number of boxes of greeting cards. In this Problem, students will explore two similar equations for the cost of tiles.

- *How did this equation differ from those you saw in earlier Units?*

Describe the Problem. Display the two equations for the cost of tiles.

- *Do these equations make sense given the information about the two companies?*
- *What information does the constant number on each side of the equal sign represent?*
- *What information does the number in front of the parentheses represent?*

> ### *Materials*
>
> **Accessibility Labsheet**
> - 3ACE: Exercise 9
> - poster paper
> - markers
> - graphing calculators (optional)

Explore

Similar to the last Problem, solving linear equations with parentheses continues in this Problem. In this context, however, there are parentheses on both sides of the equal sign for determining when the costs of the two companies are equal.

If students make a graph for the two equations, check if they represent the situations accurately. For *Cover and Surround It*, they should have a horizontal line ($y = 1000$) for tiles up to 12, which represents a fixed charge of $1,000 up to 12 tiles, then the graph of $1,000 + 25(N - 12)$ beyond the first 12 tiles. Similarly, for *Tile and Beyond*, they should have a horizontal line ($y = 740$) for tiles up to 10, which represents a fixed charge of $740 up to 10 tiles, then the graph of $740 + 32(N - 10)$ beyond the first 10 tiles.

Summarize

Call on a group to present its work for Question A, parts (1) and (2). Have the rest of the class validate the group's work and/or ask questions of the group.

- *Did any group use a different first step?*
- *For the expression $740 + 32(N - 10)$ on the right side of the equation, can you add 740 and 32 as a first step?*
- *Describe how you could use a table or graph to solve this equation.*
- *How can you determine the number of tiles for which the Tile and Beyond company is the cheaper of the two companies?*

If no one suggests using a graph, ask:

- *How can you use a table or graph to decide which company is cheaper?*

Discuss the graphs of each equation. Each graph contains a horizontal line and a nonhorizontal line. See answer to Question A, part (3).

ACE

Assignment Guide for Problem 3.2

Applications: 8–23 | Connections: 39–41, 43, 44

Extensions: 56

Answers to Problem 3.2

A. **1.** 40;

$$1{,}000 + 25(N - 12) = 740 + 32(N - 10)$$
$$1{,}000 + 25N - 300 = 740 + 32N - 320$$
$$700 + 25N = 420 + 32N$$
$$700 - 420 + 25N = 420 - 420 + 32N$$
$$280 + 25N = 32N$$
$$280 + 25N - 25N = 32N - 25N$$
$$\frac{280}{7} = \frac{7N}{7}$$
$$40 = N$$

2. One possible way to check that the solution is correct is to substitute the value for N, 40, into each equation, solve for cost, and see if it is the same value.

3. Students may graph each equation and find the point at which the two lines intersect in order to determine the number of tiles for which the cost estimates are equal. If students used a table to determine the number of tiles for which the cost is equal, they would look for the number of tiles for which both companies have the same cost values.

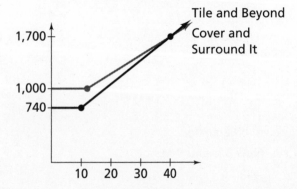

4. *Tile and Beyond* is cheaper than *Cover and Surround It* when the number of tiles is less than 40. On the graph, *Tile and Beyond* has cost values that are lower than *Cover and Surround It* when the value for N is less than 40 tiles, and this holds true for the table as well.

B. **Note:** The solutions below make use of the idea of combining like terms. For example, $3x - 8x = -5x$ may be used by some students. Others may still need to think of this idea as $3x - 8x = (3 - 8)x = -5x$ using the Distributive Property. Be sure that students check answers!

1.
$$3x = 5 + 2(3 + 4x)$$
$$3x = 5 + 6 + 8x$$
$$3x = 11 + 8x$$
$$3x - 8x = 11 + 8x - 8x$$
$$-5x = 11$$
$$x = -\frac{11}{5}$$

2.
$$3x = 5 - 2(3 + 4x)$$
$$3x = 5 - 6 - 8x$$
$$3x = -1 - 8x$$
$$3x + 8x = -1 - 8x + 8x$$
$$11x = -1$$
$$x = -\frac{1}{11}$$

3.
$$10 + 3x = 2(3 + 4x) + 5$$
$$10 + 3x = 6 + 8x + 5$$
$$10 + 3x = 11 + 8x$$
$$10 + 3x - 11 = 11 + 8x - 11$$
$$-1 + 3x = 8x$$
$$-1 + 3x - 3x = 8x - 3x$$
$$-1 = 5x$$
$$-\frac{1}{5} = x$$

4. $7 + 3(1 - x) = 5 - 2(3 - 4x)$

$7 + 3(1 - x) = 5 - 6 + 8x$

$7 + 3 - 3x = -1 + 8x$

$10 - 3x = -1 + 8x$

$10 - 3x + 1 = -1 + 8x + 1$

$11 - 3x = 8x$

$11 - 3x + 3x = 8x + 3x$

$11 = 11x$

$1 = x$

5. You can use the solution to the equation in Question B, part (3). The inequality $10 + 3x > 2(3 + 4x) + 5$ is true if $x < -\frac{1}{5}$.

C. 1. $3(2x - 5) = 2(3x - 1) + x$

$6x - 15 = 6x - 2 + x$

$6x - 15 = 7x - 2$

$6x - 6x - 15 = 7x - 6x - 2$

$-15 = x - 2$

$-15 + 2 = x - 2 + 2$

$-13 = x$

$y_1 = y_2$ has only one solution. The graph is a pair of intersecting lines, which meet at one point.

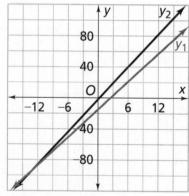

2. $3(2x - 5) = 2(3x - 1) + 7$

$6x - 15 = 6x - 2 + 7$

$6x - 15 = 6x + 5$

$6x - 6x - 15 = 6x - 6x + 5$

$-15 = 5$

$y_1 = y_2$ has no solution. It is a contradiction because there is no solution. The graph is a pair of parallel lines, which have no points in common.

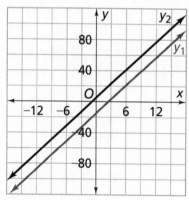

3. $3(2x - 5) = 2(3x - 1) - 13$

$6x - 15 = 6x - 2 - 13$

$6x - 15 = 6x - 15$

$6x - 6x - 15 = 6x - 6x - 15$

$-15 = -15$

$-15 + 15 = -15 + 15$

$0 = 0$

$y_1 = y_2$ has an infinite number of solutions because the graph is one line. Every possible x-value makes the equation true.

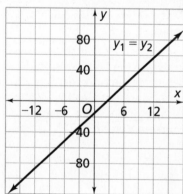

Notes

3.3 Factoring Quadratic Equations

> *Focus Question* What are some strategies for factoring a quadratic expression?

Launch

Write the equation $y = x^2 + 5x$ on the board.

- *How would you describe the shape of the graph?*
- *How can you use a table or graph to find the x-intercepts?*
- *What are the coordinates of the x-intercepts?*

Finding the x-intercepts is the same as solving the equation $0 = x^2 + 5x$ for x. This is called solving a quadratic equation for x when $y = 0$. Display Teaching Aid 3.3A.

- *What is the factored form of $x^2 + 5x$?*
- *What is the relationship between the factored form of $x^2 + 5x$ and the x-intercepts of the graph of $y = x^2 + 5x$?*
- *How would you use an area model to get the factored form?*

> *Key Vocabulary*
> - roots
>
> *Materials*
>
> **Teaching Aids**
> - 3.3A: Factoring Quadratic Equations
> - 3.3B: Quadratic Expression Model

Explore

If students are having trouble factoring, suggest that they use an area model. When they are ready, have students check if they can adapt Jakai's method for Questions B and C.

- *Will Jakai's method work?*

If you find that students need further assistance with Question B, parts (2) and (3), refer them to the first bullet of Jakai's method.

Some students may start working on Question D, and notice that Jakai's method does not apply here. Encourage them to use an area model to help find the factors.

Summarize

Go over Questions B and C. In Question C, part (1d), $x^2 - 4$ is the difference of two squares. Its factored form is $(x + 2)(x - 2)$. An area model for this special quadratic was explored in Investigation 2 of *Frogs, Fleas, and Painted Cubes*. You might want to have a student present an area model for this expression.

- *Will Jakai's method for factoring work for Question C, part (1d)?*

Write the expressions for Question D on the board.

- *What is different about these expressions?*
- *Can you use Jakai's method?*
- *Let's go back to an area model to see if we can adjust Jakai's method.*

Answers to Problem 3.3

A. 1. The area model that represents why Jakai's method worked is shown below. The simplest way to represent x^2 is x times x. Next, Jakai needed to decide how to represent 12. He had three choices that gave him 12 in the lower right-hand rectangle. He picked the pair (2, 6) because they added to 8, which was the coefficient of the middle term in $x^2 + 8x + 12$. This happened because when he used 2 and 6, they created rectangles with an area of $2x$ and $6x$, which made for a total area of $8x$ when he added them.

2. If Jakai had used another factor pair like 3 and 4, the area model would have rectangles with areas of $3x$ and $4x$, which would add to $7x$, not $8x$. So the factor pair 3 and 4 would not work. There is only one factor pair that will work for an expression using Jakai's method (though the factor pair may be commuted: 2 and 6 and 6 and 2).

B. 1. The factor pairs for 4 are (1, 4) and (2, 2). Since $1 + 4 = 5$, the factored form of $x^2 + 5x + 4$ is $(x + 4)(x + 1)$. To show that this factored form is correct, students may make an area model with one side of length $x + 4$ and the other of length $x + 1$ and show that the area of the rectangle is $x^2 + 5x + 4$. They can also make a table or graph for the two expressions $(x + 4)(x + 1)$ and $x^2 + 5x + 4$ and note that they are the same.

2. The factor pairs for 4 are (1, 4) and (2, 2). However, even though $1 + 4 = 5$, the middle term is actually -5. So for this one, Jakai's method must be modified to consider negative values in the factor pairs. Since -1×-4 still is 4, and $-1 + (-4) = -5$, the factored form of $x^2 - 5x + 4$ is $(x - 4)(x - 1)$.

3. The factor pairs for -4 are $(-1, 4)$, $(1, -4)$ and $(-2, 2)$. Since $1 + -4 = -3$, the factored form of $x^2 - 3x - 4$ is $(x - 4)(x + 1)$.

4. The factor pairs for 4 are (2, 2) and $(-2, -2)$. Since $2 + 2 = 4$, the expression in factored form is $(x + 2)(x + 2)$.

C. 1. The expressions are similar to those in Question B in that they are all quadratic. However, some of these expressions have $a \neq 1$ in the expression $ax^2 + bx + c$, whereas in Question B, $a = 1$ for all the expressions. Also, the expressions in Question C have two terms because either b or c equals zero, whereas the expressions in Question B have three terms.

2. Jakai's method will only work if the coefficient of x^2 is 1. So it only works directly for parts (a) or (d). However, students can use Jakai's method for part (b) if they first factor out a 4 from both the $4x^2$ and $32x$. See below for explanations.

a. Students may think of the c in the form $ax^2 + bx + c$ as 0. So the factor pair (0, 4) works since $0 \times 4 = 0$ and $0 + 4 = 4$. So the factored form is $(x)(x + 4)$. Students may also apply the Distributive Property directly to factor out the common factor x, or use an area model.

b. Students must factor out the 4 in order to use Jakai's method. If they do so, they will have $4(x^2 + 8x)$, which if they think of the factor pair (0, 8), yields $0 + 8 = 8$. So the factored form is $4(x)(x + 8)$. Students may also apply the Distributive Property directly to factor out the common factor $4x$, or use an area model.

c. Students may apply the Distributive Property by factoring out $2x$ and writing $2x(3x - 2)$, or they may use an area model. Also, Jakai's method could be adjusted to fit quadratic expressions in which the coefficient of x^2 is not 1. See answer to Question D, part (2). **Note:** There are other valid area models for this expression. See two of them below:

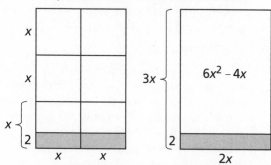

d. The factor pair $(2, -2)$ works since $2 + -2 = 0$, which is the coefficient of the middle term. So the factored form is $(x + 2)(x - 2)$. Students may also use an area model. Two models are provided below. For example, the area of the shaded part of the lower figure is $(x - 2)(x + 2) = x^2 - 2x + 2x - 4 = x^2 - 4$.

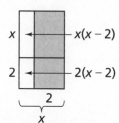

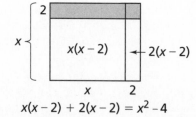

$$x(x - 2) + 2(x - 2) = x^2 - 4$$

D. 1. They are different in that the coefficients of x^2 are not equal to 1. They are similar because they all are of the form $ax^2 + bx + c$, where a, b, c all are $\neq 0$.

2. Jakai's method will not work on these because his method requires that the coefficient of x^2 is equal to 1. However, students can adapt Jakai's method for a, b, and c. For example, to factor the expression $2x^2 + 9x + 4$ for Question D, part (1c), students would need to look at the factor pairs for 4, which are (1, 4) and (2, 2), and the factor pairs for the 2 in front of x^2, which are (2, 1).

Looking at the area models for each one of these combinations:

Combination 1: (2, 1) and (4, 1)

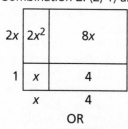

OR

$$2x^2 + 6x + 4$$

Combination 2: (2, 1) and (1, 4)

$$2x^2 + 9x + 4$$

Combination 3: (2, 1) and (2, 2)

	x	2
$2x$	$2x^2$	$4x$
2	$2x$	4

OR

	x	2
x	x^2	$2x$
x	x^2	$2x$
2	$2x$	4

$2x^2 + 6x + 4$

We see that Combination 2 gives $2x^2 + 9x + 4$.

So in adjusting Jakai's methods, students consider factor pairs of a and c in $ax^2 + bx + c$ and find combinations of the pairs for which the middle coefficient b is satisfied.

The factored forms are:

a. $(2x + 4)(x + 2) = 2(x + 2)(x + 2)$

b. $(2x + 1)(2x + 1)$

c. $(2x + 1)(x + 4)$

To explain why the expressions are equivalent, students may check that three different x-values give the same y-value in each expression. They may use a graph or table to show that the expressions produce the same graph or table. They may also use the Distributive or Commutative Property to show equivalence.

3.4 Solving Quadratic Equations

> ***Focus Question*** What are some strategies for solving quadratic equations?

Launch

Students will use their knowledge about factoring a quadratic expression to solve a quadratic equation.

Display Teaching Aid 3.4 to show the equation from the Problem introduction, $0 = x^2 + 8x + 12$. Go over the questions.

- *How can you solve the equation $0 = x^2 + 8x + 12$ by factoring?*
- *When $0 = (x + 2)(x + 6)$, what must be true about one or both of the linear factors?*
- *How can this information help you find the solutions to $0 = (x + 2)(x + 6)$?*
- *How can this information help you find the x-intercepts of $y = x^2 + 8x + 12$?*

The factoring parts are review for the students to understand how the product of two quantities could equal 0. They will connect the process of factoring a quadratic expression to solving a quadratic equation, $0 = ax^2 + bx + c$.

> ***Materials***
>
> **Teaching Aid**
> - 3.4: Solving Quadratic Equations
>
> **Assessment**
> - Check Up 2
>
> - poster paper
> - markers

Explore

If a student has factored incorrectly, challenge the student to show that his/her factored expression is correct by multiplying it out using the Distributive Property or by trying three numerical values for the factored and expanded form to see if they are equivalent expressions.

You may want some pairs to put their work for an equation on large poster paper along with the graph and table showing alternate ways to solve the equations. Students can point out the connections among solutions for an equation, x-intercepts, line of symmetry, and maximum or minimum.

Summarize

Go over each part of the Problem. Take time to connect solving quadratic equations to the bigger picture of quadratic relationships. Solving a quadratic equation, $0 = ax^2 + bx + c$, is the same as finding the x-intercepts of the graph of $y = ax^2 + bx + c$.

Discuss Question D, which introduces a context where it useful to solve a quadratic equation by factoring.

- *What does solving $0 = 32t - 16t^2$ tell you about the pole vaulter's jump? About the graph of $y = 32t - 16t^2$?*
- *How do the solutions for the quadratic equation help you determine how high the pole vaulter jumped? Can you find this maximum point without actually making the graph?*

Answers to Problem 3.4

A. 1. $(x + 4)(x + 6)$

  2. For the product of two numbers to equal 0, one or both factors must equal 0. So for the equation $(x + 4)(x + 6) = 0$, either $x + 4 = 0$ or $x + 6 = 0$. So either $x = -4$ or $x = -6$. So the equation $x^2 + 10x + 24 = 0$ has two solutions.

  3. The solutions to $0 = x^2 + 10x + 24$ are the x-intercepts since you are finding x when the y-value is 0.

B. 1. $x = -1$ or $x = -\frac{7}{2}$

  2. $x = 5$ or $x = 2$

  3. To find the solutions, students must first factor using Jakai's method or an area model. So the equation becomes $0 = (x + 3)(x + 3)$ and the solution is $x = -3$.

  4. To find the solutions, students must first factor using Jakai's method or an area model. So the equation becomes $0 = (x + 4)(x - 4)$ and the solutions are $x = -4$ or $x = 4$.

  5. To find the solutions, students must first factor using Jakai's method or an area model. So the equation becomes $0 = (x + 8)(x + 2)$, and the solutions are $x = -8$ or $x = -2$.

  6. To find the solutions, students must first factor using an area model or some other method. So the equation becomes $0 = (2x + 3)(x + 2)$, and the solutions are $x = -\frac{3}{2}$ or $x = -2$.

  7. To check the solutions, students can substitute their x-values into the equation.

C. 1. $x = 0$ or $x = 9$

  2. $x = 0$ or $x = -\frac{5}{2}$

  3. If students factor first, they should get $2x(x + 16) = 0$, so $x = 0$ or $x = -16$. Students may also make an area model to find the factors.

  4. If students factor first, they should get $9x(2 - x) = 0$, so $x = 0$ or $x = 2$.

  To check the solutions, students can either substitute their x-value into the equation or look at a table and see if the x-values they found correspond to a y-value of 0. They can also look at the graph and see if the x-intercepts are the x-values they found.

D. 1. The pole vaulter is looking for the time when he/she will land the jump.

  2. No, the maximum height given in this equation is 16 feet, which occurs at 1 second. The maximum height can be found by graphing and looking at the y-coordinate of the vertex, by using a table, or by looking at the factored form of the equation $h = 32t - 16t^2 = 16t(2 - t)$. Since the zeros are 0 and 2, the maximum occurs directly between 0 and 2, which is 1 second. Substituting 1 second into the original equation yields a maximum height of 16 feet, which is less than 17.5 feet.

4.1 Pumping Water: Looking at Patterns of Change

Focus Question How can you use an equation to answer particular questions about a function and the situation it represents?

Launch

Describe the situation about water being pumped from Magnolia Middle School's pool. Write the equation on the board. Tell students that they are to find information about the amount of water in the pool and the rate at which it is being pumped out of the pool.

Explore

Some students may write $(t - 5)(-250)$ as an equivalent expression for the amount of water in the pool. This is correct, but encourage them to find another expression for the amount of water.

- *Is there a way to write the equation in expanded form? If so, how?*

- *Does the expanded form help you find the answers for Question A?*

Summarize

Ask different pairs of students to present their work. Ask the rest of the class if they agree and if they have any questions they want to ask the pair.

For Question D, some students may have read the −450 as the rate per hour that the water is being pumped out. This will happen when students do not distribute the −450 to the 2, the coefficient of x inside the parentheses. Tables and graphs will be helpful to see the constant rate of 2 times −450 (or −900) gallons per minute. Make sure that all students understand how to use the Distributive Property to write the equations in the form $y = mx + b$.

- *Which form of the equation, $w = -250(t - 5)$ or $w = -250t + 1,250$, would an engineer most likely use to represent this situation? Why?*

- *Without making a graph, describe the shape of the graph of the equation. Is this relationship linear? Exponential? Quadratic? Why?*

- *In Question A, part (1) and Question D, part (1), how is the information about the amount of water being pumped out related to the graph of the equation?*

Materials

Accessibility Labsheets
- 4ACE: Exercises 1 and 2
- 4ACE: Exercise 25

- graphing calculators (optional)

- poster paper (optional)

AT A GLANCE 4

Assignment Guide for Problem 4.1

Applications: 1–4 | Connections: 25–28
Extensions: 56

Answers to Problem 4.1

A. 1. 250 gallons are being pumped out each hour. Students may make a table and notice the constant rate of change, which is −250, or they may recognize that −250 is the coefficient of t in a linear relationship between w and t.

2. 5 hours. Students can find in their table the corresponding t-value when w is 0, or they can find where the graph of $w = -250t + 1,250$ intersects the x-axis (t-axis). If students look at the equation $w = -250t + 1,250$, they may solve the equation for $w = 0$, which is $t = 5$.

3. 1,250 gallons; the answer can be found by looking at the equation and identifying the y-intercept (w-intercept), or by finding the y-intercept (w-intercept) on the table or graph.

B. 1. $-250t + 1,250$ or $1,250 - 250t$

2. The −250 represents that there are 250 gallons of water being pumped out each hour. 1,250 is the number of gallons of water in the tank at the start.

3. Answers will vary. The original expression tells you that the x-intercept (t-intercept) is 5, since for w to equal 0 the factor $(t - 5)$ must equal 0, so $t = 5$. The y-intercept (w-intercept) is harder to read in this expression. However, the rate of change is not hard to compute, since it is just −250 times 1. The expanded expression $-250t + 1,250$ is better for identifying the amount of water at the start and the amount of water being pumped out each hour.

C. 1. The pattern of change is linear. For every change of one hour in time, the amount of water in the pool decreases by a constant amount of 250 gallons.

2. The graph would have a y-intercept (w-intercept) at (0, 1,250) and slant down from left to right. It would cross the x-axis (t-axis) at (5, 0).

D. 1. 900 gallons are being pumped out each hour. Students may make a table on a graphing calculator.

2. 3.5 hours. Students may use their table. To get the exact time in their table, they would have to use $\frac{1}{2}$-hour intervals of time. There would be 0 gallons left in the pool between 3 and 4 hours. To check, students can substitute 3.5 hours into the equation for t to find that $w = -450[2(3.5) - 7] = -450(7 - 7) = 0$ gallons.

Some students may use the guess-and-check method in the equation and then switch to a table or graph. Others may solve the equation: $w = -450(2t - 7)$ for t when $w = 0$, since $w = 0$ means that the amount of water in the pool is 0 gallons. There are two different ways to solve the equation $0 = -450(2t - 7)$.

Method 1: You can use the Distributive Property on the right side, getting $0 = -900t + 3,150$. Solving by subtracting 3,150 from each side and then dividing by −900 results in $t = 3.5$.

Method 2: You can look at the equation $-450(2t - 7) = 0$ and notice that in order for the product on the left hand side to equal zero, $2t - 7$ must equal 0, so solve $2t - 7 = 0$ by adding 7 to each side and then dividing by 2. The result is $t = 3.5$. **Note:** When the product of two factors is 0, one or both of the factors must be zero. This is known as the Zero-Product Property.

3. 3,150 gallons. This can be found in the table when time is zero or by solving the equation $w = -450(2t - 7)$ for w when $t = 0$, $w = -450(-7) = 3,150$.

4. Using the Distributive Property, the equation becomes $w = -900t + 3,150$, which is equivalent to the original equation. Some students may say that $(2t - 7)(-450)$ is an equivalent expression, which is correct since they have just used the Commutative Property. However, their new expression does not give any new information about the Problem. The expanded form of this equation tells you that the tank started with 3,150 gallons and that the rate of change is −900 gallons per hour, so students may say that it is more useful.

Say It With Symbols **At a Glance**

4.2 Area and Profit—What's the Connection?: Using Equations

> ***Focus Question*** How can two different contexts be represented by the same equation?

Launch

Tell students the story of Tony and Paco and how the boys plan to run a concession stand and rent water tubes to the visitors at Water Town. Tony is trying to find the maximum area of the concession stand given a fixed perimeter and Paco is trying to find the maximum profit from renting water tubes.

- *Compare these contexts to others you have studied.*
- *How might these two situations be related?*

Explore

As students work on the Problem, check to see if they can write an equation for area in terms of length ℓ for Question A, part (1). If they are having difficulty with this, you may want to ask them the following questions.

- *What is area in terms of length and width?*
- *Do you have an expression that relates the length and the width?*
- *Can you use this equation to find an equivalent expression for w in terms of ℓ?*
- *How can you use this equation to write an equation for area in terms of length ℓ?*
- *How do you know that the area you got in Question A, part (2) is the maximum area?*

For Question B, make sure that students read the conditions carefully.

- *Do Equations 1 and 2 in Question B match what you know about the conditions?*
- *Does $n = 54 - (1)p$ make sense?*

If students are confused about profit, ask them to explain how to calculate it.

- *How can you calculate profit?*
- *What is the income I? What will you have to do to rewrite this in terms of n?*
- *How can you rewrite $n = 54 - p$ to find an expression for p in terms of n? How does this help you rewrite the equation for I?*
- *What are the expenses?*
- *What is the daily profit?*

Summarize

To focus your discussion on the similarity of the two equations, ask your students:

- *Compare the equations for profit and area.*

- *In the area and profit equations, different variables are used, but the relationships are the same. What does this mean in terms of particular solutions such as (44, 0) or (22, 484)?*

- *How can you use the information about maximum area in Question A to find the maximum profit in Question B?*

- *Compare the methods for combining equations or expressions to write one equation in this unit.*

Assignment Guide for Problem 4.2

Applications: 5–7 | Connections: 29–39
Extensions: 57

Answers to Problem 4.2

A. 1. $A = \ell(44 - \ell)$ or $A = 44\ell - \ell^2$; since $88 = 2(\ell + w)$, then dividing each side of the equation by 2 gives the equation $44 = \ell + w$. Then $w = 44 - \ell$ and $A = \ell(44 - \ell)$ after substitution. Students may multiply through to get $A = 44\ell - \ell^2$.

2. The maximum area is 484 m^2 when the floor plan is a 22 m by 22 m square.

B. 1. Equation 1 means that for each $1 increase in the price to rent, the number of rentals decreases by 1. The starting value is 54 rentals for a price of $0. This equation matches the conditions described in Question B. The y-intercept is 54 and the slope is -1.

2. $I = n(54 - n)$; first solve $n = 54 - p$ for p to get $p = 54 - n$. Then substitute the expression into the income equation for p to get $I = n(54 - n)$.

3. $D = n(54 - n) - 10n$ or $D = 44n - n^2$; since $D = $ income $-$ expenses and expenses $= 10n$, $D = n(54 - n) - 10n$ or $D = 54n - n^2 - 10n = 44n - n^2$, which is the daily profit.

4. 22 rentals will produce a maximum profit of $484; you can find the maximum value by graphing the equation or by looking at a table of the equation $D = 44n - n^2$ or any equivalent equation. Students should also realize that the maximum profit is the same as the maximum area that they found in Question A, part (2).

A price of $32 produces the maximum daily profit; since the maximum profit occurs at 22 rentals, you need to find p when $n = 22$. In the equation $n = 54 - p$, substitute 22 for n, $22 = 54 - p$, and solve for p, $p = 54 - 22 = 32$. Students may also use a graph or table to get the answer.

5. The equations in Questions B, part (3) and Question A, part (1) represent the same quadratic relationship. The only difference is that they use different variables.

4.3 Generating Patterns:
Linear, Exponential, Quadratic

Focus Question How can you determine the patterns of change of a function from a table of data for the function?

Launch

Explain to your students that they will make their own linear, exponential, and quadratic patterns. Then they will write equations to represent their patterns.

Give your students the coordinates of two points for a linear, an exponential, and a quadratic function. Their task is to generate four more points, or coordinate pairs, that fit each pattern of change. Then they will write an equation to represent each pattern of change.

Explore

Ask students how they chose the patterns they did.

- *How did you check whether your pattern was linear? Exponential? Quadratic?*

For the exponential pattern, some students may need prompting.

- *What is an example of an exponential equation? What do exponential equations look like?*

- *Can you figure out either of the values of a or b from the points given? Does this help you find additional points or find an equation?*

For students that are working on the quadratic equation, you may need to remind them of the general form of a quadratic: $y = ax^2 + bx + c$.

Summarize

Display the posters of student work around the classroom. Give the class a few minutes to examine the posters and to leave a sticky note with a comment or question on each poster. Then have students explain their work on their posters and why the patterns they found are linear, exponential, or quadratic.

- *Is there a way to check whether your pattern is quadratic like the checking you did for your linear and exponential patterns?*

- *I notice that there is only one example for the linear equation. Is there one that we didn't think of that is not equivalent to the one we got? Why or why not?*

- *Do you think there is another possible exponential pattern if you have to go through (1, 1) and (2, 4)? Why or why not?*

- *How many points do you need to determine a line?*

- *How many points do you need to determine an exponential function?*

Materials

Teaching Aid
- 4.3: Check for Understanding

- poster paper (optional)

- graphing calculators (optional)

- *Can you think of another quadratic pattern that is not on the board?*
- *What if the point (3, 9) had to be included in your table? How many different quadratic patterns could you find?*

ⒶⒸⒺ
Assignment Guide for Problem 4.3

Applications: 8–10 | Connections: 40–51
Extensions: 58

Answers to Problem 4.3

A. There is only one possible linear pattern because once you have fixed two points, (1, 1) and (2, 4), the constant rate of change is determined and can be calculated; in this case, it is + 3.

There is only one possible exponential pattern because once you have fixed two points, (1, 1) and (2, 4), the constant growth factor is determined and can be calculated; in this case, it is 4.

There are infinitely many patterns that students can generate for the quadratic; the table shows 3 possible patterns. Second differences must have a constant nonzero rate of change. The y-values for the points (1, 1) and (2, 4) determine a first difference, in this case 3, but the second difference depends on what the student puts in for the third value. For example, if a student uses 9 for the value for 3, then the second difference is fixed (at 2 in this case). This is why if you are given three points of a quadratic pattern, the quadratic is fixed. Three possible equations are show in Figure 1 below.

i. $y = x^2$

ii. $y = -\frac{1}{2}x^2 + \frac{9}{2}x - 3$

iii. $y = \frac{1}{2}x^2 + \frac{3}{2}x - 1$

Note: A common mistake is to simply make a symmetrical pattern for the y-values. For example, {1, 4, 6, 7, 8, 7, 6, 4, 1} is symmetric, but second differences are not constant because the first differences are not linear.

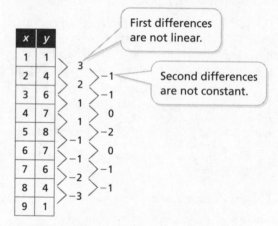

B. A linear relationship always has a constant rate of change. For every change of 1 in the x-values, there is a constant change of 3 in the y-values.

Figure 1

x	Linear, y	Exponential, y	i. Quadratic, y	ii. Quadratic, y	iii. Quadratic, y
1	1	1	1	1	1
2	4	4	4	4	4
3	7	16	9	6	8
4	10	64	16	7	13
5	13	256	25	7	19
6	16	1,024	36	6	26

Say It With Symbols **At a Glance**

An exponential relationship has the same value (the growth factor) for the quotients between successive y-values. To find the y-value corresponding to consecutive x-values in an exponential relationship, multiply the previous y-value by the growth factor (in this case by 4).

A quadratic relationship has a constant second difference. When you take the differences between successive y-values, the first differences show a constant rate of change, and the second differences are a nonzero constant.

C. 1. The linear equation is $y = 3x - 2$ and is unique; the 3 is the rate of change, and the -2 is the y-intercept. Some students may write $y = 1 + 3(x - 1)$, which is equivalent. The exponential equation is $y = 4^{x-1}$ and is unique. It is equivalent to $y = \frac{1}{4}(4^x)$. The 4 is the growth factor; the $\frac{1}{4}$ is the initial value, or y-intercept. In the table shown for Question A,

    i. Quadratic is $y = x^2$. Other equations are more difficult for students to find.

    ii. Quadratic is $y = -\frac{1}{2}x^2 + \frac{9}{2}x - 3$

    iii. Quadratic is $y = \frac{1}{2}x^2 + \frac{3}{2}x - 1$

2. The linear and exponential equations should be the same, except for equivalent forms $y = 3x - 2$ or $y = 1 + 3(x - 1)$ and $y = 4^{x-1}$ or $y = \frac{1}{4}(4^x)$. For linear and exponential functions, two points on the graph uniquely determine the function. That is, the pattern of change for these two points is unique, while for a quadratic function, a third point is needed to uniquely determine the pattern of change.

The quadratic equation will vary. A third point is needed to make it unique. Some students may choose (3, 9) which makes the equation fairly simple to observe, $y = x^2$. Some may choose (3, 6) for the third point, which makes the second difference -1. In *Frogs, Fleas, and Painted Cubes*, some students correctly conjecture

that the coefficient of x^2 is always one half the value of the second difference if x increases by 1 each time in the table. So if the second difference is -1, then the coefficient of x^2 is $-\frac{1}{2}$. Students can also find the y-intercept by working backward in the table, which in this case will be -3. One way to find the equation of a quadratic is to find the value for a and the y-intercept value c, substitute them into the equation $y = ax^2 + bx + c$, and solve for b. The equation is now $y = -\frac{1}{2}x^2 + bx - 3$. Substituting the point (1, 1) into the equation, $b = 4.5$. The equation is $y = -\frac{1}{2}x^2 + 4.5x - 3$.

The following is an example of finding a quadratic equation to fit the points (1, 1) and (2, 4) by generating a linear pattern for the first differences.

Marty's Quadratic Relationship

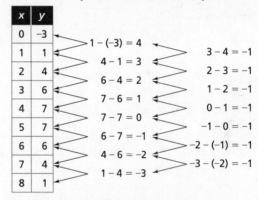

The general quadratic is $y = Ax^2 + Bx + C$. A is half the constant second difference, or $A = -0.5$. The y-intercept is $(0, -3)$, so $C = -3$. Substitute these values into the general equation. The result is $y = -0.5x^2 + Bx - 3$. Substitute the point (1, 1) into that equation and solve for B.

$$1 = -0.5(1)^2 + B(1) - 3$$
$$B = 1 + 0.5 + 3 = 4.5$$

So the equation is $y = -0.5x^2 + 4.5x - 3$.

Notes

4.4 What's the Function?: Modeling With Functions

> *Focus Question* How can you determine which function to use to solve or represent a problem?

Launch

Describe the challenge. Students are going to be given eight situations. Each situation involves some kind of relationship between variables. The task is to figure out which function relationship fits the situation. Then students have to write an equation and ask a question that can be answered by using their equation.

- *When you are given a relationship in words, how do you decide what kind of function represents the relationship?*

Explore

If students need prompting to get started, you can help them look for clues.

- *What clues suggest that a situation is a linear, exponential, or quadratic function, an inverse variation, or none of these?*

Summarize

Use the student posters to discuss the Problem or make a table on the board with four columns: Linear, Exponential, Quadratic, Inverse Variation, and Other. Have students share their ideas about which situations belong with a function type.

Discuss the various strategies that students used to decide which function matches each situation. Ask them to think of other situations that are linear, exponential, quadratic, or inverse variation. Ask them about the similarities and differences of the situations grouped within a column.

Be sure to have students share by describing the features of a graph and examining the equation without graphing it.

Ask students to share the questions that they made that could be answered by the equation. Try to get examples of linear, exponential, and quadratic functions. Ask the class if the equations and questions fit the situations. You could have groups exchange their questions and answer them using the equations.

Materials

Labsheet
- 4.4: Function Matching

- poster paper (optional)

- graphing calculators (optional)

ACE

Assignment Guide for Problem 4.4

Applications: 11–24 | Connections: 52–55
Extensions: 59, 60

Answers to Problem 4.4

A–B. For each part of Question A, students have three tasks for each given situation: (1) students match situations with linear, quadratic, exponential, or inverse variation functions, or none of these; (2) they write an equation to represent the situation; and (3) they write a question that can be answered with the equation and answer it. For Question B, students describe the shapes of the graphs of the equations with as much detail as possible. In each of the situations, both the independent and dependent variables are positive, so the graphs are limited to the first quadrant. Functions used to model the situations extend outside of the graph of the situation. This is an important distinction for students to understand.

For each situation, possible answers are shown below.

1. This is a quadratic function. $V = 16\pi r^2$ or $y = 16\pi x^2$.

   Possible question: What is the volume of the cylinder if the radius is 3 inches? Answer: $16\pi(3)^2 = 144\pi \approx 452.4$ in.^{3}

   The independent variable is raised to the 2nd power. Its graph is a parabola with a minimum point at (0, 0).

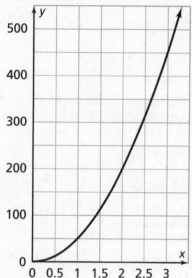

2. This is an inverse variation function. $W = \frac{24}{L}$ or $y = \frac{24}{x}$.

   Possible question: What is the width of the rectangle if the length is 3 inches? Answer: $\frac{24}{3} = 8$ in.

In the first quadrant, the graph is a decreasing function with no intercepts.

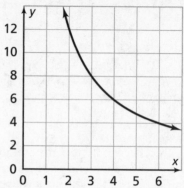

3. This is an exponential function.

   $V = 800(0.5)^t$ or $y = 800(0.5)^x$.

   Possible question: When will the laptop's value be $50? Answer: $800(0.5)^t = 50$. $t = 4$ years.

   The independent variable is the exponent. The function has an exponential decay factor of 0.5, which is the base, with a y-intercept of (0, 800).

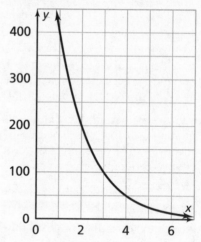

4. This is a linear function. $M = 2c$ or $y = 2x$.

Possible question: What is the total amount of magazines sold for 5 customers?
Answer: $2(5) = 10$ magazines

The function has a constant rate of change (2) with an y-intercept of $(0, 0)$.

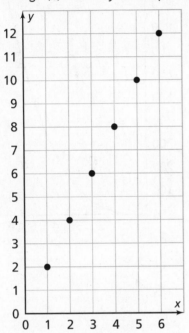

5. This is a linear function. $V = 16\pi h$ or $y = 16\pi x$.

Possible question: What is the height of the cylinder if the volume is 302 in.^{3}? Answer: $16\pi(x) = 302$ in.^{3} $x = 6$ in.

This line has a constant rate of change of 16π and a y-intercept at $(0, 0)$.

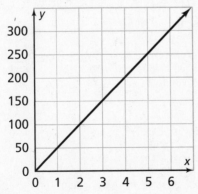

6. This is an exponential function. $V = 3^d$ or $y = 3^x$.

Possible question: How many visitors will there be on day 10?
Answer: $3^{10} = 59,049$ visitors

The curve has an exponential growth factor of 3 and a y-intercept at $(0, 1)$.

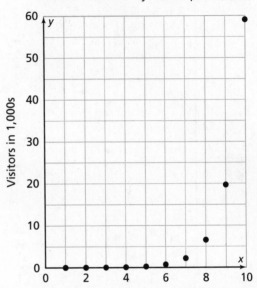

7. This is a quadratic function.
$R = \dfrac{f(f + 1)}{2}$ or $y = \dfrac{x(x + 1)}{2}$.

Note: Students may record their data in a table, determine that the numbers are triangular numbers, and recognize triangular numbers as a quadratic function. They may also use the numbers from the table to determine that the second difference is 1, which is an indicator that this situation can be modeled by a quadratic function.

Possible question: What Figure has 28 squares? Answer: $\dfrac{7(7 + 1)}{2} = 28$. $n = 7$.

This quadratic function has two x-intercepts, $(0, 0)$ and $(0, -1)$, a y-intercept at $(0, 0)$, and a minimum of $\left(-\dfrac{1}{2}, -\dfrac{1}{8}\right)$. Students may find the minimum of the function using the symmetry of the intercepts to find the midpoint at $-\dfrac{1}{2}$.

AT A GLANCE 4

Then they can substitute this value into the original function to find the *y*-value for the minimum.

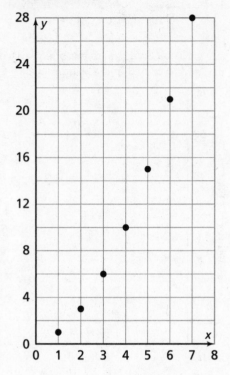

8. None of these. $V = \frac{4}{3}\pi r^3$ or $y = \frac{4}{3}\pi x^3$.

Possible question: What is the volume if the radius is 4.5 inches? Answer: $\frac{4}{3}\pi(4.5)^3 = 121.5\pi \approx 381.7$ in.^{3}

This is a cubic function with an intercept at (0, 0).

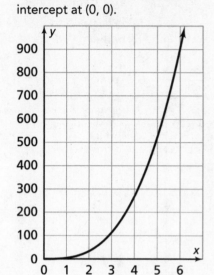

5.1   Using Algebra to Solve a Puzzle

> *Focus Question*   How can you use algebra to solve a number trick?

Launch

Briefly tell the story about the e-mail message that Elizabeth (or you) received. Ask students to pick a number from 1 to 9 and to perform the steps as you read them aloud.

- *You should have a three-digit number. What is your three-digit number?*

Ask students to use their algebraic knowledge to figure out the puzzle for Questions B and C.

Explore

To help your students get started, you can ask:

- *How can you indicate multiplication of the number n by 2?*
- *How can you indicate the addition of 5 to this expression?*
- *How can you indicate multiplying this expression by 50?*

Continue this line of questioning as needed.

Summarize

Ask one or two students to show their work.

- *How does the current year figure into the series of statements?*

To reinforce the use of symbolic statements to illustrate how a number trick works, use one of the number tricks in ACE Exercises 1 or 2 or use one that the students made up.

> *Materials*
>
> **Accessibility Labsheet**
>
> - 5ACE: Exercises 1–3
> - graphing calculators (optional)
> - poster paper (optional)

Answers to Problem 5.1

A. 1. Students work through the steps of the puzzle.

2. The first number is the number you choose, and the last two numbers represent your age in the year 2013.

B. 1. Let n be the number chosen in the first step and x be your age in 2013. Then, assuming you have already had your birthday this year, you can write the symbolic statement
$50(2n + 5) + 1{,}763 - (2{,}013 - x) =$
$100n + 250 + 1{,}763 - 2{,}013 + x =$
$100n + x$

So it makes sense that the hundreds digit is the initial value chosen and that the last two digits represent your age in 2013. If the number 1,762 is added instead of 1,763, then age is one less, which makes sense for the person who has not had a birthday yet in 2013.

2. The puzzle is for 2013. To adjust for the current year, for those who have had their birthday in the current year, subtract 250 from the current year and add this result in step 5 instead of 1,763. For those who have not had their birthday in the current year, subtract 251 from the current year and add this result in step 5 instead of 1,762.

5.2 Odd and Even Revisited

> *Focus Question* How can you use algebra to represent and prove a conjecture about numbers?

Launch

Pose the questions in the introduction.

- *Daphne claims that you can represent an even number with the expression 2n, where n is any integer. Is this true? Why?*

- *Write an algebraic expression that will generate all odd numbers. Explain why it works.*

- *What conjectures can you make about operations with rational and irrational numbers?*

If the following conjectures are not suggested, you can ask:

- *Is a rational + a rational always a rational? What about a rational + an irrational? What about the product of a rational and an irrational?*

> ### Materials
>
> **Teaching Aid**
> - 5.2: Bianca's Method
>
> - graphing calculators (optional)
>
> - poster paper (optional)

Explore

If students find Question B challenging, give them some square tiles or cut some out of grid paper to show them how to represent even and odd numbers. This was done in the Grade 6 Unit *Prime Time*.

For Question C, some students may want to write $2n$ and $2n + 1$ for an even and an odd. You may have to use examples for n to show that these two will not randomly represent an even and odd number, because once the n is picked, then both the even and the odd are determined. That is, they will be consecutive integers. The odd number should not depend on the even number.

You might suggest using area models to do Question C, part (2). Some students may be more comfortable with geometric arguments.

If students are challenged by the proof for an irrational + an irrational, you can show a couple of sample student proofs. Then ask students to analyze the proof. Most should be able to use number facts as a proof. See the answer for arguments.

Summarize

Go over the steps students provided for Question A. Compare the two methods for proving that the sum of two even numbers is even. You can ask students to associate the algebraic steps with the geometric model. Some students may choose to use a geometric argument for Question C. Encourage the class to try both methods.

The product of an even and an odd number (or two odds) is a direct application of multiplying two binomials. $2n(2m + 1) = 4nm + 2n$. Since you can factor out 2 to write $2(2mn + n)$, you now have an even number that is the product of 2 and the number $2mn + n$.

Answers to Problem 5.2

A. Student reasoning will vary. Students may be challenged by the idea that $2(n + m)$ is an even integer. One way to think about it is that $n + m$ is "some integer number" and $2(n + m)$ is "some integer number" multiplied by two, which is the characteristic of an even number.

B. Yes; Bianca's argument confirms the conjecture because $2n + 2m$ can be written as a rectangular array with one dimension equal to 2 and the other dimension equal to $n + m$. That is, it can be written as a product of 2 and another integer.

C. **1.** Students may use different expressions to represent odd numbers: $2n + 1$ or $2n - 1$, for example. One possible argument: Let n and m represent any two integers. Then $2n$ is even and $2m + 1$ is odd. $2n + 2m + 1$ is the sum of an even and an odd and $2n + 2m + 1 = 2(n + m) + 1$. $2(n + m) + 1$ is an odd number. Thus the sum of an even and an odd is odd.

2. Let n and m represent any integer. Then $2n$ is even and $2m + 1$ is odd. $2n(2m + 1)$ is the product of an even and an odd. $2n(2m + 1) = 4nm + 2n = 2(2nm + n)$. $2(2nm + n)$ is an even number. Thus the product of an even and an odd is even.

D. **1.** Let $\frac{a}{b}$ and $\frac{c}{d}$ be rational numbers with a, b, c, and d integers, $b \neq 0$, and $d \neq 0$. Then $\frac{a}{b} \times \frac{c}{d} = \frac{ac}{bd}$, which is also a rational number, because ac and bd are integers and $bd \neq 0$ because both b and d are nonzero.

2. Let $\frac{a}{b}$ and $\frac{c}{d}$ be rational numbers with a, b, c, and d integers, $b \neq 0$, and $d \neq 0$. Then to find $\frac{a}{b} + \frac{c}{d}$ requires a common denominator, which can be bd. $\frac{a}{b} + \frac{c}{d} = \frac{ad}{bd} + \frac{bc}{bd} = \frac{ad + bc}{bd}$, which is rational because $ad + bc$ is an integer and bd is a nonzero integer.

E. This question may challenge students. You might consider assigning this as a homework problem to give students additional time to think about solution strategies.

1. Students might look at some examples to support their reasoning. For example, suppose a student chooses π as an irrational number and then 0.25 as the rational number. The sum $\pi + 0.25$ will have the same decimal expansion as π, except the tenths and hundredths digit will be changed. In general, if a rational number terminates, adding it to an irrational number will only change finitely many decimal places resulting in the sum being irrational. This argument, however, only pertains to rational numbers whose decimal expansions terminate.

General argument: Let p be a rational number and q be an irrational number. The sum is either rational or irrational since all real numbers are either rational or irrational. The argument to show that $p + q$ is irrational is called a Proof by Contradiction. We will assume one of the two possible results and show that it cannot be true because it contradicts the original assumption. Suppose the sum $p + q$ is rational. Let $p + q = s$, or equivalently, $q = s - p$. Now, $s - p$ is rational because it is the difference of two rational numbers. **Note:** In Question D, part (2), students showed that the sum of two rational numbers is rational. This works for differences as well because $s - p = s + (-p)$. Since $s - p$ is rational, then so is q because they are equal. However, q is irrational from the starting assumption and cannot be both rational and irrational. Therefore, the assumption that $p + q$ is rational must be false, which means that the sum of a rational number and an irrational number must be irrational.

Alternate reasoning: Suppose p is rational and q is irrational. Let $p + q = s$. If s is rational, then $s - p$ is irrational and this contradicts the finding in Question D, part (2). So, $p + q$ must be irrational.

2. Use similar reasoning as in Question E, part (1). Let p be rational ($p \neq 0$) and q be irrational. Assume that their product $pq = y$ is a rational number. We can rewrite the equation in terms of q, as $q = y\left(\frac{1}{p}\right)$. Now, $\frac{1}{p}$ is just the reciprocal of p, and because p is rational, its reciprocal $\frac{1}{p}$ will be rational. From Question D, part (1), the product of two rational numbers is rational. This means that q is rational, the product of two rational numbers. However, the original assumption was that q was irrational and cannot be both rational and irrational. Thus, the original assumption that $pq = y$ is rational must be false. Therefore, the product of a nonzero rational number and an irrational number must be an irrational number.

Note: Students may conjecture other properties of rational and irrational numbers. There are some surprising results. For example, the sum of two irrational numbers can be rational (e.g., $\pi + (-\pi) = 0$), and the product of two irrational numbers can be rational (e.g., $\sqrt{2} \cdot \sqrt{2} = 2$). In fact, the question "Is $\pi + e$ a rational or not?" remains unanswered. (e is an important mathematical constant like π. It is the base of the natural logarithm.)

AT A GLANCE 5

Notes

Say It With Symbols   **At a Glance**

5.3 Squaring Odd Numbers

> **Focus Question** What are some strategies for making and proving a conjecture?

Launch

Pick an odd number, square it, and then subtract 1. Have the class do this for several odd numbers. Then they will look for patterns, explain why the patterns work, and make conjectures.

Your students will organize their work in a table for the first few odd numbers and observe patterns. They may even give verbal explanations for why their conjectures work. Some conjectures are that the numbers are even, 4 and 8 are factors, the pattern of change looks quadratic, and so forth.

Explore

Encourage your students to find interesting patterns and conjectures. When students are ready, encourage them to write a general expression of an odd number to carry out the procedure. They should be able to see that 4 is a factor of the final expression. To get the factor of 8, they will need to multiply the numerator and denominator by 2. This shows that 8 is a factor or multiple of the number, which is the expression for triangular numbers from *Frogs, Fleas, and Painted Cubes*.

Some students have used a geometric argument to prove the conjecture that $s^2 - 1$ for all odd numbers s is 8 times the triangular number for $n - 1$. An example is shown in the Summarize.

If different strategies come up, have students put them on poster paper to use in the Summarize.

Summarize

Let students share their work. You may have conjectures other than the one that involves triangular numbers.

Some students may use a table, some may use a geometric argument with a diagram, and some may use algebraic reasoning.

Materials

Teaching Aid
- 5.3: Student Examples

Assessments
- Self-Assessment
- Notebook Checklist
- Unit Test

- graphing calculators (optional)
- poster paper (optional)

B. Answers will vary. Possible patterns: The numbers in the last column are multiples of 4; they are multiples of 8; or they are even.

C. Answers will vary. See Teaching Aid 5.3: Student Examples for some conjectures and proofs.

Answers to Problem 5.3

A.

x	x^2	$x^2 - 1$
1	1	0
3	9	8
5	25	24
7	49	48
9	81	80
11	121	120
13	169	168
15	225	224

At a Glance

Pacing ☐ Day

Mathematical Goals

_____

_____

_____

_____

Launch

_____

_____

_____

_____

_____

Materials

Explore

_____

_____

_____

_____

_____

Materials

Summarize

_____

_____

_____

_____

Materials

Notes

Applications

1. a. $2(10) + 2(5) + 4 = 34$ tiles

b. Possible expressions:
$2L + 2W + 4$
$2(L + 1) + 2(W + 1)$
$2(L + 2) + 2W$
$2L + 2(W + 2)$

c. See part (b) for some expressions; explanations will vary. Students might draw sketches. For example:

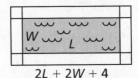

$2L + 2W + 4$

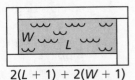

$2(L + 1) + 2(W + 1)$

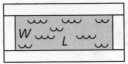

$2(L + 2) + 2W$

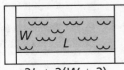

$2L + 2(W + 2)$

They might substitute values for L and W in the expressions; for example, when $W = 2$ and $L = 3$:
$2L + 2W + 4 = 2(3) + 2(2) + 4 = 14$
$2(L + 1) + 2(W + 1) = 2(4) + 2(3) = 14$
$2(L + 2) + 2W = 2(5) + 2(2) = 14$
$2L + 2(W + 2) = 2(3) + 2(4) = 14$

2. a. $4(7) + 4(0.5) = 30$ tiles

b. Possible answers:
$4s + 2$
$4(s + 0.5)$
$2s + 2(s + 1)$

c. See expressions in part (b). Students might substitute values for s [in this case two values (s, N) are sufficient because these are linear relationships], generate tables for both equations, or make a geometric argument to show that the two equations are equivalent. They may also graph each equation.

d. The relationship is linear; students may say that this is because the graphs are straight lines; the table increases by a constant value of 4 for every increase of 1 ft in the side length.

3. a. $2(30) + 2(20) + 2 = 102$ tiles

b. Possible answers:
$2L + 2W + 2$
$2(L + 0.5) + 2(W + 0.5)$
$2(W + 1) + 2L$

c. Students might substitute values for L and W, make tables or graphs, or make geometric arguments to show that their two expressions are equivalent.

4. a. First equation: $4\left(\frac{0}{2} + \frac{0}{4}\right) = 4(0) + 4 = 4$;
Second equation: $2(0 + 0.5) + 2(0 + 1.5) = 2(0.5) + 2(1.5) = 1 + 3 = 4$;
Third equation: $4\left[\frac{0 + (0 + 2)}{2}\right] = 4\left(\frac{2}{2}\right) = 4$

b. You cannot determine whether the expressions are equivalent by checking them at one point, although students may think that they are equivalent since these expressions produced the same number of tiles for $s = 0$.

c. First equation: $4\left(\frac{12}{2} + \frac{12}{4}\right) + 4 = 4(6 + 3) + 4 = 40$;
Second equation: $2(12 + 0.5) + 2(12 + 1.5) = 2(12.5) + 2(13.5) = 52$;
Third equation: $4\left[\frac{12 + (12 + 2)}{2}\right] = 4\left(\frac{26}{2}\right) = 4(13) = 52$

d. Since you can determine nonequivalency of linear equations by checking one point, the first expression is not equal to the second and third expressions because they did not produce the same number of tiles when you checked using the same side value.

In general, it is not enough to show that two expressions are equivalent when they have the same value at two different points, because you need to check all points, which is impossible. However, for linear equations such as those in this Exercise, checking only two values would be enough because only one line can pass through the two points. So linear expressions that agree on two values (two points) contain the same two points. So, the lines that they represent must be the same.

Students will either need to check all points, which is impossible, or know that two points uniquely determine a line.

5. a. The shape is the area between the circle and the square.

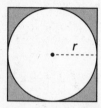

b. The shape is all the area inside the square except a quarter of the area of the circle.

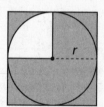

6. a. ii and iv

b. i and iii

c. For part (a), ii and iv are equivalent since:
$(s - 10)^2 = (s - 10)(s - 10)$
$= s(s - 10) - 10(s - 10)$
$= s^2 - 10s - 10s + 100$
$= s^2 - 20s + 100$

For part (b), i and iii are equivalent since $s(3s - 10) = 3s^2 - 10s$ and $2s^2 + s(s - 10) = 3s^2 - 10s$.

d. Answers will vary, but must be equivalent to $A = (s^2 - 20s + 100) + (3s^2 - 10s)$.

e. The equation in part (d) is a quadratic relationship.

7. a.

x	−3x + 6 + 5x	6 + 2x
−3	0	0
−2	2	2
−1	4	4
0	6	6
1	8	8
2	10	10
3	12	12

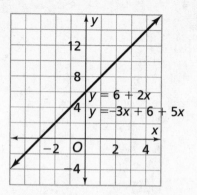

b. The expressions are equivalent because the table values are the same and the graph is a single line. **Note:** These are linear expressions, so it is enough to show that they pass through the same two points.

c. $-3x + 6 + 5x = 6 + -3x + 5x$
$= 6 + (-3 + 5)x = 6 + 2x$

8. a.

x	10 − 5x	5x − 10
−3	25	−25
−2	20	−20
−1	15	−15
0	10	−10
1	5	−5
2	0	0
3	−5	5

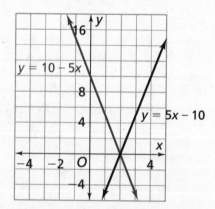

b. The expressions are not equivalent because the table values are different and the graphs are separate lines; one has a negative slope and one has a positive slope.

c. $10 - 5x = -5x + 10 \neq 5x - 10$

9. a.

x	(3x + 4) + (2x − 3)	5x + 1
−3	−14	−14
−2	−9	−9
−1	−4	−4
0	1	1
1	6	6
2	11	11
3	16	16

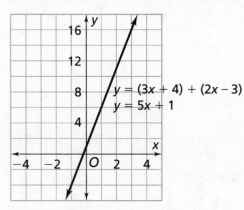

b. The expressions are equivalent because the table values are the same and the graph is a single line. **Note:** These are linear expressions, so it is enough to show that they all pass through the same two points.

c. $(3x + 4) + (2x − 3) = 3x + 2x + 4 − 3$
$= (3 + 2)x + 1 = 5x + 1$

10. a. $3x + 21$

b. $25 − 5x$

c. $8x − 16$

d. $x^2 + 4x + 2x + 8 = x^2 + x(4 + 2) + 8 = x^2 + 6x + 8$

11. a. $2(x + 3)$

b. $7(2 − x)$

c. Possible answers: $2(x − 5x)$ or $x(2 − 10) = −8x$

d. $x(3 + 4)$

12. a. equal; $3x + 7x = (3 + 7)x = 10x$

b. not equal; $5x − 10x = (5 − 10)x = −5x \neq 5x$

c. equal; $4(1 + 2x) − 3x = 4 + 8x − 3x = 4 + 5x = 5x + 4$
Using the Commutative Property of addition, $5x + 4 = 4 + 5x$.

d. equal; $5 − 3(2 − 4x) = 5 − 6 + 12x = −1 + 12x$

13. Step (1): Distributive Property
Step (2): Commutative Property
Step (3): Distributive Property
Step (4): Addition

14. Possible answers: $3(2x + 1)$, $x + 5x + 3$, $2x + 2 + 4x + 1$

15. $(7 + 5)p − p = 11p$

16. $7 + 5(p − p) = 7$

17. Parentheses are not needed.

Connections

18.

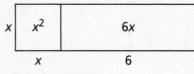
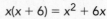

$x(x + 6) = x^2 + 6x$

19.

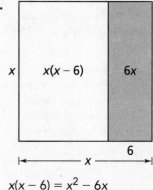

$x(x − 6) = x^2 − 6x$

20.

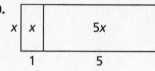

$x(5 + 1) = x + 5x$, or $6x$

21.

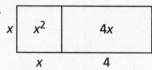

$x^2 + 4x = x(x + 4)$

22.

$x^2 - 2x$ 2

|← x →|

$x^2 - 2x = x(x - 2)$

23.

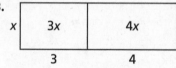

$3x + 4x = x(3 + 4)$, or $7x$

24. **a.** Area of water $= \pi(4)^2 = 16\pi \approx 50$ ft^2

b. Area of border $= \pi(5^2) - \pi(4^2) =$
$25\pi - 16\pi = 9\pi \approx 28$ ft^2

c. Area of water $= \pi r^2$

d. Area of border $= \pi(r + 1)^2 - \pi r^2$, or
$2\pi r + \pi$

25. B

26. I

27. **a.** For $s = 1$, 8 tiles are needed.
For $s = 2$, $8 + 4$ tiles are needed.
For $s = 3$, $8 + 4 + 4$ tiles are needed.
Thus, for any s, the number of tiles
needed is equal to 8 plus $(s - 1)$ fours,
or $N = 8 + 4(s - 1)$.

b. Percy's equation is equivalent to Stella's
equation, $4(s + 1)$. Explanations will
vary; they may be based on tables,
graphs, the substitution of specific
values of s, or the sameness of the
expressions.

28.

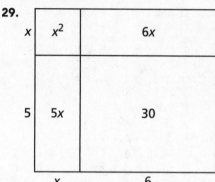

$(x + 1)(x + 4) = x^2 + 1x + 4x + 4$, or
$x^2 + 5x + 4$

29.

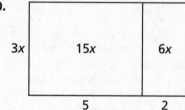

$(x + 5)(x + 6) = x^2 + 5x + 6x + 30$, or
$x^2 + 11x + 30$

30.

$3x(5 + 2) = 15x + 6x$, or $21x$

31.

$x^2 + x + 2x + 2 =$
$x^2 + 3x + 2 = (x + 1)(x + 2)$

32.

$x^2 + 7x + 10 = (x + 5)(x + 2)$

33.

$$x^2 + 14x + 49 = (x + 7)(x + 7)$$

34. For $2(s + 0.5) + 2(s + 1.5)$; the picture should look like:

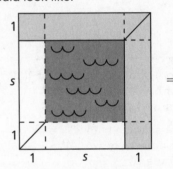

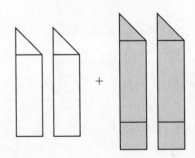

For $4\left[\dfrac{s + (s + 2)}{2}\right]$, the picture should look like:

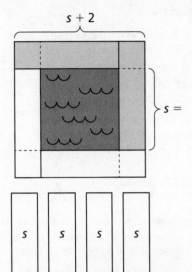

where $4\left[\dfrac{s + (s + 2)}{2}\right]$ is the area of half the shaded region multiplied by 4. Half the shaded region can be represented by one of the four rectangles to the right of the equal sign.

35. $\dfrac{8}{21}$

36. $\dfrac{17}{6}$

37. x

38. $\dfrac{1}{6}x$

39. 28

40. 12

41. $\dfrac{1}{7}$

42. 66

43. 5

44. -5

45. $-54x$

46. $3x$

47. $-6x$

48. 5

49. 12

50. 25

51. 3

52. a. Possible answers: $(2x)(4x) + \pi(x)^2$ or $\dfrac{1}{2}\pi(x)^2 + \dfrac{1}{2}\pi(x)^2 + 8x^2$

b. The fencing needed for the rectangular region is $4x + 4x = 8x$ since you do not count the two shorter sides. The two half circles each have a perimeter of $\dfrac{1}{2}\pi(2x)$, which is half of the circumference $\pi(2x)$. So the perimeter is $8x + 2\left[\dfrac{1}{2}\pi(2x)\right]$, or $2\pi x + 8x$.

c. Possible answers: $\pi x + \pi x + 4x + 4x$ or $(2\pi + 8)x$

53. a. Yes. $8 + 4(s - 1) = 8 + 4s - 4 =$
$8 - 4 + 4s = 4 + 4s = 4s + 4$

b. Hank

54. a. Since the expression represents her money after one year, she would have the money she put in, which is D, plus the interest the account accrues in that year, which is 0.10 times D, so the expression $D + 0.10D$ is correct.

b. $D(1 + 0.10)$

c. $\$1,500(1.1) = \$1,650$

55. a. Corey's estimate is correct:
$C = 200 + 10(50) = 200 + 500 = \$700$.

b. Duncan performed the operations incorrectly by doing the addition first:
$C = (200 + 10)50 = \$10,500$.

56. a. $S = \dfrac{200 + 10(20)}{20} = \dfrac{200 + 200}{20} = \dfrac{400}{20}$
$= \$20$

b. $S = \dfrac{200 + 10(N)}{N}$

c. $S = \dfrac{200 + 10(40)}{40} = \dfrac{200 + 400}{40} = \dfrac{600}{40}$
$= \$15$

57. a. Sarah performed the calculations correctly.

b. Emily did not use the Order of Operations correctly. In the second line, she added 4 and 11 instead of multiplying 11 and 3. In the third line, she added 15 and 10 to get 25 instead of multiplying the 15 by 3 (her incorrect calculation).

Extensions

58. The number of tiles in the first pool =
$4(3 \times 1) + 4(1)$
The number of tiles in the second pool =
$4(3 \times 2) + 4(2^2)$
The number of tiles in the third pool =
$4(3 \times 3) + 4(3^2)$

Therefore, the equation is $N = 4(3W) + 4W^2$, or $N = 4W^2 + 12W$.
(See Figure 1.)

Another solution path is $N = 4W(3 + W)$, which simplifies to $N = 4W^2 + 12W$.
(See Figure 2.)

Figure 1

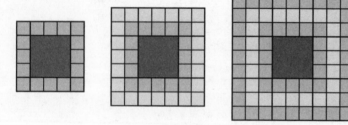

Figure 2

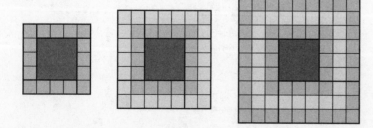

Say It With Symbols   **ACE Answers**

59. The number of tiles in the first pool =
$2(3 \times 1) + 2(5 \times 1) + 4(1^2)$
The number of tiles in the second pool =
$2(3 \times 2) + 2(5 \times 2) + 4(2^2)$
The number of tiles in the third pool =
$2(3 \times 3) + 2(5 \times 3) + 4(3^2)$
Therefore, the equation is $N = 2(3 \times W) + 2(5 \times W) + 4(W^2)$, which simplifies to
$N = 2(3W + 5W) + 4W^2 = 4W^2 + 16W$.
(See Figure 3.)

60. Puzzle1:

a. $2(n - 3) + 4n + 6n + 1 = 12n - 5$

b. $2(n - 3) + 4n + 6n + 1$
$= 2n - 6 + 4n + 6n + 1$ Distributive Prop.
$= 2n - 6 + (4 + 6)n + 1$ Distributive Prop.
$= 2n - 6 + 10n + 1$
$= 2n + 10n - 6 + 1$ Comm. Property
$= (2 + 10)n - 5$ Distributive Prop.
$= 12n - 5$

Puzzle 2:

a. $2n - 3 + 4n + 6(n + 1) = 12n + 3$

b. $2n - 3 + 4n + 6(n + 1)$
$= 2n - 3 + 4n + 6n + 6$ Distributive Prop.
$= 2n - 3 + (4 + 6)n + 6$ Distributive Prop.
$= 2n - 3 + 10n + 6$
$= 2n + 10n - 3 + 6$ Comm. Property
$= (2 + 10)n + 3$ Distributive Prop.
$= 12n + 3$

Puzzle 3:

a. $2n - 3 + 4n + 6n + 1 = 12n - 2$; no need for parentheses

b. $2n - 3 + 4n + 6n + 1$
$= 2n - 3 + (4 + 6)n + 1$ Distributive Prop.
$= 2n - 3 + 10n + 1$
$= 2n + 10n - 3 + 1$ Comm. Property
$= (2 + 10)n - 2$ Distributive Prop.
$= 12n - 2$

Puzzle 4:

a. $2n - (3 + 4)n + 6n + 1 = n + 1$

b. $2n - (3 + 4)n + 6n + 1$
$= 2n - 7n + 6n + 1$
$= (2 - 7 + 6)n + 1$ Distributive Prop.
$= n + 1$

Figure 3

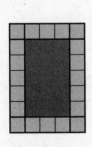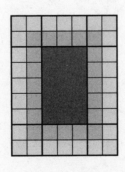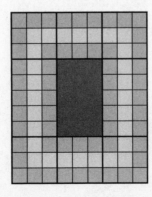

ACE ANSWERS 1

Applications

1. a. $I = 12n + 150$

b. $E = 250 + 4.25n$

c. $675; if you substitute 100 T-shirts into the income equation, you will get $12(100) + 150 = 1,350$ in income, and if you substitute 100 into the expense equation, you will get $E = 250 + 4.25(100) = 675$. So, the profit is $1,350 - 675 = 675$.

d. Possible answers:
$P = 12n + 150 - (250 + 4.25n)$,
$P = 12n + 150 - 4.25n - 250$, or
$P = 7.75n - 100$

2. a. $E = 125n + 30n + 700$ or
$E = 155n + 700$

b. $I = 350n$

c. $P = 350n - (125n + 30n + 700)$,
$P = 350n - 125n - 30n - 700$, or
$P = 195n - 700$

d. $4,175; substituting 25 for n into the profit equation,
$P = 195(25) - 700 = 4,175$

e. 9 bikers; after substituting 1,055 for P in the equation $P = 195n - 700$ and solving for n, the equation is $1,055 = 195n - 700$ or $1,755 = 195n$. After dividing each side by 195, the number of bikers is 9.

f. Acceptable answers: The profit equation is a linear equation because it can be written in the form $y = mx + b$. It has a constant rate of change and a linear graph.

3. B

4. F

5. C

6. $375; since the probability of rain is 50% or 0.50, the number of predicted visitors is $V = 600 - 500(0.50) = 350$. Based on this number, the profit will be $P = 2.50(350) - 500 = 375$.

7. 72%; if students use the combined equation, which is $P = -1,250R + 1,000$ and solve for R when $P = 100$, they should get 72%. If students use both equations separately, then $P = 10$, and the number of visitors would be 240, which can be found by solving the equation $100 = 2.50n - 500$ for n. So, to find the probability of rain, solve the other equation $240 = 600 - 500R$ for R to get 0.72 or 72%.

8. a. $325; combining both equations into one results in the equation $B = 100 + 0.50(600 - 500R)$, or $B = 400 - 250R$. If the probability of rain is 30%, the daily employee-bonus fund is $325. Students may use both equations separately to find the number of visitors.
$V = 600 - 500R$ when $R = 30\%$, which is 450. Then substitute 450 into the equation $B = 100 + 0.50V$ and solve for V to get $325.

b. $B = 100 + 0.50(600 - 500R)$ or $B = 400 - 250R$

c. $275; $B = 400 - 250(0.5)$, which is $B = \$275$

d. 10%; solving the equation $375 = 400 - 250R$ for R gives $R = 0.1$, or 10%.

9. a. 65°F;
$$V = 50(T - 45)$$
$$1,000 = 50(T - 45)$$
$$1,000 = 50T - 2,250$$
$$1,000 + 2,250 = 50T - 2,250 + 2,250$$
$$3,250 = 50T$$
$$\frac{3,250}{50} = \frac{50T}{50}$$
$$65 = T$$

b. To find the profit based on the temperature, substitute $50(T - 45)$ for V in the equation $P = 4.25V - 300$ to get $P = 4.25[50(T - 45)] - 300$.

c. $P = -9,862.5 + 212.5T$; to simplify $P = 4.25[50(T - 45)] - 300$, first distribute the 50 by multiplying it by T and -45. Then multiply each of those terms by 4.25, and combine like terms:
$P = 4.25[50(T - 45)] - 300$
$P = 4.25[50T - 2,250] - 300$
$P = -9,562.5 + 212.5T - 300$
$P = -9,862.5 + 212.5T$

The 212.50 represents the rate of change for the profit when the temperature increases 1°. The y-intercept is $-9,862.5$. However, $-9,862.5$ does not have a physical meaning since T must always be greater than or equal to 458 to have a positive number of visitors. T represents the independent variable, or the temperature, and P represents the dependent variable, or the profit, which depends on the temperature because it changes at the rate of 212.50 dollars per 18° change in temperature.

d. $5,012.50; students may choose to use either of their equations from Question B, parts (b) or (c).

10. a. Consider the formula for volume of a cylinder, $V = \pi r^2 h$. With the radius doubled, $V = \pi(2r)^2 h$, which equals $V = 4\pi r^2 h$. So, when the radius is doubled, the volume increases by a factor of 4.

b. When the height is doubled, the volume increases by a factor of 2, $V = \pi r^2(2h) = 2\pi r^2 h$.

11. a. Consider the formula for volume of a cone, $V = \frac{1}{3}\pi r^2 h$. With the radius doubled, $V = \frac{1}{3}\pi(2r)^2 h$, which equals $V = \frac{4}{3}\pi r^2 h$. So, when the radius is doubled, the volume increases by a factor of 4.

b. When the height is doubled, the volume increases by a factor of 2; $V = \frac{1}{3}\pi r^2(2h) = \frac{2}{3}\pi r^2 h$.

12. a. Consider the formula for volume of a sphere, $V = \frac{4}{3}\pi r^3$. With the radius doubled, $V = \frac{4}{3}\pi(2r)^3$, which equals $V = \frac{4}{3}\pi \cdot 8r^3 = \frac{32}{3}\pi r^3$. So, when the radius is doubled, the volume increases by a factor of 8, or 2^3.

b. Similarly, when the radius is tripled, the volume increases by a factor of 27, or 3^3.

c. Similarly, when the radius is quadrupled, the volume increases by a factor of 64, or 4^3.

13. a. $A = \pi \times 5^2 \approx 78.54$ square feet

b. $A = \pi r^2$

c. $V = \pi \times 5^2 \times 3 + \frac{4}{6} \times \pi \times 5^3 \approx 497$ cubic feet

d. $V = \pi r^2 h + \frac{4}{6} \times \pi r^3$

14. The volume of the cylindrical portion of the rocket plus the conical tip is $V = \pi r^2 \ell + \frac{1}{3}\pi r^2 h$.

15. The volume of the hemisphere plus the cylindrical body plus the conical end is $V = \frac{4}{6}\pi r^3 + \pi r^2 \ell + \frac{1}{3}\pi r^2 h$.

16. a. The volume of the prism is $6 \times 6 \times 4$ cubic units $= 144$ cubic units. So, the volume of the pyramid is $\frac{144}{3} = 48$ cubic units.

b. A cube with edge length 2 units would have volume 8 cubic units. A pyramid that fits inside of this cube would have the given volume.

c. A cube with edge length 3 units would have volume 27 cubic units. A pyramid that fits inside this cube would have the given volume.

d. A cube with edge length $3x$ units would have volume $27x^3$ cubic units. So, a pyramid with base $3x$ by $3x$ and height $3x$ units would have a volume of $\frac{1}{3}(27x^3) = 9x^3$.

Connections

17. J; students can try an example like $a = 1$ and $b = 2$ to check that J is false. The other letters are true; F and H are the Associative Property of Addition and Multiplication, respectively, and G is the Commutative Property of Multiplication.

18. $x(x + 5) = x^2 + 5x$

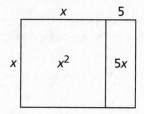

19. $(2 + x)(2 + 3x) = (2 + x)2 + (2 + x)3x = 4 + 2x + 6x + 3x^2 = 4 + 8x + 3x^2$

	2	3x
2	4	6x
x	2x	$3x^2$

20. $(x + 2)(2x + 3) = (x + 2)2x + (x + 2)3 = 2x^2 + 4x + 3x + 6 = 2x^2 + 7x + 6$

	2x	3
x	$2x^2$	3x
2	4x	6

21. a.
$$11x - 12 = 30 + 5x$$
$$11x - 12 + 12 = 30 + 12 + 5x$$
$$11x = 42 + 5x$$
$$11x - 5x = 42 + 5x - 5x$$
$$6x = 42$$
$$\frac{6x}{6} = \frac{42}{6}$$
$$x = 7$$

b. To check, substitute 7 into the original equation for x and see if the values on each side of the equal sign are equal to each other.
$$11x - 12 = 30 + 5x$$
$$11(7) - 12 = 30 + 5(7)$$
$$77 - 12 = 30 + 35$$
$$65 = 65$$

c. To solve the equation using a graph, first graph each of the equations $y = 11x - 12$ and $y = 30 + 5x$ and use the x-value of their point of intersection for the solution. To solve the equation using a table, look on the tables for each equation and see for which value of x their y-values are equal.

22. a. $1,000

b.

Number of Soccer Balls	Income From Soccer Balls (dollars)	Expenses of Soccer Balls (dollars)
500	500	1,250
1,000	1,000	1,500
3,000	3,000	2,500

c. To find the profit of soccer balls, subtract the expenses from the income. See table below.

Number of Soccer Balls	Profit of Soccer Balls (dollars)
500	$500 - 1,250 = -750$
1,000	$1,000 - 1,500 = -500$
3,000	$3,000 - 2,500 = 500$

d. The break-even point is at 2,000 soccer balls; the income and expenses are both $2,000.

e. Income = 1 times the number of soccer balls or $I = 1n$
Expenses = 1,000 + 0.5 times number of soccer balls or $E = 1,000 + 0.5n$
Profit = Income − Expenses,
$P = 1n - (1,000 + 0.5n)$,
$P = n - 1,000 - 0.5n$, or
$P = 0.5x - 1,000$

f. $-125 or a loss of 125 dollars
(See Figure 1.)

g. $22,000;

$$\text{Profit} = -1,000 + 0.5(\text{number of soccer balls})$$
$$\$10,000 = -1,000 + 0.5n$$
$$10,000 + 1,000 = -1,000 + 1,000 + 0.5n$$
$$11,000 = 0.5n$$
$$\frac{11,000}{0.5} = \frac{0.5n}{0.5}$$
$$22,000 = n$$

The number of soccer balls produced and sold if the profit is $10,000 is 22,000.

23. One possible solution:

$$7x + 15 = 12x + 5$$
$$7x - 7x + 15 = 12x - 7x + 5$$
$$15 = 5x + 5$$
$$15 - 5 = 5x + 5 - 5$$
$$10 = 5x$$
$$\frac{10}{5} = \frac{5x}{5}$$
$$2 = x$$

Check:

$$7x + 15 = 12x + 5$$
$$7(2) + 15 = 12(2) + 5$$
$$14 + 15 = 24 + 5$$
$$29 = 29$$

24. $x = 2$; the solution is the same as Exercise 23 because the Commutative Property does not change the value of the variables when you are solving an equation.

25. One possible solution:

$$-3x + 5 = 2x - 10$$
$$-3x - 2x + 5 = 2x - 2x - 10$$
$$-5x + 5 = -10$$
$$-5x + 5 - 5 = -10 - 5$$
$$-5x = -15$$
$$\frac{-5x}{-5} = \frac{-15}{-5}$$
$$x = 3$$

Check:

$$-3x + 5 = 2x - 10$$
$$-3(3) + 5 = 2(3) - 10$$
$$-9 + 5 = 6 - 10$$
$$-4 = -4$$

26. One possible method:

$$14 - 3x = 1.5x + 5$$
$$14 - 3x - 14 = 1.5x + 5 - 14$$
$$-3x = 1.5x - 9$$
$$-3x - 1.5x = 1.5x - 9 - 1.5x$$
$$(-3 - 1.5)x = -9$$
$$-4.5x = -9$$
$$x = 2$$

Check:

$$14 - 3(2) = 1.5(2) + 5$$
$$8 = 3 + 5$$
$$8 = 8$$

27. One possible solution:

$$9 - 4x = \frac{(3 + x)}{2}$$
$$2(9 - 4x) = 2 \cdot \frac{(3 + x)}{2}$$
$$18 - 8x = 3 + x$$
$$18 - 8x - x = 3 + x - x$$
$$18 - 9x = 3$$
$$18 - 9x - 18 = 3 - 18$$
$$-9x = -15$$
$$\frac{-9x}{-9} = \frac{-15}{-9}$$
$$x = 1\frac{2}{3}$$

Check:

$$9 - 4\left(1\frac{2}{3}\right) = \frac{3 + \left(1\frac{2}{3}\right)}{2}$$
$$9 - 6\frac{2}{3} = \frac{4\frac{2}{3}}{2}$$
$$2\frac{1}{3} = 2\frac{1}{3}$$

Figure 1

Number of Soccer Balls	Income = # of Soccer Balls $I = 1n$	Expenses = 1,000 + 0.5 (# of soccer balls)	Profit = Income − Expenses or $P = 0.5n - 1,000$
1,750	1,750	1,000 + 0.5(1,750) = 1,000 + 875 = 1,875	1,750 − 1,875 = −125, or 0.5(1,750) − 1,000 = 875 − 1,000 = −125

ACE Answers

28. One possible solution:

$$-3(x + 5) = \frac{(2x - 10)}{3}$$

$$-3x - 15 = \frac{(2x - 10)}{3}$$

$$3(-3x - 15) = 3 \cdot \frac{(2x - 10)}{3}$$

$$-9x - 45 = 2x - 10$$

$$-9x - 2x - 45 = 2x - 2x - 10$$

$$-11x - 45 = -10$$

$$-11x - 45 + 45 = -10 + 45$$

$$-11x = 35$$

$$\frac{-11x}{-11} = \frac{35}{-11}$$

$$x = -3\tfrac{2}{11}$$

Check:

$$-3\left(-3\tfrac{2}{11} + 5\right) = \frac{2\left(-3\tfrac{2}{11}\right) - 10}{3}$$

$$-3\left(-1\tfrac{9}{11}\right) = \frac{\frac{-70}{11} - 10}{3}$$

$$\frac{-60}{11} = \frac{\frac{-180}{11}}{3}$$

$$\frac{-60}{11} = \frac{-60}{11}$$

29. a. The two bids are equal when the y-values for a common x-value are equal. This occurs when $x = 25$ and $y = 200$, meaning the bids are both $200 for 25 books.

x (Number of books printed)	y = 100 + 4x (dollars)	y = 25 + 7x (dollars)
10	140	95
15	160	130
20	180	165
25	200	200
30	220	235

b.

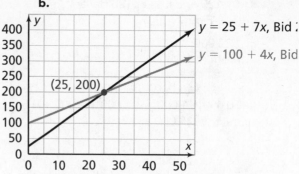

c. For 25 books, the bids are equal. The graph shows that for more than 25 books, Bid 1 is less than Bid 2 because the graph for Bid 1 is below the graph for Bid 2. For example, if the number of books is 26, Bid 1 is $204 and Bid 2 is $207. Since Bid 2 increases more for each book, if the number of books is greater than 25, Bid 1 is lower.

30. a. Bid 1: $100 + 4(75) = \$400$,
Bid 2: $25 + 7(75) = \$550$

Students might also find these values from the table or graph.

b. The greatest number of books that can be printed is 50 for Bid 1 and 39 for Bid 2. Explanations will vary. Students might extend their tables or graphs, use trial-and-error, or apply methods for solving linear equations.

31. The related equations are $y = 8x$ and $y = 30 + 6x$. The two bids are equal when $x = 15$ and $y = 120$, meaning they are both $120 for 15 books. Explanations will vary: students may use tables, graphs, or begin to see a pattern and solve the equations $8x = 30 + 6x$ symbolically.

32. $3.14 \times 4.25^2 \times 5.5$ represents the volume of a cylinder with radius 4.25 and height 5.5.

33. $\frac{1}{3} \times 3.14 \times 4.25^2 \times 5.5$ represents the volume of a cone with radius 4.25 and height 5.5.

34. $\frac{4}{3} \times 3.14 \times 4.25^3$ represents the volume of a sphere with radius 4.25.

35. $\frac{1}{3} \times 3.14 \times 4.25^2 \times 5.5 + \frac{4}{6} \times 3.14 \times 4.25^3$ represents the volume of a cone with radius 4.25 and height 5.5 and a hemisphere with a radius of 4.25.

36. $3.14 \times 4.25^2 \times 5.5 + \frac{4}{6} \times 3.14 \times 4.25^3$ represents the volume of a cylinder with radius 4.25 and height 5.5 and a hemisphere with a radius of 4.25.

37. $3.14 \times 4.25^2 \times 5.5 + \frac{1}{3} \times 3.14 \times 4.25^2 \times 3.5$ represents the volume of a cylinder with radius 4.25 and height 5.5 combined with a cone with a radius of 4.25 and a height of 3.5.

38. $3.14 \times 4.25^2 \times 5.5 - \frac{4}{6} \times 3.14 \times 4.25^3$ represents the volume of a cylinder with radius 4.25 and height 5.5 with a hollow space of a hemisphere with a radius of 4.25 carved out.

39. $3.14 \times 4.25^2 \times 5.5 - \frac{1}{3} \times 3.14 \times 4.25^2 \times 3.5$ represents the volume of a cylinder with radius 4.25 and height 5.5 with a hollow space of a cone with a radius of 4.25 and height of 3.5 carved out.

Extensions

40. a. $P = 15x - 500 + 106x - x^2$

   b. The maximum profit is $3,160.25, which occurs between 60 and 61 people. That is, the maximum profit occurs when $x = 60.5$, which means 6,050 people since x is in hundreds.

41. a. The vertical slice of a cylinder results in a rectangular face.

   b. The horizontal slice of a cylinder results in a circular face.

42. a. The vertical slice of a cone results in a triangular face.

   b. The horizontal slice of a cone results in a circular face.

43. a. The vertical slice of a sphere results in a circular face.

   b. The horizontal slice of a sphere results in a circular face.

Applications

1. a. Income will be
$1{,}000 + 5(40) + 15(30) = \$1{,}650$.
Expenses will be
$500 + 250 + 6(40) + 8.50(30) = \$1{,}245$.
The profit is thus
$\$1{,}650 - \$1{,}245 = \$405$.

b. $P = (1{,}000 + 5c + 15a) - (750 + 6c + 8.50a)$

c. $P = 1{,}000 + 5c + 15a - 750 - 6c - 8.50a$
$P = 250 - c + 6.50a$

d. $P = 250 - 40 + 6.50(30)$
$P = 250 - 40 + 195$
$P = 210 + 195$
$P = 405$
The answer is the same as in part (a): $405 profit.

e.
$P = 250 - c + 6.50a$
$\$1{,}099 = 250 - 100 + 6.50a$
$1{,}099 = 150 + 6.50a$
$1{,}099 - 150 = 150 - 150 + 6.50a$
$949 = 6.50a$
$\dfrac{949}{6.50} = \dfrac{650a}{6.50}$
$146 = a$
There are 146 adults registered for the event.

2. a. When evaluating the second set of parentheses, Marcel distributed the minus sign to the 500, but not to the other three terms.

b. Kirsten combined $5c - 6c$ and got c instead of $-c$.

3. $1{,}000 = 200 + 50(T - 70)$
$1{,}000 = 200 + 50T - 3{,}500$
$1{,}000 = 50T - 3{,}300$
$4{,}300 = 50T$
$86 = T$
Other logical arguments are possible. Students might choose to solve this problem with a table or graph.

4. $10 + 2(3 + 2x) = 0$
$10 + 6 + 4x = 0$
$16 + 4x = 0$
$16 + 4x - 16 = 0 - 16$
$4x = -16$
$x = -4$

5. $10 - 2(3 + 2x) = 0$
$10 - 6 - 4x = 0$
$4 - 4x = 0$
$4 - 4x - 4 = 0 - 4$
$-4x = -4$
$x = 1$

6. $10 + 2(3 - 2x) = 0$
$10 + 6 - 4x = 0$
$16 - 4x = 0$
$16 - 4x - 16 = 0 - 16$
$-4x = -16$
$x = 4$

7. $10 - 2(3 - 2x) = 0$
$10 - 6 + 4x = 0$
$4 + 4x = 0$
$4 + 4x - 4 = 0 - 4$
$4x = -4$
$x = -1$

8. a. 30;
$750 + 22(N - 12) = 650 + 30(N - 10)$
$750 + 22N - 264 = 650 + 30N - 300$
$486 + 22N = 350 + 30N$
$486 - 350 + 22N = 350 - 350 + 30N$
$136 + 22N = 30N$
$136 + 22N - 22N = 30N - 22N$
$\dfrac{136}{8} = \dfrac{8N}{8}$
$17 = N$

Note: For this context to make sense, $N \geq 12$.

b. One possible way to check that the solution is correct is to substitute the value for N, 17, into each equation, solve for cost, and see if both equations have the same value.

c. The point on the graphs at which the two lines intersect is the number of tiles for which the cost estimates are equal. Using a table, you would look for the number of tiles for which both companies have the same cost values.

d. *Tile and Beyond* is cheaper than *Cover and Surround It* when the number of tiles is less than 17. *Tile and Beyond* charges less start-up cost than *Cover and Surround It*; thus it is cheaper when fewer than 30 tiles are used.

e. $C = 650 + 30(N - 10)$
$C = 650 + 30N - 300$
$C = 30N + 350$
The 30 means that each tile costs 30 dollars and the 290 is the start-up cost.

9. 80 boxes; students may graph the two equations and find the x-coordinate of the intersection point. Or they may make a table for each equation and find for which x-coordinate the profits are equal. If students solve symbolically:

$4s - 2(10 + s) = 5s - (100 + 2s)$
$4s - 20 - 2s = 5s - 100 - 2s$
$2s - 20 = 3s - 100$
$2s - 20 + 100 = 3s - 100 + 100$
$2s + 80 = 3s$
$2s + 80 - 2s = 3s - 2s$
$80 = s$

10. One possible answer method:
$8x + 16 = 6x$
$8x + 16 - 8x = 6x - 8x$
$16 = -2x$
$-8 = x$

Check:
$8(-8) + 16 = 6(-8)$
$-64 + 16 = -48$
$-48 = -48$

11. One possible answer method:
$8(x + 2) = 6x$
$8x + 16 = 6x$
$8x + 16 - 8x = 6x - 8x$
$16 = -2x$
$-8 = x$

Check:
$8(-8 + 2) = 6(-8)$
$8(-6) = -48$
$-48 = -48$

12. One possible answer method:
$6 + 8(x + 2) = 6x$
$6 + 8x + 16 = 6x$
$22 + 8x = 6x$
$22 + 8x - 8x = 6x - 8x$
$22 = -2x$
$-11 = x$

Check:
$6 + 8(x + 2) = 6x$
$6 + 8(-11 + 2) = 6(-11)$
$6 + 8(-9) = -66$
$6 + (-72) = -66$
$-66 = -66$

13. One possible answer method:
$4 + 5(x + 2) = 7x$
$4 + 5x + 10 = 7x$
$14 + 5x - 5x = 7x - 5x$
$14 = 2x$
$7 = x$

Check:
$4 + 5(7 + 2) = 7(7)$
$4 + 5(9) = 49$
$49 = 49$

14. One possible answer:
$2x - 3(x + 6) = -4(x - 1)$
$2x - 3x - 18 = -4x + 4$
$-x - 18 = -4x + 4$
$-x - 18 - 4 = -4x + 4 - 4$
$-x - 22 = -4x$
$-x - 22 + x = -4x + x$
$-22 = -3x$
$x = \frac{22}{3}$, or $x = 7\frac{1}{3}$

Check:
$2\left(\frac{22}{3}\right) - 3\left(\frac{22}{3} + 6\right) = -4\left(\frac{22}{3} - 1\right)$
$\frac{44}{3} - 22 - 18 = -\frac{88}{3} + 4$
$\frac{44}{3} - 40 = -\frac{88}{3} + \frac{12}{3}$
$\frac{44}{3} - \frac{120}{3} = -\frac{88}{3} + \frac{12}{3}$
$-\frac{76}{3} = -\frac{76}{3}$

15. One possible answer:
$2 - 3(x + 4) = 9 - (3 + 2x)$
$2 - 3x - 12 = 9 - 3 - 2x$
$-3x - 10 = 6 - 2x$
$-3x - 10 - 6 = 6 - 2x - 6$
$-3x - 16 = -2x$
$-3x - 16 + 3x = -2x + 3x$
$-16 = x$

Check:
$2 - 3(-16 + 4) = 9 - (3 + 2(-16))$
$2 - 3(-12) = 9 - (3 - 32)$
$2 + 36 = 9 - (-29)$
$38 = 38$

16. One possible answer:
$2.75 - 7.75(5 - 2x) = 26$
$2.75 - 38.75 + 15.5x = 26$
$-36 + 15.5x = 26$
$-36 + 36 + 15.5x = 26 + 36$
$15.5x = 62$
$x = 4$

Check:
$$2.75 - 7.75(5 - 2(4)) = 26$$
$$2.5 - 7.75(5 - 8) = 26$$
$$2.75 - 7.75(-3) = 26$$
$$2.75 + 23.25 = 26$$
$$26 = 26$$

17.
$$\frac{1}{2}x + 4 = \frac{2}{3}x$$
$$\frac{1}{2}x + 4 - \frac{1}{2}x = \frac{2}{3}x - \frac{1}{2}x$$
$$4 = \frac{1}{6}x$$
$$4 \div \frac{1}{6} = x$$
$$24 = x$$

Check:
$$\frac{1}{2}(24) + 4 = \frac{2}{3}(24)$$
$$12 + 4 = 16$$
$$16 = 16$$

18. $x = -5$. The equation is conditional. The graph is a pair of intersecting lines, which meet in one point. There is only one solution to this Exercise.

19. $-15 = -15$. The equation is an identity. The graph is one line, so there are an infinite number of solutions.

20. $x = 0$. The equation is conditional. The graph is a pair of intersecting lines, which meet in one point. There is only one solution to this Exercise.

21. $-15 = -20$. The equation is a contradiction. The graph is a pair of parallel lines, which have no points in common. There is no solution.

22. $0 = 0$. The equation is an identity. The graph is one line, so there are an infinite number of solutions.

23. $7 = 13$. The equation is a contradiction. The graph is a pair of parallel lines, which have no points in common. There is no solution.

24. a. $x^2 - 4$ **b.** $x^2 - 25$
    c. $x^2 - 16$ **d.** $x^2 - 144$

25. a. $(x + 1)(x + 4)$
    b. $(x + 2)(x + 4)$
    c. $(x - 5)(x - 2)$
    d. $x(x + 7)$

    e. $(x - 1)(x + 6)$
    f. $(2x + 3)(x - 4)$
    g. $(x + 1)(x - 8)$
    h. $x(x - 5)$

26. a. $(x + 3)(x - 3)$
    b. $(x + 6)(x - 6)$
    c. $(x - 7)(x + 7)$
    d. $(x + 20)(x - 20)$
    e. $(x - 8)(x + 8)$
    f. $(x - 12)(x + 12)$

27. $x^2 + 1.5x = 0$
$x(x + 1.5) = 0$
$x = 0$ or $x = -1.5$

28. $x^2 + 6x + 8 = 0$
$(x + 2)(x + 4) = 0$
$x = -2$ or $x = -4$

29. $8x - x^2 = 0$
$x(8 - x) = 0$
$x = 0$ or $x = 8$

30. a. The jump equation is quadratic.

    b. $-8t(2t - 1)$ or $8t(-2t + 1)$. Some students may write an equivalent form like $2(-8t^2 + 4t)$, for example; however, this will not help them when they try to solve symbolically in part (c), since there is still a quadratic factor in this expression.

    c. $\frac{1}{2}$; the flea lands on the ground when the height is 0 ft. So by solving the equation $0 = -16t^2 + 8t$, which is the same as solving $0 = 8t(-2t + 1)$, students should get $8t = 0$ or $-2t + 1 = 0$. So $t = 0$, which is when the flea starts the jump, or $t = \frac{1}{2}$, which is when the flea lands back on the ground.

31. a.

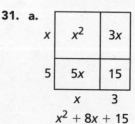

$$x^2 + 8x + 15$$

b.

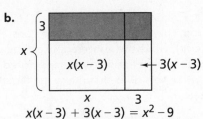

$x(x - 3) + 3(x - 3) = x^2 - 9$

c.

1	x	x	3
x	x^2	x^2	$3x$

x x 3

$2x^2 + 5x + 3$

Note: There are other area models that use $2x + 3$ and $x + 1$.

32. a. $x^2 + 8x + 15 = 0$
$(x + 5)(x + 3) = 0$
$x + 5 = 0$ or $x + 3 = 0$
$x = -5$ or $x = -3$

b. $x^2 - 9 = 0$
$(x - 3)(x + 3) = 0$
or $x^2 - 9 = 0$
$x^2 = 9$
$x = 3$ or $x = -3$

c. $2x^2 + 5x + 3 = 0$
$2x^2 + 2x + 3x + 3 = 0$
$2x(x + 1) + 3(x + 1) = 0$
$(2x + 3)(x + 1) = 0$
$x = -\frac{3}{2}$ or $x = -1$

33. $6x^2 - x = 1$
Solution:
$6x^2 - x - 1 = 0$
$(3x + 1)(2x - 1) = 0$
$3x + 1 = 0$ or $2x - 1 = 0$
$x = -\frac{1}{3}$ or $x = \frac{1}{2}$
The factors the student gave were $(3x - 1)$ $(2x + 1)$, which are the wrong factors, since when you use the Distributive Property you get $6x^2 - 2x + 3x - 1$ or $6x^2 + x - 1$, and you need the middle term to be $-1x$, not $1x$. With trial and error, students may find that if they switch the signs, they can find the correct factorization. So the correct factorization is $(3x + 1)(2x - 1)$ with solutions of $-\frac{1}{3}$ and $\frac{1}{2}$.
To help the student, first I would tell the student to check answers in the original equation to see if the answers are correct. When factoring $6x^2 - x - 1$, students may suggest an alteration of Jaime's method that they found in Problem 3.3, or they can make an area model.

34. The mistake is that the student attempted to isolate the n on the left side of the equal sign by multiplying each side by $\frac{1}{24n}$. By doing this, the solution of $n = 0$ disappears so the student is only partially correct. To help the student, I would tell the student to factor the expression $24n^2 - 16n$ by factoring out $8n$ and getting the new equation $8n(3n - 2) = 0$ to solve. By setting the expression equal to zero, you get $n = 0$ or $n = \frac{2}{3}$.

Connections

35. a. Substitute $11n$ (total number of boxes sold based on the number of choir members) for s, the number of boxes sold, in the equation $P = 5s - (100 + 2s)$ and you will get $P = 5(11n) - [100 + 2(11n)]$.

b. You can simplify the new equation for profit in part (a) by multiplying inside the parentheses, multiplying outside the parentheses, then applying the Distributive Property by multiplying -1 by the numbers inside the brackets, and then combining like terms.

$P = 5(11n) - [100 + 22n]$
$P = 55n - 100 - 22n$
$P = 33n - 100$

c. If the number of choir members is 47, you would substitute it for n in the equation and solve for P.
$P = 33(47) - 100$
$P = 1,551 - 100$
$P = \$1,451$

d. Substitute 1,088 for P and solve for n.

$$1,088 = 33n - 100$$
$$1,088 + 100 = 33n - 100 + 100$$
$$1,188 = 33n$$
$$\frac{1,188}{33} = \frac{33n}{33}$$
$$36 = n$$

There are 36 choir members when the profit is $1,088.

e. The number of boxes s is 11 times the number of choir members, $s = 11n$. Therefore, when there are 36 choir members, there are $11(36) = 396$ boxes.

36. a. 11; $48 = 2s + 2(s + 2)$
$$48 = 2s + 2s + 4$$
$$44 = 4s$$
$$11 = s$$

b. 11; $48 = 4(s + 2) - 4$
$$48 = 4s + 8 - 4$$
$$48 = 4s + 4$$
$$48 - 4 = 4s + 4 - 4$$
$$44 = 4s$$
$$s = 11$$

c. The answers are the same since the expressions are equivalent expressions. So for any N-value, the corresponding s-value for both equations is the same.

37. D; since $\frac{3}{4}(20 - 4) = \frac{3}{4}(16) = 12$

38. H; since $5^2(7 - 5) + 1 = 25(2) + 1 = 50 + 1 = 51$

39. The largest square pool that can be built for the 40 tiles is a 9-tile-by-9-tile pool because that would use (9 tiles $\times$ 4 sides) + the 4 corner tiles, totaling 40 tiles.

40. $16x + 22$; $2(9x + 15) - (8 + 2x) = 18x + 30 - 8 - 2x = 16x + 22$

41. $x - 32$; $(7x - 12) - 2(3x + 10) = 7x - 12 - 6x - 20 = x - 32$

42. a. If the coefficient of the x^2 term is positive, then the graph has a minimum point.

If the coefficient of the x^2 term is negative, then the graph has a maximum point.

Either form can be used, but the coefficient of x^2 is immediately available in the expanded form. In the factored form, some mental calculation may have to be done to find the coefficient.

b. The y-intercept can be read directly from the expanded form (the constant term), while the x-intercepts can be determined easily from the factored form (the values that make the factors zero).

c. The line of symmetry is a vertical line perpendicular to the x-axis through a point with an x-coordinate half way between the x-intercepts. The factored form can be used to find this point.

d. The x-coordinate of the maximum/minimum point lies on the line of symmetry. The factored form can be used to find the x-coordinate. To find the y-coordinate, substitute the value of x into either form to calculate the y-value.

43. Approximately 4.899 meters; since $x^2 = 24$, $x = \sqrt{24} \approx 4.899$.

44. Approximately 2.76 meters; using the formula $A = \pi x^2$, you get $24 = \pi x^2$, and so $x^2 = \frac{24}{\pi}$ and $x \approx 2.76$.

45. Approximately 7.44; you can find the height by using the Pythagorean Theorem. When the height (altitude) is drawn, the resulting triangle has a side of length $\frac{1}{2}x$ and a hypotenuse of length x. Substitute these into the Pythagorean Theorem to solve $\left(\frac{1}{2}x\right)^2 + h^2 = x^2$ for the height h. So the height is $\frac{\sqrt{3}}{2}x$. Since the area is 24, you can use the equation $24 = \frac{1}{2}(x)\left(\frac{\sqrt{3}}{2}x\right)$ to find the value of x. Simplifying the right side gives $24 = \frac{\sqrt{3}}{4}x^2$. Dividing each side by $\frac{\sqrt{3}}{4}$, you get $x^2 \approx 55.4256$, so $x \approx 7.44$.

46. The triangle has base 12 and height 4; since $24 = \frac{1}{2}(3x)(x) = \frac{1}{2}(3x^2) = \frac{3}{2}x^2$ and $24 = \frac{3}{2}x^2$ simplifies to $16 = x^2$, the dimensions of the triangle are 4 and $3 \times 4 = 12$.

47. 3 and 8 meters; since $(x + 5)x = 24$, you need two factors of 24 that are 5 apart. These are 8 and 3, so $x = 3$. The dimensions of the rectangle are 3 and 8.

48. About 1.06 meters; the volume of the sphere is $V = \frac{4}{3}\pi\left(\frac{3}{2}\right)^3 = \frac{4}{3}\pi\left(\frac{27}{8}\right) = \frac{9}{2}\pi$ and the volume of the cylinder is $V = \pi x^2(4)$, so you need $\pi x^2(4) = \frac{9}{2}\pi$. Dividing each side by 4π, you get $x^2 = \frac{9}{8}$. So the radius, x, of the cylindrical tank must be $\sqrt{\frac{9}{8}}$ or about 1.06 meters. (**Note:** This is an opportunity to see how students deal with irrational numbers involving fractions.)

49. a. Some possible answers: $y = x^2 + 4x + 4$, $y = x^2 + 6x + 9$, $y = x^2 - 4x + 4$

   b. Some possible answers: $y = x^2 - 16$, $y = x^2 + 7x + 10$ and $y = x^2 + 6x - 7$

50. a. 3 seconds; to find out how long the ball is in the air, students could find out at what time the ball hits the ground, or when height is zero. Students can do this by looking at a table or a graph for the value of t for which h is zero. Alternatively, they can solve the equation $0 = 48t - 16t^2$ for t.

Since solving $0 = 48t - 16t^2$ is the same as solving $16t(3 - t) = 0$, you have $t = 0$ or $t = 3$. So since it is back on the ground after 3 seconds, it is in the air for 3 seconds.

   b. Yes; The maximum height of the ball will occur at $t = 1.5$. At this time the height of the ball will be 36, which can be found on a graph or on a table, or by substituting 1.5 into the equation to get $48(1.5) - 16(1.5)^2 = 36$, which is greater than 30 feet.

51. If $g = n^2 - n$, then $g = n(n - 1)$. The x-intercepts are $n = 0$ or $n = 1$. This means that for a league with 0 teams or 1 team, there are no league games.

52. 50,000 feet; the x-intercepts are 0 and 1,000. (The equation $0.2x(1,000 - x) = 0$ has solutions $x = 0$ and $x = 1,000$.) The axis of symmetry would be $x = 500$, so the maximum occurs when the x-coordinate is 500. This makes the height $h = 0.2(500)(1,000 - 500) = 0.2(250,000) = 50,000$ feet.

Extensions

53. $c = -1$; when $x = 3$ for $3x + c = 2x - 2c$

$$3(3) + c = 2(3) - 2c$$
$$9 + c = 6 - 2c$$
$$9 - 6 + c = 6 - 6 - 2c$$
$$3 + c = -2c$$
$$3 + c - c = -2c - c$$
$$3 = -3c$$
$$\frac{3}{-3} = \frac{-3c}{-3}$$
$$-1 = c$$

54. $c = 5.5$; when $x = 3$ for $3x + c = cx - 2$

$$3(3) + c = c(3) - 2$$
$$9 + c = 3c - 2$$
$$9 + 2 + c = 3c - 2 + 2$$
$$11 + c = 3c$$
$$11 + c - c = 3c - c$$
$$11 = 2c$$
$$\frac{11}{2} = \frac{2c}{2}$$
$$5.5 = c$$

55. Some possible answers: $2x = 6$, $9 - x = 6$, $15 = 2x + 9$, or $10 = 5(x - 1)$. Not everyone will have the same equation. All the equations of the form $y = mx + b$ that have $x = 2$ as a solution when $y = 0$ will intersect at the point $(0, 2)$.

56. The parentheses should be around $(2 - 2x)$:

$$13 = 3 + 5x - (2 - 2x) + 5$$
$$13 = 3 + 5(1) - (2 - 2(1)) + 5$$
$$13 = 3 + 5(1) - (2 - 2) + 5$$
$$13 = 3 + 5(1) - 0 + 5$$
$$13 = 3 + 5 - 0 + 5$$
$$13 = 8 - 0 + 5$$
$$13 = 8 + 5$$
$$13 = 13$$

57. a. $x^2 - 4$　　**b.** $x^2 - 156.25$

   c. $x^2 - 5$　　**d.** $x^2 - 2$

58. **a.** $(x - 10)(x + 10)$

b. $(x - 1.2)(x + 1.2)$

c. $(x - \sqrt{7})(x + \sqrt{7})$

d. $(x - \sqrt{24})(x + \sqrt{24})$

59. **a.** $a = 1$, $b = -6$, and $c = 8$, so, using the quadratic formula:

$$x = \frac{-(-6) \pm \sqrt{(-6)^2 - 4(1)(8)}}{2(1)}$$

$$x = \frac{6 \pm \sqrt{36 - 32}}{2}$$

$$x = \frac{6 \pm \sqrt{4}}{2} = \frac{6 \pm 2}{2}$$

$$x = 4 \text{ or } x = 2$$

b. $a = -1$, $b = -1$, and $c = 6$, so, using the quadratic formula:

$$x = \frac{-(-1) \pm \sqrt{(-1)^2 - 4(-1)(6)}}{2(-1)}$$

$$x = \frac{1 \pm \sqrt{1 - (-24)}}{-2} = \frac{1 \pm \sqrt{25}}{-2} = \frac{1 \pm 5}{-2}$$

$$x = -3 \text{ or } x = 2$$

c. $a = 1$, $b = -7$, and $c = 10$, so, using the quadratic formula:

$$x = \frac{-(-7) \pm \sqrt{(-7)^2 - 4(1)(10)}}{2(1)}$$

$$x = \frac{7 \pm \sqrt{49 - 40}}{2}$$

$$x = \frac{7 \pm \sqrt{9}}{2} = \frac{7 \pm 3}{2}$$

$$x = 5 \text{ or } x = 2$$

d. $a = 4$, $b = -1$, and $c = 0$, so, using the quadratic formula:

$$x = \frac{-(-1) \pm \sqrt{(-1)^2 - 4(4)(0)}}{2(4)}$$

$$x = \frac{1 \pm \sqrt{1 - 0}}{8}$$

$$x = \frac{1 \pm 1}{8}$$

$$x = 0 \text{ or } x = 0.25$$

e. $a = 2$, $b = -12$, and $c = 18$, so, using the quadratic formula:

$$x = \frac{-(-12) \pm \sqrt{(-12)^2 - 4(2)(18)}}{2(2)}$$

$$x = \frac{12 \pm \sqrt{144 - 144}}{4} = \frac{12 \pm 0}{4}$$

$$x = 3$$

f. $a = 1$, $b = 3$, and $c = -4$, so, using the quadratic formula:

$$x = \frac{-(3) \pm \sqrt{(3)^2 - 4(1)(-4)}}{2(1)}$$

$$x = \frac{-3 \pm \sqrt{9 + 16}}{2}$$

$$x = \frac{-3 \pm \sqrt{25}}{2} = \frac{-3 \pm 5}{2}$$

$$x = 1 \text{ or } x = -4$$

60. **a.** The equation of line 1 is $y = -2x + 15$. The equation of line 2 is $y = 1.5x + 6$.

b. $x \approx 2.6$; $y \approx 10$. (Previous discussion about the x-scale and the y-scale will be helpful here.)

c. Solve $1.5x + 6 = -2x + 15$ to get $x \approx 2.571$, $y \approx 9.857$.

d. Values of x that satisfy $1.5x + 6 < -2x + 15$ are those values of x such that $x < 2.571$. The graph of $y = 1.5x + 6$ is below the graph of $y = -2x + 15$ for values of $x < 2.571$, i.e., to the left of the line $x = 2.571$.

e. $1.5x + 6 > -2x + 15$ when $x > 2.571$. The graph of $y = 1.5x + 6$ is above the graph of $y = -2x + 15$ for values of $x > 2.571$, i.e., to the right of the line $x = 2.571$.

61. **a.** The coordinates of the points where this graph crosses the x-axis are $(0, 0)$ and $(9, 0)$.

b. Rewrite the equation in factored form as $y = x(x - 9)$. The desired points are those whose x-coordinates are the x-intercepts for the given equation (the values of x for which $y = 0$).

c. The values of x that satisfy $x^2 - 9x < 0$ are x such that $0 < x < 9$. The portion of the graph below the x-axis shows that.

d. The values of x that satisfy $x^2 - 9x > 0$ are x such that $x > 9$ or $x > 0$. The portion of the graph to the right of the line $x = 9$ or to the left of the line $x = 0$ show that.

e. The minimum value of y occurs when $x = 4.5$. That minimum value is -20.25.

62.
$$x^2 + 5x + 7 = 1$$
$$x^2 + 5x + 7 - 1 = 1 - 1$$
$$x^2 + 5x + 6 = 0$$
$$(x + 2)(x + 3) = 0$$
$$x = -2 \text{ or } x = -3$$

Check: If $x = -2$, then
$$(-2)^2 + 5(-2) + 7 = 1$$
$$4 - 10 + 7 = 1$$
$$1 = 1$$

Check: If $x = -3$, then
$$(-3)^2 + 5(-3) + 7 = 1$$
$$9 - 15 + 7 = 1$$
$$1 = 1$$

63.
$$x^2 + 6x + 15 = 6$$
$$x^2 + 6x + 15 - 6 = 6 - 6$$
$$x^2 + 6x + 9 = 0$$
$$(x + 3)(x + 3) = 0$$
$$x = -3$$

Check: If $x = -3$, then
$$(-3)^2 + 6(-3) + 15 = 6$$
$$9 - 18 + 15 = 6$$
$$6 = 6$$

ACE ANSWERS 3

Applications

1. a. 275 gallons are being pumped out each hour; students may make a table and notice the constant rate of change, which is -275, or they may recognize that -275 is the coefficient of t in a linear relationship between w and t.

b. 1,925 gallons. This can be found using a table and finding the value when $t = 0$, or by substituting 0 for t into the equation and finding w.

c. 3 hours. Students can find 3 in their table as the corresponding t-value when w is 1,100, or they can solve the equation $w = -275t + 1,925$ for t when $w = 1,100$.

d. 7 hours. Students can find 7 in their table as the corresponding t-value when w is 0, or they can solve the equation $w = -275t + 1,925$ for t when $w = 0$.

e. $w = -275(t - 7)$. The original equation tells you that before the pump started working, there were 1,925 gallons of water in the pool, and that for every hour the pump emptied 275 gallons of water from the pool. In this equation, when $t = 7$, the amount of water is 0, or the tank is empty.

f. The relationship is linear because there is a constant rate of change.

2. a. 550 gallons. Students may use a table and notice the constant rate of change is -550, after multiplying -275 by 2, or they may recognize that -550 is the coefficient of t in a linear relationship between w and t.
$$w = -275(2t - 7)$$
$$w = -550t + 1,925$$

b. 1,925 gallons. This can be found using a table and finding the value when $t = 0$, or by substituting 0 for t into the equation and finding w.

c. 1.68 hours or 1 hour, 41 minutes. Students can find 1.68 in their table as the corresponding t-value when w is 1,000, or they can solve the equation $w = -275(2t - 7)$ for t when $w = 1,000$ after applying the Distributive Property:
$$1,000 = -550t + 1,925$$
$$1,000 - 1,925 = -550t$$
$$\frac{-925}{-550} = \frac{-550t}{-550}$$
$$1.68 \approx t$$
The pump has been running for about 1.68 hours.

d. 3.5 hours; students can find in their table the corresponding t-value when w is 0, or they can solve the equation $w = -275(2t - 7)$ for t when $w = 0$.
$$0 = -550t + 1,925$$
$$-1,925 = -550t$$
$$\frac{-1,925}{-550} = \frac{-550t}{-550}$$
$$3.5 = t$$
The pool will be empty in 3.5 hours.

e. $w = -550t + 1,925$. This equation tells you that before the pump started working there were 1,925 gallons of water in the pool, and that for every hour the pump emptied 550 gallons of water from the pool.

3. a. 25 gallons. Let $m = 0$, since 0 miles have been driven after the last fill-up. From the equation, $g = 25$, meaning the tank holds 25 gallons of gas.

b. Approximately 21.7 gallons.
$g = 25 - \frac{50}{15} \approx 21.7$ gallons.

c. Substitute 5 for g into the equation, $5 = \frac{1}{15}m$. Solve for m, so $m = 300$ miles.
Note: A graph and a table would also show that 5 gallons remain after 300 miles.

d. 375 miles. Students may use their table to find the value of m that corresponds to $g = 0$, or solve the equation $g = 25 - \frac{1}{15}m$ for m when g equals 0. Since m has a coefficient of $-\frac{1}{15}$, students may have a difficult time deciding how to apply the properties of equality, they may multiply by 15, or they could also divide by $\frac{1}{15}$.

e. The tank holds 25 gallons, so $g = 25 - 1 = 24$ when 1 gallon has been used. Therefore, $24 = 25 - \frac{1}{15}m$, so $m = 15$. The driver would have to travel 15 miles to use 1 gallon of gas.

f. 25 is the number of gallons of gas in the tank after a fill-up, and $\frac{1}{15}$ indicates that the truck uses $\frac{1}{15}$ of a gallon of gas every 1 mile.

4. The variable y represents how much money they still need to pay for the printing bill, depending on the number of books sold. N represents the number of books sold or given away, 2,500 is the amount they owe for printing at the start of the project, 15 is the price they charge for each book, and 8 represents the free copies they gave to the yearbook advisor and staff.

5. a. $A = \ell(120 - \ell)$; since $A = \ell w$, you need to write w in terms of ℓ. Perimeter is 240 from the given amount of fencing. So, using the equation $240 = 2\ell + 2w$ and solving for w, $w = 120 - \ell$ and $A = \ell(120 - \ell)$.

b. The maximum area is when ℓ and w each equal 60.

c. If you graph the equation $A = \ell(120 - \ell)$, you get a parabola that opens down. To find the maximum area, you look at the maximum point on the parabola, or the vertex. The x-coordinate is the length of the rectangle with the greatest area. To find the width, substitute this x-coordinate into the equation $w = 120 - \ell$ and solve for w.

d. The equation is quadratic because it is the product of two linear factors that are in terms of ℓ. The equation $A = \ell(120 - \ell)$ can be written as $A = 120\ell - \ell^2$, where the exponent on ℓ is 2. Also, 2 is the highest exponent to which ℓ is raised.

6. a. $A = \ell(120 - 0.5\ell)$. Since $A = \ell w$, write w in terms of ℓ. Since the fencing is 240 meters, use the equation $240 = w + \ell + w$. Solve to find $w = 120 - 0.5\ell$.

b. The length would be 120 meters, so the width could be found using the equation $w = 120 - 0.5\ell$. The width would be 60 meters.

c. The equation is quadratic because it is the product of two linear factors that are in terms of ℓ. The equation $A = \ell(120 - 0.5\ell)$ can be written as $A = 120\ell - 0.5\ell^2$, where the exponent on ℓ is 2. This is the highest exponent to which ℓ is raised.

7. a. First you need to write the equation $n = 20 - x$ in terms of $x = 20 - n$. So, substituting into $P = xn - 6n$, $P = (20 - n)n - 6n$, or $P = 20n - n^2 - 6n$, which is equivalent to $P = 14n - n^2$.

b. \$40; using the equation $P = 14n - n^2$, substitute 10 for n. The profit is $P = 14(10) - 10^2 = 40$.

c. The selling price can be found using the equation $n = 20 - x$. So, when $n = 10$, the selling price is \$10.

d. \$49; the greatest profit can be found by making a table or graph for the profit equation $P = 20n - n^2 - 6n = 14n - n^2$. The greatest profit occurs when 7 posters are sold, which yields a value of $P = 14(7) - 7^2 = 49$.

8. a. Table 1 is quadratic with a second difference of 1. Table 2 is linear with a constant rate of change of 30. Table 3 is exponential with a growth factor of 3.

b. Possible answers: Table 1: Let N be the number of deer and x be the number of years after 2010 (so when $x = 1$, the year is 2011); then the equation is $N = \frac{1}{2}x^2 + \frac{59}{2}x + 1{,}000$.

Table 2: Let N be the number of deer and y be the year. Then $N = 1{,}000 + 30(y - 2{,}000)$. Or, let N be the number of deer and x be the number of years after 2010 (so when $x = 1$, the year is 2011); then the equation is $N = 1{,}000 + 30x$.

Table 3: Let N be the number of deer and y be the year. Then $N = 1{,}000(3)^{y-2{,}000}$. Or, let N be the number of deer and x be the number of years after 2010 (so $x = 1$ represents the year 2011), then the equation is $N = 1{,}000(3)^x$.

c. Table 3 shows the deer population growing at a rate of 300% per year.

9. a. For Species 1, 10,000 is the starting population. 100 is the rate at which the population grows every year. So, for every year the population increases by 100 animals, P_1 is the total population after x years.

For Species 2, 10 is the starting population, and 3^t means that the population triples every year. P_2 is the total population after t years.

For Species 3, 800 is the starting population and $10t^2$ means that the population increases by the product of 10 and the number of years passed multiplied by itself. P_3 is the total population after t years.

b. The pattern of growth for Species 1 is linear. The pattern of growth for Species 2 is exponential. The pattern of growth for Species 3 is quadratic. After a certain time, the population of Species 2 will surpass the other two populations, since exponential growth patterns increase at an increasing rate.

c. Answers will vary; however, any two populations will be the same at some value for t.

The populations of Species 1 and 2 are the same when t is between 6.3 and 6.4.

The populations of Species 2 and 3 are the same when t is between 4.1 and 4.2.

The populations of Species 3 and 1 are the same when t is about 35.74 and -25.74. A negative answer does not make sense in this situation, so -25.74 is not a solution.

One way to find these values for t is to use a graphing calculator. If you use the table function and set the increments to 0.1 or 0.01, you can get close estimates for the values for which the equations are equal.

10. a. Answers will vary.

b. 70. Students may draw the next two figures and count the number of toothpicks, or make a table of values and use the pattern in the table to find the number of toothpicks in the seventh figure.

Figure	Toothpicks
1	4
2	10
3	18
4	28
5	40
6	54
7	70

c. Linear. Possible answer: The figure number times 4 equals the perimeter. The figure number equals the number of toothpicks on the bottom and the number of toothpicks going up (height). If you double the figure number, you get the number of toothpicks that make up the "stairs" on the left side of the figure giving $n + n + 2n = 4n$. This pattern shows that the data will go up at a constant rate. The graph will be a straight line with a slope of 4.

d. Quadratic. Possible answer: In the data table, as x increases by 1, the y-value has a second difference of 2.

e. $P = 4N$. To find the perimeter, you take the figure number and multiply it by 4.

f. Possible answers: $T = N^2 + 3N$, where T is the total number of toothpicks and N is the figure number. If you work backward on the table, you find that the y-intercept is 0. This means that in the quadratic equation form of $y = ax^2 + bx + c$, $c = 0$. Because the second difference is 2, the value of $a = 1$, since $2a = $ the second difference. Substituting into the quadratic equation, $y = 1x^2 + bx + 0 = x^2 + bx$. You can use a table to find b. See below.

Figure Number	x^2	bx	Total Toothpicks
0	0	$+ 0(3 \times 0)$	0
1	1	$+ 3(3 \times 1)$	4
2	4	$+ 6(3 \times 2)$	10
3	9	$+ 9(3 \times 3)$	18
4	16	$+ 12(3 \times 4)$	28
x	x^2	$3x$	$x^2 + 3x$

$T = N(N + 3)$, where T is total number of toothpicks and N is figure number.

Figure (N)	$N + 3$	Total Toothpicks $N(N + 3)$
1	4	4
2	5	10
3	6	18
4	7	28

If you divide the total number of toothpicks by the figure number, the result is the second column of numbers. This number is the figure number plus 3. To get the total number of toothpicks, you multiply the $N + 3$ and the figure number.

11. Graph 1 is linear since it is a straight line with a constant rate of change of 3. Graph 2 is exponential since it has an increasing graph with a growth factor of 3. Graph 3 is quadratic since it has an upside-down U shape and a second difference of -2. Graph 4 is an inverse variation and was studied in *Thinking With Mathematical Models*.

12.

Graph 1		Graph 2	
x	y	x	y
1	1	1	3
2	4	2	9
3	7	3	27
4	10	4	81
5	13	5	243
6	16	6	729

Graph 3		Graph 4	
x	y	x	y
1	2	1	1
2	2	2	0.5
3	0	3	0.33
4	-4	4	0.25
5	-10	5	0.2
6	-18	6	0.17

13. **Graph 1: $y = 3x - 2$**. To find this equation you need to find the y-intercept and the slope or rate of change. Students may use the formula $m = \frac{\Delta y}{\Delta x}$ (i.e., $m = \frac{y_2 - y_1}{x_2 - x_1}$) to find slope by using two of their points in the table. They may look at the constant rate of change, which is 3. To find the y-intercept, they may look at the graph and see that it is -2.

Graph 2: $y = 3x$. To find this equation, students need the starting point and the growth factor. By looking at the table, each y-value increases by a growth factor of 3. The starting point can be found by dividing the y-value for $x = 1$ by 3 to get the y-value for $x = 0$. Doing this, $y = 1$ for the starting value. So, the equation is $y = 1(3)^x$ or $y = 3^x$.

Graph 3: Since the x-intercepts are 0 and 3, the factors could be $x(3 - x)$, and the equation could be $y = x(3 - x)$. By checking the point $(1, 2)$ in this equation, you can verify that this is correct, since three points, the x-intercepts and the point $(1, 2)$, determine a parabola.

Graph 4: Graph 4 is neither linear, exponential, nor quadratic. It is an inverse variation that students studied in *Thinking With Mathematical Models*.

Note: The equation for Graph 4 is $y = \frac{1}{x}$, or equivalently $xy = 1$.

14. G

15. D

16. B

17. F

18. E

19. C

20. A

21. **a.** Linear: Equations 2 and 4. Quadratic: Equations 1, 5, 8, and 9. Exponential: Equations 3, 6, and 7.

    b. Equations 2 and 4 represent the same function. Equations 1 and 5 represent the same function. Equations 3 and 6 represent the same function.

    c. The graph of Equations 2 and 4 is a line with a starting point of $(0, 0)$, a rate of change of 2, and an increasing pattern from left to right. The graph of Equations 1 and 5 is a parabola that opens up with a y-intercept of $(0, 0)$, x-intercepts of $(0, 0)$ and $(-8, 0)$, and a minimum point at $(-4, -16)$. The graph of Equations 3 and 6 is an increasing curve with y-intercept $(0, 1)$ and a growth factor of 4.

22. Answers will vary. Possible answer for the linear equation is $y = 2x$. You get 2 dollars for every kilometer you walk, where x is the number of kilometers walked and y is the total amount of money collected.

    Possible answer for the quadratic equation: $y = x^2 + 8x$. This represents the number of handshakes between two teams if one team has x members and the other team has $x + 8$ members.

    Possible answer for the exponential equation: $y = 4^{x-1}$. y is the number of rubas on the xth square of a checkerboard if the King puts 1 on the first square, 4 on the second, and 16 on the third and then continues to quadruple the number of rubas for each successive square.

23. **a.** Linear: Equations 3, 7, 14, 18

    Exponential: Equations 2, 6, 13

    Quadratic: Equations 1, 9, 10, 11, 12, 15, 17

    b. Equations 1 and 9; Equations 2 and 13; Equations 3 and 14; Equations 11 and 17

    c. Equations 1 and 9: Quadratic pattern with y-intercept of 16 and x-intercept of -4. The minimum is $(-4, 0)$.

    Equations 2 and 13: Exponential patterns with starting point $\left(0, \frac{1}{3}\right)$ and a growth factor of 3.

    Equations 3 and 14: Linear pattern, x-intercept is $(5, 0)$ and y-intercept is 10. The rate of change is -2. The line has a negative slope, so it falls left to right.

    Equations 11 and 17: Quadratic pattern with y-intercept of $(0, 0)$ and x-intercepts of $(0, 0)$ and $(5, 0)$. The maximum is $(2.5, 25)$.

24. Answers will vary. An example for equation 2 is that the King of Montarek will put one ruba on the first square on a chessboard, 3 on the next square, 9 on the next square, and so on, multiplying by 3 for each successive square. Equation 2 represents the number of rubas on square x of the chessboard.

Connections

25. a. Plan 1: 17 weeks; Plan 2: 12 weeks; Plan 3: 8 weeks

Cookie Prices

Week	Price (dollars)		
	Plan 1	Plan 2	Plan 3
0	1.00	1.00	1.00
1	1.05	1.05	1.10
2	1.10	1.10	1.20
3	1.15	1.16	1.30
4	1.20	1.22	1.40
5	1.25	1.28	1.50
6	1.30	1.34	1.60
7	1.35	1.41	1.70
8	1.40	1.48	1.80
9	1.45	1.55	
10	1.50	1.63	
11	1.55	1.71	
12	1.60	1.80	
13	1.65		
14	1.70		
15	1.75		
16	1.80		

b.

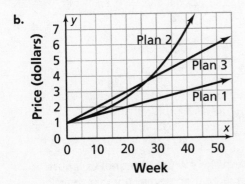

c. The graphs of Plans 1 and 3 are linear because they are straight lines. The price of cookies in Plan 1 grows at a constant rate of $.05 per week, and the price of cookies in Plan 3 grows at a constant rate of $.10 per week. Plan 2 is not linear because it grows by $.05 from week 1 to week 2, and then the amount of growth increases each week. Plan 2 is exponential growth.

d. Possible answer: Customers will notice the change in Plan 3 more quickly than in either of the other plans. Plan 1 would be the least noticeable to customers. **Note:** Students should justify their choice based on the mathematics of the problem.

26. a. $1{,}000{,}000 - 40{,}000x = 0$, where x is the number of days since the canister was opened; $1{,}000{,}000 \div 40{,}000 = 25$ days

b.

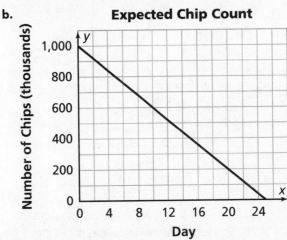

c. $y = -40{,}000x + 1{,}000{,}000$

ACE ANSWERS 4

d.

Expected vs. Actual Chip Count

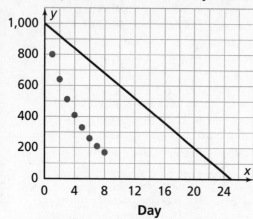

Betty is going to suspect something strange is happening. The decrease in the number of chips is not constant and is greater than what is expected.

27. a.

Cookie Price Survey

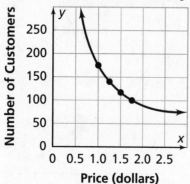

b. Answers will depend on the curve that students draw. About 130 customers would be willing to pay $1.35; about 90 would be willing to pay $2.00.

c. Answers will vary. The predictions above are probably pretty accurate.

d. Students may say that this graph model is similar to the inverse relationships they have seen in the bridge-length, teeter-totter, and travel-time problems from *Thinking With Mathematical Models*. They may also say it is like an exponential decay problem they have seen in *Growing, Growing, Growing*. The graphs of inverse relationships and decreasing exponential relationships have different shapes, but this is

probably too subtle a point for students who have only seen a few examples of each at this point and time.

28. a. First, Tara distributed $(x + 2)$ to x and 3. Second, she distributed x to x and 2. Third, she distributed 3 to x and 2. Then she applied the Distributive Property when she said that $2x + 3x = x(2 + 3)$. To get the term $5x$, she used the Commutative Property: $x(2 + 3) = (2 + 3)x = 5x$.

b. Finding the area of the left-hand column of the table, which is $(x + 2)x$, and adding it to the right hand column area $(x + 2)3$, is the same as her first step. Her second step is just expressing the two column's areas as a sum of the parts that make them up. The last two steps are just to combine the two x-terms and are not represented in the area model.

c. i. $x^2 + 8x + 15$
$(x + 5)(x + 3) = (x + 5)x + (x + 5)3$
$\quad = x^2 + 5x + 3x + 15$
$\quad = x^2 + x(5 + 3) + 15$
$\quad = x^2 + 8x + 15$

ii. $x^2 + 5x + 4$
$(x + 4)(x + 1) = (x + 4)x + (x + 4)1$
$\quad = x^2 + 4x + 1x + 4$
$\quad = x^2 + x(4 + 1) + 4$
$\quad = x^2 + 5x + 4$

iii. $x^2 + 2x - 8$
$(x - 2)(x + 4) = (x - 2)x + (x - 2)4$
$\quad = x^2 - 2x + 4x - 8$
$\quad = x^2 + x(-2 + 4) - 8$
$\quad = x^2 + 2x - 8$

29. a. 210; $(21 \times 20) \div 2 = 420 \div 2 = 210$

b. $h = \dfrac{n(n - 1)}{2}$

c. $h = \dfrac{n^2 - n}{2}$ or $h = \dfrac{1}{2}(n^2 - n)$

30. a. $x^2 + 7x + 10$ or $x^2 + 2x + 5x + 10$

b. Answers will vary. Students may use an area model to justify that their expressions are equivalent, or they may use a graph or a table to show that their expressions are equivalent. **Note:** If three points satisfy different quadratic expressions, then the expressions are equivalent.

31. a. y-intercept is 10; students may find this by looking at a graph or a table when $x = 0$.

b. The x-intercepts are -2 and -5. Students can find the x-intercepts by looking at a graph or a table when $y = 0$.

c. The minimum is at $x = -3.5$ where the value of y is -2.25. The students may use a table or graph. There is no maximum.

d. The line of symmetry is the vertical line through the value $x = -3.5$.

x	y
−5	0
−4	−2
−3	−2
−2	0
−1	4
0	10
1	18
2	28
3	40
4	54
5	70
6	88

32. x^5

33. x^6

34. x^4

35. x^3

36. $\frac{1}{x^3}$

37. $2x^3$

38. a. \$34,500; she gets $30,000 \times 1.15 = 34,500$.

b. \$33,600; $30,000 \times 1.12 = 33,600$.

c. \$63,000. A 110% increase means that the new salary is 210% of the original salary. Thus, the salary is $30,000 \times 2.10 = \$63,000$.

39. a. Cylinder A is fatter and shorter than either of the other 2 cylinders. Cylinder C is the same height as Cylinder B but skinnier. Cylinders B and C are both twice as tall as Cylinder A.

b. Cylinder A has the greatest surface area. Students may count squares on the grid pattern to estimate the surface area. If they use formulas, they will probably use the actual measurements. Cylinder A has radius 2 and height 4 and surface area = $2\pi(2)^2 + \pi(4)(4) = 24\pi$. Cylinder B has radius 1 and height 8 and surface area = $2\pi(1)^2 + \pi(2)(8) = 18\pi$. Cylinder C's surface area is less than Cylinder B's surface area since its rectangle and circles are smaller.

c. Cylinder A; since volume equals $\pi r^2 h$, find V when $r^2 h$ is the greatest. For Cylinder A, $r^2 h = 16$; for Cylinder B, $r^2 h = 8$; and for Cylinder C, $r^2 h = 2$.

40. a. 7.94 feet; $d = -16(0.1^2) + 16(0.1) + 6.5 = 7.94$

b. 9.86 feet; $d = -16(0.3^2) + 16(0.3) + 6.5 = 9.86$. **Note:** Ask students if this is reasonable.

c. 6.5 feet; $d = -16(1^2) + 16(1) + 6.5 = 6.5$

d. The operations are exponentiation, multiplication, and addition. The exponentiation is done first, then the multiplication, and lastly the addition. **Note:** The multiplication of numbers not involving exponents could be done before the exponentiation.

41. a. 40,000 and 160,000; to find the population after 3 hours, substitute 3 into the equation $b = 5,000(2^t)$ for t. Then $b = 5,000(8) = 40,000$. To find the population after 5 hours, substitute 5 into the equation for t. Then $b = 5,000(32) = 160,000$.

b. First, perform the repeated multiplication defined by the 2^t in the parentheses; then take this product and multiply it by 5,000.

42. Possible answers: $-59 - 6x$, $1 - 6x - 60$, or $5 - 6x - 60 - 4$

43. Possible answers: $-4x + 9$, $-3x + 12 - (x + 3)$, $-3x + 12 - x - 3$, $-3(x - 4) - x - 3$, $-4x + 12 - 3$, or $-3x + 9 - x$

44. Possible answers: $x^2 + 2x - 5x + 6$, or $x^2 - 3x + 6$

45. Possible answers: $6x^2 + 5x^2 - 50x + 10$, or $11x^2 - 50x + 10$

46. Possible answers: $\frac{3}{4}x^2 + x^2 + 3x$, $\frac{7}{4}x^2 + 3x$, $x\left(\frac{7}{4}x + 3\right)$, or $\frac{7}{4}x\left(x + \frac{12}{7}\right)$

47. Possible answers: $7x^2 - 2.75x - 8$, or $3.5x(2x - 1) + 0.25(3x - 32)$

48. **a.** $y = 6(2z - 7) + 10$, or equivalently, $y = 12z - 42 + 10$, or $y = 12z - 32$

   b. $P = (12 - n)n - 6n$, or equivalently, $P = 12n - n^2 - 6n$, or $P = 6n - n^2$, or $P = n(6 - n)$

   c. $A = (15 - w)w$, or equivalently, $A = 15w - w^2$

49. Possible answer: $y = (x + 3)(x - 2) = x^2 + x - 6$. Some students may have equations that are quadratics in factored form of $a(x + 3)(x - 2)$, where a is a nonzero real number. As long as the linear factors have -3 and 2 as their solutions for x when the factor is set equal to zero, the answer is valid. Also, equations that are not of the form $a(x + 3)(x - 2)$ may work, too. For example, $3\left(\frac{4}{3}x + 4\right)(x - 2)$, which expands to $y = 4x^2 + 4x - 24$, is a possible answer.

50. $y = -4x + 8$ is the only possible equation unless the student writes another equation that is equivalent to this.

51. Possible answers: $y = 1.25^x$, $y = a(1.25)^x$, where a is a real number.

52. **a.** (See Figure 1.)

Figure 1

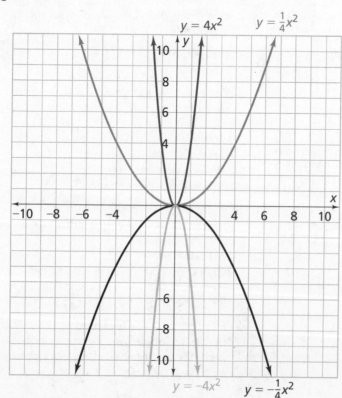

$y = 4x^2$ $y = \frac{1}{4}x^2$

$y = -4x^2$ $y = -\frac{1}{4}x^2$

Say It With Symbols   **ACE Answers**

b. If a is positive, then the parabola opens up and if a is negative, then the parabola opens down. As $|a|$ increases, the parabola becomes narrower, and as $|a|$ decreases, the parabola becomes wider.

53. a. (See Figure 2.)

b. The c-value is the y-intercept, so changes in the c-value move the parabola up or down. If c is 0, the y-intercept is at the origin, and when c increases, the parabola moves up, since the y-intercept value is increasing. As c decreases, the parabola moves down, since the y-intercept value is decreasing.

54. About 53.67 feet. To find h in the diagram above right using the Pythagorean Theorem, solve the equation $h^2 + \left(\frac{1}{2}h\right)^2 = 60^2$, which is the same as solving the equation $h^2 + \frac{1}{4}h^2 = 3{,}600$, or $\frac{5}{4}h^2 = 3{,}600$. Students may either divide

each side by $\frac{5}{4}$ to obtain the equation $h^2 = 2{,}880$, or they may look at the table of $y = \frac{5}{4}h^2$ on the graphing calculator to find h when $y = 3{,}600$.

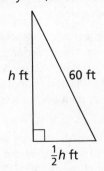

h ft   60 ft

$\frac{1}{2}h$ ft

55. Cone 2; the base area of the first cylinder is πx^2. The volume of cylinder 1 is $\pi x^2(3)$, so the volume of the cone is a third of that, or πx^2. The base area of the cylinder on the right is $\pi(3x)^2 = 9\pi x^2$, so the volume of this cylinder is $9\pi x^2(1)$ and the volume of cone 2 is a third of the volume of the cylinder, or $3\pi x^2$ cubic units.

....

Figure 2

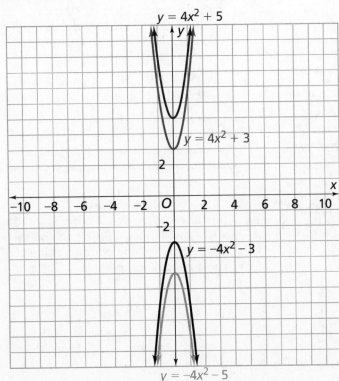

$y = 4x^2 + 5$

$y = 4x^2 + 3$

$y = -4x^2 - 3$

$y = -4x^2 - 5$

Extensions

56. a. Plan 2. If Caley uses Plan 1, she will owe $25 + 0.50 \times 100 = \$75$. If she uses Plan 2, she will owe $\$50$. So, Plan 2 is the better choice.

b. The equations are the same when you use 150 minutes. In order to pay $\$50$ for Plan 1, you would pay $\$25$ for up to 100 minutes and then $\$25$ more for 50 more minutes for a total of $100 + 50 = 150$ minutes.

c. Suppose that M_1 and M_2 are the monthly bill amounts and n is the number of minutes used. Plan 1's equation is $M_1 = 25$ when n is from 0 to 100 minutes and $M_1 = 25 + (100 - n)0.5$ for more than 100 minutes. Plan 2's equation is $M_2 = 50$. The growth pattern for M_1 is linear and M_2 is linear in pieces.

Cell Phone Offers

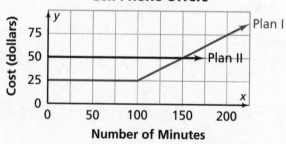

d. Plan 1 is a horizontal line, and then after 100 minutes, it has a positive slope. Plan 2 remains a horizontal line no matter how many minutes you use. So, Plan 1 will always cost more money if you talk more than 150 minutes.

57. Overall Rating $= 100\dfrac{(CR + YR + TR + IR)}{6} <$
$100\dfrac{(1.538 + 1.197 + 1.181 + 2.368)}{6} \approx 105$.

Since the Completion Rating is $0 < CR = 5\left(\dfrac{288}{474}\right) - 1.5 < 2.375$, $CR \approx 1.538$; the

Yards Rating is $0 < YR = \dfrac{\dfrac{3,692}{474} - 3}{4} < 2.375$, $YR \approx 1.197$;

the Touchdown Rating is $0 < TR = 20\left(\dfrac{28}{474}\right) < 2.375$, $TR \approx 1.181$;

and the Interception Rating is

$0 < IR = \dfrac{19 - 2\left(\dfrac{14}{474}\right)}{8} < 2.375$, $IR \approx 2.368$.

Note: The four statistics, CR, YR, TR, and IR, cannot be negative or exceed 2.375. When a statistic is negative, then 0 is used in the Overall Rating for that statistic. When a statistic exceeds 2.375, then 2.375 is used in the Overall Rating for that statistic.

58. a. 122.5 feet; a car should be $S = \dfrac{44^2}{32} + 44 + 18$, or 122.5 feet away.

b. 30 mph; 44 ft/sec is $44 \times 60 = 2,640$ feet per minute and $2,640 \times 60 = 158,400$ feet per hour. Then $\dfrac{158,400}{5,260} = 30$ miles per hour

c. About 37.5 or 38 ft/s (25.57 or 25.9 mi/h). If a car is trailing 100 feet behind a car, the car's safe speed would be 37.5 or 38 feet per second, which is about 25.57 or 25.9 miles per hour. Students can find these values by putting the equation $S = \dfrac{v^2}{32} + v + 18$ into a graphing calculator and using the table to find the value for v when S is 100.

59. a. Solutions of $(x + 2)(x - 1)(x - 5) = 0$ are $x = -2$, $x = 1$, and $x = 5$. Those solutions are shown on the graph; they are the points where the graph crosses the x-axis.

b. The values of x that satisfy $(x + 2)(x - 1)(x - 5) < 0$ are $x < -2$ and $1 < x < 5$. This can be seen on the graph where portions of the curve are below the x-axis.

c. Using only the equation and answers to part (a), you can find answers to part (b) by substituting a number less than 2 for x in the expression $(x + 2)(x - 1)(x - 5)$ and asking if the result is positive or negative. Repeat the process for a number between -2 and 1, for a number between 1 and 5, and for a number greater than 5. When the result is a negative number for the chosen interval, the x-values in that interval satisfy the given inequality $(x + 2)(x - 1)(x - 5) < 0$.

60. a. Graph $y = x^2 + 4$. It is not possible to find x when y is zero, since there are no x-intercepts. Also, solving the equation $0 = x^2 + 4$ means finding a number that, when you square it and add 4, gives you zero, which is not possible with real numbers because whether negative or positive, a number squared is positive. Furthermore, adding 4 only results in a positive number. Therefore, the result cannot be zero.

b. Answers will vary. Some possible answers: $0 = x^2 + 4$, $0 = x^2 + 1x + 8$.
Note: Any answer for $y = ax^2 + bx + c$ in which the value of $b^2 - 4ac$ is a negative number is a possible answer. This is because in the quadratic formula given in the *Did You Know?* after Problem 3.4, if $b^2 - 4ac$ is negative, the result is a negative value under the radical in the formula. This results in roots that are not in the real number system. When this happens, the parabola does not cross the x-axis in the coordinate (real) plane.

c. Answers will vary. Some possible answers: $0 = x^2 + 4x + 4$, $0 = x^2 + 8x + 16$; any quadratic that can be factored into the form $a(yx + z)^2$ where a, y, and z are real numbers.

d. Answers will vary. Some possible answers: $0 = x^2 - 4$, $0 = x^2 + 6x + 8$.

ACE Answers

Applications

1. Students may explain the result using an equation such as $(2x + 6) \div 2 - x$, where x is the number picked. In order to simplify this equation, students will need to make sense of $(2x + 6) \div 2$. They need to rewrite $2x + 6$ in two parts as $x + x + 3 + 3$, with the result that $(2x + 6) \div 2 = x + 3$. Thus $(2x + 6) \div 2 - x = x + 3 - x = 3$ for any number x a student picks.

2. Students may explain the result using an equation such as $(2(x + 4) - 6) \div 2 - x = 1$. In order to simplify this equation, students will need to make sense of $(2(x + 4) - 6) \div 2$, which is equal to $(2x + 2) \div 2$. Since $2x + 2 = x + x + 1 + 1$, dividing $x + x + 1 + 1$ in two parts results in $x + 1$, or $[2(x + 4) - 6] \div 2 = (2x + 2) \div 2 = x + 1$. Thus $[(2(x + 4) - 6) \div 2] - x = x + 1 - x = 1$ for any number x a student picks.

3. Answers will vary.

4. Answers may vary, but they should make logical sense. Possible argument:
Let n and m represent any integers.
Then $2n + 1$ and $2m + 1$ are two odd numbers.
But, $(2n + 1) + (2m + 1) = 2n + 2m + 2 = 2(n + m + 1)$, and
$2(n + m + 1)$ is an even number because it is a multiple of 2.
So, the sum of two odd integers is even.

5. Again, answers may vary; one possible argument:
Let n and m represent any integers.
Then $2n$ and $2m$ are two even numbers.
But $(2n)(2m) = 4nm = 2(2nm)$.
$2(2nm)$ is an even integer.
So, the product of two even numbers must be even.

6. Answers may vary; one possible argument:
Take two odd numbers represented by $(2n + 1)$ and $(2m + 1)$, where m and n are integers.
Then $2n$ and $2m$ are two even numbers.
But, $(2n + 1)(2m + 1) = 4nm + 2n + 2m + 1 = 2(2nm + n + m) + 1$, and
$2(2nm + n + m) + 1$ is an odd number, since it is 1 more than a multiple of 2.
So, the product of two odd integers is odd.

7. **a.** Possible answers: The product of three consecutive whole numbers will always yield an even number. The product of three consecutive whole numbers is always a multiple of 6.

   b. The product of three consecutive whole numbers is even. There are two cases for a set of 3 consecutive numbers. Case 1: Two evens and an odd. Using the facts from Exercise 5 and Problem 2.2, (even $\times$ odd) $\times$ even = even $\times$ even = even.

   Case 2: Two odds and an even, (odd $\times$ even) $\times$ odd = even $\times$ odd = even. The product of three consecutive whole numbers is a multiple of 6 since there is at least one even (multiple of 2) and at least one multiple of 3 (there are 3 numbers so one must be a multiple of 3), so the product must be a multiple of 6.

8. **a.** The product of four consecutive whole numbers will always be even. It is also divisible by 24. For any four consecutive numbers, one of them is divisible by 4, another is divisible by 2 (but not 4), and at least one of the four is divisible by 3. For example, $(4 \times 3 \times 2) \times 1 = 24 \times 1$. Therefore, 24 is a factor of the product of any four consecutive numbers.

   b. In a set of four consecutive whole numbers, there will be two odd whole numbers and two even whole numbers. This is symbolically shown with E = any even whole number and O = any odd whole number:
   $O \times E \times O \times E$; since $O \times E = E$,
   $O \times E \times O \times E = E \times E = E$

9. **a.** rational

   b. irrational

   c. irrational

   d. rational

   e. rational

   f. rational

10. **a.** 10,034 is divisible by 2; 69,883 is not. Students may reason that they could tell because 4 is divisible by 2, but 3 is not.

b. Answers will vary. Some students may suggest that as long as the last digit is even, then the number is divisible by 2, using the reasoning of long division. One explanation is that any digit except the last is a multiple of 10, which is clearly divisible by 2, and thus the only important digit is the ones digit.

11. Answers will vary, but students should note that the last two digits must be divisible by 4. For example, 4,516 is divisible by 4 whereas 4,519 is not, because 16 is divisible by 4 and 19 is not. This is not easy to see. Since all powers of 10 greater than 10 (100, 10,000, etc.) are divisible by 4, you only have to check the last two digits.

12. Answers will vary, but students should note that the last digit must be 0 or 5. This is true because the other digit is a multiple of 10, and thus is divisible by 5. The ones digit is the only important one to check.

Connections

13. **a.** Answers will vary. Some possibilities are below.
These buildings are composed of a central cube and 5 arms that contain 0 cubes, then 1 cube, then 2 cubes, then 3 cubes, and so on. This pattern is described in the student edition.
The buildings are composed of a central tower that contains 1 cube, then 2 cubes, and so on. Each new building is the previous building with 5 cubes added.

b. There are many possible equivalent expressions for the number of cubes in the nth building. Some examples: $1 + 5(n - 1)$, $n + 4(n - 1)$, or $5n - 4$.

c. The fifth building contains 21 cubes, which can be found by substituting 5 into any of the above equations or other correct equations.

d. Answers will vary since they depend on what the students had for part (b). However, the expression $5n - 4$ is the simplest form of the expression possible. This expression can be thought of as representing an addition of five blocks for every new tower starting with $n = 1$.

e. Students may either find a different pattern that relates to one of the previous expressions, or they may find a new expression altogether. Other possibilities include rewriting $n + 4(n - 1)$ as $n + 4n - 4$.

14. **a.** Students may list all the combinations or make a table. For 2 participants, 2 games must be played; for 3 participants, 6 games must be played; for 4 participants, 12 games must be played; for 5 participants, 20 games must be played; and for 6 participants, 30 games must be played.

b. The expression for the number of games played g in relation to the number of participants in the league n is $n(n - 1) = g$ or $n^2 - n = g$.

15. **a.** n^2, where n is the number of participants in the league

b. n; the diagonal is not filled in because participants do not play themselves.

c. Students should combine the two equations to create a new expression $n^2 - n$, but some students may recognize that this is the same as $n(n - 1)$ and use this as their expression.

d. Answers may vary since they depend on which expressions students used for parts (a) and (b). Students should note that, regardless, the expressions are equivalent.

16. 4 and -3; $(x - 4)(x + 3) = 0$, so $x = 4$ or $x = -3$.

17. 0 and -4; $x^2 + 4x = x(x + 4) = 0$, so $x = 0$ or $x + 4 = 0$, and thus $x = 0$ or $x = -4$.

ACE ANSWERS 5

18. -4 and -5; $x^2 + 9x + 20 = (x + 4)(x + 5) = 0$, so $(x + 4) = 0$ or $(x + 5) = 0$, and thus $x = -4$ or $x = -5$.

19. -8 and 1; $x^2 + 7x - 8 = (x + 8)(x - 1) = 0$, so $(x + 8) = 0$ or $(x - 1) = 0$, and thus $x = -8$ or $x = 1$.

20. 10 and 1; $x^2 - 11x + 10 = (x - 10)(x - 1) = 0$, so $(x - 10) = 0$ or $(x - 1) = 0$, and thus $x = 10$ or $x = 1$.

21. 9 and -3; $x^2 - 6x - 27 = (x - 9)(x + 3) = 0$, so $(x - 9) = 0$ or $(x + 3) = 0$, and thus $x = 9$ or $x = -3$.

22. 5 and -5; $x^2 - 25 = (x + 5)(x - 5) = 0$, so $x = -5$ or $x = 5$.

23. 10 and -10; $x^2 - 100 = (x + 10)(x - 10) = 0$, so $x = -10$ or $x = 10$.

24. -0.5 and -1; $2x^2 + 3x + 1 = (2x + 1)(x + 1) = 0$, so $x = -0.5$ or $x = -1$.

25. $-\frac{4}{3}$ and -2; $3x^2 + 10x + 8 = (3x + 4)(x + 2) = 0$, so $x = -\frac{4}{3}$ or $x = -2$.

26. a. $6r + 2(r - 30) = 8r - 60 = $ distance traveled

b. Possible question: How many miles are traveled if the rate is 70 miles per hour? Substitute 70 for r, the rate of speed, in the simplest expression and get $4(70) - 30 = 280 - 30 = 250$ miles traveled.

27. a. If x is the number of dimes, then $0.10x + 0.25(1,000 - x) = 0.10x + 250 - 0.25x = 250 - 0.15x = $ amount of money in dollars

b. Possible question: If the amount of money in the bag is $10, how many of each coin are in the bag? Set $10 equal to your expression and solve for the number of coins:
$$10 = 250 - 0.15x$$
$$10 - 250 = 250 - 250 - 0.15x$$
$$-240 = -0.15x$$
$$\frac{-240}{-0.15} = \frac{-0.15x}{-0.15}$$
$$1,600 = x$$
So, in theory, there are 1,600 dimes and -600 quarters. **Note:** Students may recognize that this answer does not

make sense since the number of dimes and quarters each should be greater than or equal to zero. So, x should be less than or equal to 1,000 and greater than or equal to zero, since you want to account for only a nonnegative number of coins. Thus, having the value of the coins add up to anything less than $100 is not possible.

To check, substitute the values into the equation:
$$0.10x + 0.25(1,000 - x)$$
$$0.10(1600) + 0.25(1,000 - 1,600)$$
$$160 - 150 = 10, \text{ which is the amount of}$$
money in dollars in the bag.

28. a. $P = 2(2w + 4) + 2w = 4w + 8 + 2w = 6w + 8 = 2(3w + 4)$

b. Find the dimension of the rectangle if the perimeter is 80. If the perimeter of a rectangle is 80, then you could substitute 80 into your simplest equation, solve for w, and calculate the length using the value of w.
$$80 = 6w + 8$$
$$80 - 8 = 6w + 8 - 8$$
$$72 = 6w$$
$$\frac{72}{6} = \frac{6w}{6}$$
$$12 = w$$
Therefore, the width is 12 feet and the length is $2(12) + 4$ or 28 feet.

29. a. $15x + 9(4,000 - x) = 15x + 36,000 - 9x = 6x + 36,000 = 6(x + 6,000)$

b. If the total amount of money collected at a concert was $60,000, find the number of reserved and unreserved seats. Set 60,000 equal to your simplest expression and solve for the number of tickets.
$$60,000 = 6x + 36,000$$
$$60,000 - 36,000 = 6x$$
$$24,000 = 6x$$
$$\frac{24,000}{6} = \frac{6x}{6}$$
$$4,000 = x$$
The number of reserved seats was 4,000 and the number of unreserved seats was $4,000 - 4,000$, or 0.

Say It With Symbols **ACE Answers**

30. a. 32 feet. Students may substitute the value 2 into the equation for t and get 32.

b. 36 feet. To find the maximum height, students would first find the x-intercepts (See part (c).). Then, the maximum height occurs between the two intercepts, so it is at $t = \frac{3}{2}$. When $t = \frac{3}{2}$, $h = -16\left(\frac{3}{2}\right)^2 + 48\left(\frac{3}{2}\right) = 36$.

c. 3 seconds; students can use the equation $h = -16t^2 + 48t$ and the factored form $h = -16t(t - 3)$, or $h = 16t(-t + 3)$. They find the x-intercepts, which are 0 and 3. The intercepts are the points where the height is 0, so the ball is in the air from 0 to 3 seconds.

d. Answers will vary; students who use a graph may see the highest point on the graph as the maximum height and use the x-intercepts to find the total time the ball was in the air. Students who use a table will look for the greatest y-value in the table for part (b) and the x-values when y is 0 for part (c).

31–32. a. The two expressions in both Exercises 31 and 32 are not equivalent. For part (a), students should make a table or graph and find that the two equations have either the same table and graph, or that they are different, in which case they are not equivalent.

b. They can simplify the expressions using the Distributive Property and/or Commutative Property to see if the expressions are equivalent. For Exercise 31, the first expression simplifies to $4x - 5$, and for Exercise 32, the first simplifies to $6x - 7$ and the second to $6x - 3$. To show that the expressions are not equivalent, students can show that a value for x when substituted into both expressions yields different values.

33. The expression is linear.

x	−7	−5	−3	5
$y = 4(x - 7) + 6$	−50	−42	−34	−2

34. The expression is linear.

x	−7	−5	−3	5
$y = -3 - 7(x + 9)$	−17	−31	−45	−101

35. The expression is exponential. The values for y in the table are approximations.

x	−7	−5	−3	5
$y = 2(3)^x$	0.001	0.008	0.074	486

36. The expression is quadratic.

x	−7	−5	−3	5
$y = 3x^2 - x - 1$	153	79	29	69

37. The expression is quadratic.

x	−7	−5	−3	5
$y = 5(x - 2)(x + 3)$	180	70	0	180

38. For Exercise 33, $4x - 28 + 6$, or $4x - 22$; for Exercise 34, $-3 - 7x - 63$, or $-66 - 7x$.

39. Table 1: linear, $y = 9 - 3x$
Table 2: quadratic, $y = x^2 - 16$
Table 3: none of these
Table 4: exponential, $y = 3(4^x)$
Table 5: none of these. **Note:** This is inverse variation, $y = \frac{4}{x}$.

40. a. Yes, the perimeter can be a rational number if the three numbers form a Pythagorean Triple. For example, a 3-4-5 right triangle will have perimeter 12 units, which is rational since all integers are rational numbers.

b. Yes, the perimeter can be irrational if the three numbers do not form a Pythagorean Triple. For example, 1, 1, and $\sqrt{2}$.

ACE ANSWERS 5

ACE Answers   385

41. a. No, the perimeter cannot be a rational number. If the length of the hypotenuse is an integer, then the length of the shortest leg will be rational. However, the length of the longer leg will be irrational because it is square root of three times the length of the shorter leg. The perimeter is the sum of two rational numbers plus an irrational number.

For example, a 30-60-90 triangle with a hypotenuse of 10 inches will have a shorter leg measuring 5 inches, and a longer leg measuring $5\sqrt{3}$ inches. The perimeter will be $15 + 5\sqrt{3}$ inches.

b. Using similar reasoning as in part (a), the perimeter will always be irrational.

Extensions

42. a. $5^2 + 6^2 = 31^2 - 30^2$

b. Let a be the first number and $a + 1$ be the second number.
Then $a^2 + (a + 1)^2 = (a(a + 1) + 1)^2 - (a(a + 1))^2$.

c. Begin with the right-hand side of the equation to show that it is equal to the left-hand side.
$a^2 + (a + 1)^2 = (a(a + 1) + 1)^2$
$\qquad - (a(a + 1))^2$
$= (a^2 + a + 1)^2 - (a^2 + a)^2$
by the Distributive Property
$= (a^2 + a + 1)(a^2 + a + 1)$
$\quad - (a^2 + a)(a^2 + a)$ by
Definition of Exponents
$= (a^4 + 2a^3 + 3a^2 +$
$2a + 1) - (a^4 + 2a^3 + a^2)$
by the Distributive Property
$= 2a^2 + 2a + 1$ by
combining like terms
$= a^2 + a^2 + 2a + 1$ by
rewriting the first term
$= a^2 + a^2 + a + a + 1$ by
rewriting the third term
$= a^2 + a(a + 1) + 1(a + 1)$
$= a^2 + (a + 1)^2$ by
factoring the last two terms
Since the left-hand side and the right-hand side of the equation are equal, the conjecture is true.

43. a. Answers may vary depending on the choice for n.

b. George is correct. All it takes is one counterexample to disprove a conjecture. So, even if there are many examples that work, that is not sufficient proof. This conjecture fails when n is 41, for example.

44. a. $\sqrt{2} + \left(-\sqrt{2}\right)$

b. $\left(0.5 + \sqrt{2}\right) + \left(-\sqrt{2}\right)$; the sum $0.5 + \sqrt{2}$ is an irrational number.

c. $\sqrt{2} + \sqrt{2} = 2\sqrt{2}$, which is irrational because it is the product of a rational number and an irrational number.

45. If the sum of the digits of a number is divisible by 3, then the number must also be divisible by 3. Also, if a number is divisible by 3, then the sum of the digits is divisible by 3. The following proofs are written symbolically. This is not something that students are expected to be able to do at this point. Students may talk informally about parts of the proof without the symbols. Suppose n is a three-digit number whose digits sum to a number that is divisible by 3. Then $n = a(100) + b(10) + c$, where a, b, and c are the digits of n. Rewriting, $n = 99a + a + 9b + b + c$. Using the Commutative Property, $n = (99a + 9b) + (a + b + c)$. Using the Distributive Property, $(99a + 9b)$ is divisible by 3, or $3(33a + 3b)$. In order for the entire number to be divisible by 3, $a + b + c$ must also be divisible by 3.

For example,
$n = 651$

$= 6 \times 100 + 5 \times 10 + 1$

$= (6 \times 99) + (6 \times 1) + (5 \times 9) + (5 \times 1) + 1$

$= (6 \times 99) + (5 \times 9) + (6 \times 1) + (5 \times 1) + 1$

$= (99 \times 6 + 9 \times 5) + (6 \times 1 + 5 \times 1 + 1)$

$= 3(33 \times 6 + 3 \times 5) + (6 + 5 + 1)$

$= 3(33 \times 6 + 15) + (12)$

$= 3(198 + 15 + 4)$

So, given that n is divisible by 3,
$6 + 5 + 1 = 12$ is divisible by 3.

Now let's look at another case: If a number is divisible by 3, then the sum of its digits is divisible by 3. Say a number n is divisible by 3, then we can write $n = 3k$, where k is an integer. Thus, $n = a(100) + b(10) + c = 3k$. Again, $n = 99a + 9b + a + b + c = 3k$, so dividing each side by 3, $k = 33a + 3b + \frac{a + b + c}{3}$. But since k is an integer, then $\frac{a + b + c}{3}$ must be an integer, so $a + b + c$ (the sum of the digits of n) must be divisible by 3.

46. If the sum of the digits of a number is divisible by 3 and it is even, then the number is divisible by 6. Suppose n is an even number whose digits sum to a number that is divisible by 3. Since it is even, it must be divisible by 2. It must also be divisible by 3, by Exercise 45. By the Fundamental Theorem of Arithmetic (the prime factorization of), n must be of the form $n = 2 \times 3 \times \ldots$ If we rewrite, $n = 6 \times \ldots$ Thus, n is divisible by 6.

47. a. Answers will vary.

   b. Students may find it easiest to explain why this method works by forming an equation to represent the value of any number ending in five, such as $10x + 5$, where x can be any whole number. Then a student taking the square of this value will get $(10x + 5)(10x + 5) = 100x^2 + 100x + 25 = 100(x^2 + x) + 25$. This equation represents Judy's method of finding the square.

Index